# CHRONICA BOTANICA
# AN INTERNATIONAL BIOLOGICAL AND
# AGRICULTURAL SERIES

*Consulting Editor, Frans Verdoorn*

No. 20

Albert Francis Blakeslee
(1874–1954)

# BLAKESLEE:
# THE
# GENUS DATURA

AMOS G. AVERY

SOPHIE SATINA

JACOB RIETSEMA

ALL FORMERLY OF THE
SMITH COLLEGE GENETICS EXPERIMENT STATION

Foreword and Biographical Sketch

By

EDMUND W. SINNOTT

YALE UNIVERSITY

THE RONALD PRESS COMPANY · NEW YORK

Library of Congress Catalog Card Number: 59-8388

PRINTED IN THE UNITED STATES OF AMERICA

To the Memory

of

*Albert Francis Blakeslee*

(1874–1954)

Flower in the crannied wall,
I pluck you out of the crannies,
I hold you here, root and all, in my hand,
Little flower—but *if* I could understand
What you are, root and all, and all in all,
I should know what God and man is.

—TENNYSON

# Foreword

The present volume is an account of the broad program of genetic investigations on the genus *Datura* carried on by A. F. Blakeslee and his associates over a period of more than forty years. The significance of that program lies not only in the contributions it made to our knowledge of heredity but in its demonstration of the fruitful results that can be obtained by studying the genetics of a single organism from many different points of view where each supplements the rest. No other organism, not even *Drosophila*, has involved so many aspects of biology in its genetic investigation as has *Datura*. Not only has its genetics, in the narrower sense, been examined, but its cytology, morphology, anatomy, physiology, embryology, geographical distribution, and evolutionary history have contributed to an understanding of its genetic constitution and behavior.

*Datura stramonium* is an excellent species for such a broad genetic study. Its life cycle is short and, being almost a weed, its nutritional requirements are not high, so that it will flower and fruit at relatively small size and many individuals may be grown in a limited space. It has few serious insect or fungus pests. Its flowers are large and it produces great quantities of seed. Its chromosomes can easily be studied. It lends itself readily to investigation through various chemical, physical, and physiological techniques. It is widespread through the temperate regions of the world and local races have developed that can be used to explore the processes of evolution. There are other species in its genus that provide opportunities to study problems of interspecific hybridization. *Datura* has fully justified its selection as a plant for genetic investigation.

This work with *Datura* began just after Morgan and his group, in their studies of *Drosophila*, had shown that chromosomes are indeed the structures in which the genes are carried; but the *Datura* program approached this problem from a somewhat different direction. It stressed especially the genetic contributions of entire chromosomes, or large pieces of them, rather than those of single genes. This is the particular significance of the *Datura* work.

The choice of *Datura* as material for research grew out of its use for class demonstrations in genetics. In cultures for this purpose grown in the Botanic Garden at the Connecticut Agricultural College, an exceptional individual was found by B. T. Avery, Jr., Blakeslee's first assistant. This plant was ultimately shown to be a trisomic or $2n + 1$ plant and was thus the first of the many chromosomal types recognized. After Blakeslee's removal in 1915 to the Station for Experimental Evolution at Cold Spring Harbor, many more *Datura* plants were grown and a considerable number of other exceptional individuals of various kinds kept appearing. Many of these were puzzling plants. Most of them were not gene mutations, for they neither bred true nor did their differences segregate in Mendelian fashion, and much of their pollen was bad. The clue to their behavior did not come until 1920 when John Belling, a distinguished cytologist who was working at the laboratory, made the critical observation that these aberrant types were each distinguished by having an extra chromosome in one of their twelve sets. Belling also developed the acetocarmine staining technique, thus very greatly reducing the time needed for chromosome determinations and making possible the chromosome analysis of a much larger number of plants than could have been studied with the techniques usually employed.

With the chromosomal correlates of these mutant types better understood, progress was rapid. There are twelve pairs of chromosomes in *Datura,* and it was therefore to be expected that there should be twelve of these trisomic types, each with a different extra chromosome. But more problems appeared. With the unexpected discovery of a thirteenth trisomic, it was evident that other hypotheses must be found; when the facts were all in, it was possible to distinguish twelve *primary* mutants, each with one of the normal chromosomes as an extra, and, for many of these, two *secondary* mutants, where the extra chromosome was a reduplicated half of one of the normal ones. In the *tertiaries,* the extra chromosome was made up of parts of two nonhomologous chromosomes. *Compensating* types, also $2n + 1$, showed the further difference that one member of a normal pair was missing but that this deficiency was made up by having the two halves of this chromosome attached to two others.

Parallel with these studies on the various kinds of trisomic mutants and their relationships went work on polyploids. The first of these was found in 1916. It was self-fertile, true-breeding but largely sterile in crosses, and proved to be a tetraploid. From this type, in crosses with diploids, came triploids; these in turn were a fertile source of $2n + 1$ trisomic types. Tetraploids had been found in other plants, but much more exciting was the discovery in the *Datura* cultures of an undoubted haploid. This was the first haploid to be found in vascular plants and created something of a sensation. Haploid plants, one thought, should be gametophytes, but here was a little plant, rather weak and nearly sterile, that was clearly a sporophyte but that had only one set of chromosomes in its cells.

The differences in appearance between the members of this extensive polyploid series now available ( *1n, 2n, 3n,* and *4n* ) were not great; but they were important, and much interest in polyploidy, both in nature and in culture, was aroused. This was further stimulated by the later discovery that polyploidy could be induced by the use of colchicine, which made possible the production of large numbers of such plants.

It was evident that the members of the polyploid series differed much less from one another than one of the trisomics did from normal. Why should a single added chromosome make so much greater difference to a plant than the addition of an entire set? From this problem came the concept of genic balance. One added chromosome presumably increased the effect of all the genes in that chromosome, since there were now three of them in the cell instead of two. Adding an entire set, however, did not change the relative proportions of the chromosomes or the balance between them. Many characters, according to this concept, would probably be intensified by certain chromosomes and reduced by others. If the genetic effect of each chromosome could be determined by studying the twelve primaries, the normal diploid should prove to be the average of the twelve effects. With some traits, especially easily measurable ones, it was found that the diploid *was* indeed approximately the average of the twelve primaries.

The present writer was fortunate enough to have an opportunity to examine the anatomy of members of the polyploid series and the various trisomics in a study of the effects of chromosomal differences on the internal structure of the plant. To get tissues that were strictly comparable was not easy but, by using the middle region of the flower stalk on the day of flowering, this difficulty was largely overcome. Definite anatomical differences, particularly as to cell size, bundle shape, and relative development of the various tissues were found among the trisomics. These illustrated well the fact of genic balance.

But there was much more to come out of the study of the trisomic plants. The behavior of one of the genes in crosses between normal Line 1A and Line B was abnormal, and in the $F_1$ of these and similar crosses Belling no longer found twelve pairs of chromosomes but some of them joined in circles of four at meiosis. To explain this it was suggested that in certain races segmental interchange (reciprocal translocation) had taken place between nonhomologous chromosomes. These races had all the chromosomal material of normals, but it was arranged in a different order. When two types were crossed, certain chromosomes had no homologs, but, since similar ends attracted each other at meiosis, rings were inevitably formed. If one race had chromosomes (named by their ends) $1 \cdot 2$ and $17 \cdot 18$, for example, and another $1 \cdot 17$ and $2 \cdot 18$, then in the hybrid between the two the following ring configuration was formed:

$$
\begin{array}{ccc}
1 \cdot 2 & \!\!\!\!-\!\!\!\!- & 2 \cdot 18 \\
| & & | \\
1 \cdot 17 & \!\!\!\!-\!\!\!\!- & 17 \cdot 18
\end{array}
$$

This idea was of much general interest and it was used in explaining the peculiar genetic behavior of *Oenothera*. Blakeslee and R. E. Cleland wrote an important joint paper on this subject.

Segmental interchange was also of much significance in studies of evolution. The only way to recognize types that had been changed was to cross them with a standard line (here chosen arbitrarily as Line 1A) and see what the chromosome configuration of the offspring was at meiosis. Such different races, outwardly similar but inwardly transformed, were at first called *cryptic types* but later *prime types*. This idea provided a new approach to a study of the origin of some of the differences between plants and thus to certain evolutionary problems.

The question of what prime types existed in nature and how they were distributed posed new problems. Blakeslee arranged to have seed collected and sent to him, and he himself traveled extensively to gather it. As a result, eleven prime types of *D. stramonium* were found growing in the wild (and many more were developed in culture); the distribution of these began to throw light on the evolutionary history of this species from a new direction. Similar prime types were found to exist in the races available of the other *Datura* species.

Almost from the beginning an endeavor was made to obtain mutations or new chromosomal types by the use of various environmental agents, particularly certain types of radiation. During the early years, in collaboration with C. S. Gager, the effect of radium emanations was studied and a considerable number of mutations were induced. These were among the first mutations to be induced in flowering plants by the use of radiation. Later, several series of experiments using x-ray treatments were carried out and these produced many new types. Other forms of radiation were tried though with less success. In recent years, through collaboration with the Atomic Energy Commission, the mutagenic effects of thermal neutrons were studied.

During these investigations the interesting fact came to light that plants grown from seeds kept in laboratory storage showed increasing numbers of mutations the longer the seeds had been stored. Other work, however, indicated that age alone was not responsible for this increase, and therefore the mutagenic effects of heat and moisture on seeds were studied in cooperation with the Boyce Thompson Institute for Plant Research.

The *Datura* work soon began to involve problems that, although they had important genetic implications, were concerned primarily with questions of growth, physiology, anatomy, and morphology. One of these concerned the growth of pollen tubes. In a number of crosses fertilization did not occur although pollen germinated on the stigma and pollen tubes started to grow. J. T. Buchholz carried on a series of studies on pollen-tube growth. He was able to find a differential stain that made it possible to distinguish the tubes from the stylar tissue. By this means it was discovered that in many cases a large group of tubes grew so slowly that they did not reach the ovary in time to effect fertilization. In other cases the pollen tubes burst in the style. Sometimes Buchholz was able to induce these slow-growing tubes to reach the ovules by cutting off the upper part of the style and splicing it to the tip of the ovary. This shortened the distance to be traversed by the tubes and resulted in crosses that had otherwise been impossible.

The general problem of barriers to crossability between races and between species received much attention. Some of these barriers operate early by preventing fertilization, but others are concerned with later events that produce embryo abortion. Many factors, genetic and physiological, are concerned here. Ovular tumors frequently appear in aborting seeds, probably as a result and not as a cause of abortion. These are of much interest as simple instances of atypical growth.

The use of colchicine led not only to the easy production of polyploids but to the formation in *Datura* of some very significant chimeras. These tissue mixtures were of significance not only to genetics but in clearing up some problems of morphology. In their study, as in other parts of the *Datura* work, Sophie Satina had an important part. The chimeras involved three types of polyploid tissue: $2n$, $4n$, and $8n$. The cells of each could readily be distinguished by their size, which was roughly proportional to the number of chromosome sets. Of particular interest were the periclinal chimeras, where the outer one or two cell layers are different from those beneath. These were produced by treating seed with colchicine, which sometimes affected certain layers but not others or affected the layers to a different degree. At the apical meristem the one or two outer layers could thus be "tagged" and could be recognized through all later growth as different from the ones underneath. By studying the development of leaves and flowers from the meristem, it was possible to determine from which layers they were produced and thus to make clear the morphological derivation of various structures, especially the different parts of the flower. Blakeslee regarded these layers of the meristem as true germ layers, comparable in a sense to the germ layers of embryonic animals.

Particularly in the later years much attention was given to the growth of embryos in culture media. The problem of suitable culture techniques had been studied earlier in collaboration with van Overbeek, who had attempted to induce parthenogenesis. Using the techniques he developed, it was found possible to remove the embryos from the seeds at very early stages and grow them to adult plants. By this means it was possible to obtain a full history of the growth and development of the *Datura* embryo from shortly after fertilization to the ripe seed.

This material also provided an opportunity for studying the physiology of the young embryo, especially as to its nutrient requirements and metabolism. Most of this work was carried on after the *Datura* program had been moved to Smith College. It was the first extensive study of early embryo physiology in the higher plants and was done in collaboration with J. Rappaport and J. Rietsema.

In these various approaches to *Datura* genetics the more familiar methods of genetic analysis were not neglected, although they were not used in developing the central core of the work. Five hundred and forty-one genes were identified and, of these, 81 were located in particular chromosomes and found to be distributed among all twelve. Forty-two were placed in particular chromosome-halves. Gene location was determined not only by the usual method of plotting linkage data but by other methods not generally available in other genetic material, such as the use of trisomic ratios of several sorts, compensating types, pollen-abortion genes, and crossing with certain prime types. This work alone constitutes a valuable addition to genetic knowledge.

It is evident from this brief survey that the *Datura* program has touched on a very wide range of problems and transcended a study simply of the genetics of *Datura*. Few organisms have yielded such a wealth of scientific information as has come from this plebian weed. The *Datura* program may serve as a model of careful and imaginative scientific work. In all of it, although Blakeslee was the leader and directed and coordinated the program, many others made important contributions. Belling was the source of many ideas in cytology, and this aspect of the program was ably carried on later by A. Dorothy Bergner. Buchholz was responsible for most of the work on pollen tubes and contributed many ideas on techniques. Sophie Satina was an invaluable collaborator, particularly in the studies on chimeras and in the analyses of the chromosomal differences between incompatible species. J. L. Cartledge had an important share in the work, especially in pollen analysis. Blakeslee was fortunate over the years in the men and women who were his staff and assistants. They are too numerous to mention individually, but without their cooperation the program could not have had the great success that it attained. Particular mention should be made of Amos G. Avery who, a few years after his brother's death, took the latter's place in the program and worked in it for thirty-one years. Under his guidance the present volume has been prepared and much of it has been written by him.

It is fortunate that the story of forty years of fruitful research can thus be brought together, condensed, and made clear so that the interested reader need not search through the long series of over 200 papers in which the original results are published. In this volume the whole course of the *Datura* program is presented, each advance being described against the background of those preceding it. The way in which the various problems have been solved is set forth. Not all the problems, of course, *have* been solved—and it is hoped that there will be others to carry them on still further—but much has been achieved and is built into the permanent framework of scientific advance. In reading the history of this piece of research, one experiences the same enlightenment and satisfaction that he has in reading a biography in which he can trace the development of a man's mind. This book, indeed, constitutes a large part of the scientific biography of a notable man of science. To read it is not only to understand the genetics of *Datura* but also to see how Blakeslee's mind worked—posing the important problems as they arose, meeting them with ingenuity, persistence, and critical judgment, and leading them finally toward solution.

All students of *Datura* and friends of Blakeslee are grateful both to those whose foresight and generosity have made this book possible and to those who have labored to complete it so satisfactorily. It is a fitting monument to a great geneticist.

EDMUND W. SINNOTT

Yale University
New Haven, Connecticut

# *Preface*

The Smith College Genetics Experiment Station was discontinued at the end of 1955, slightly over a year after the death of Dr. Albert F. Blakeslee, its founder and director since 1942. Many geneticists and botanists, as well as Dr. Blakeslee's immediate associates, hoped that ways and means would be found to publish some of the important recent results, and a general summary, of the *Datura* research to which he had devoted much of his lifetime. Late in 1954 a committee of the Genetics Society of America, consisting of R. E. Cleland, M. Demerec, P. C. Mangelsdorf, and E. W. Sinnott, and under the chairmanship of H. H. Plough, was organized to consider possibilities. Dr. Frans Verdoorn, then Editor of Chronica Botanica, offered to publish such a volume if the manuscript could be provided. The preparation of the manuscript was made possible by a special grant to Smith College from the National Science Foundation. Smith College has generously made available office space and other facilities necessary in the preparation of the manuscript. Actual publication of the volume was later assumed by The Ronald Press Company.

The history of the *Datura* investigations carried on from 1915 to 1955 by Dr. Blakeslee and his many co-workers is related in Chapter 1. From 1915 to 1942 the work was conducted with the liberal support of the Carnegie Institution of Washington at the Department of Genetics, Cold Spring Harbor, New York. From 1942 to 1955 the research was continued by the Genetics Experiment Station within the Department of Botany of Smith College, Northampton, Massachusetts. The continued support of the *Datura* program by these two institutions is a measure of its scientific importance.

Various projects, or problems, within the broad *Datura* research program have been supported by special grants to one or the other of the above institutions. Such grants have been received from the American Philosophical Society, National Academy of Sciences, Carnegie Corporation of New York, American Association for the Advancement of Science, National Research Council, the Rockefeller Foundation, National Cancer Institute, and the National Heart Institute of the U. S. Public Health Service, the Atomic Energy Commission, the National Science Foundation, the Research Corporation, and the Office of Naval Research. Several individuals have also given material help to the program. The generous support received from so many sources is largely responsible for the extent of the *Datura* research.

Many individuals have had a share in the *Datura* investigations. Some of these are mentioned in the Foreword or in Chapter 1. Many others appear as authors or co-authors of the *Datura* papers listed on pages xxxi to xli. Two of the present authors who were associated with Dr. Blakeslee in the research program for many years wish to take this opportunity to pay special tribute to former co-workers who gave much of scientific value to the program: Dr. A. Dorothy Bergner (cytology), the late Drs. J. Belling (cytology), J. T. Buchholz (pollen-tube growth), and J. L. Cartledge (pollen research). To the several artists and the photographers who have assisted with illustrations for the many papers as well as for this volume we extend our grateful thanks. We regret that we cannot mention the many assistants and workers who have so well performed the many technical details that have been involved in this research. We sincerely appreciate the help of librarians from the several institutions where we worked and of Mrs. Elizabeth P. Avery, who checked the literature and who assisted in proofreading and in indexing.

The authors extend thanks to Dr. E. Leete for preparing the review of investigations on the alkaloids of *Datura* (Chapter 3). We also wish to thank Dr. R. F. Dawson, who has read the manuscript of this chapter. Although not directly concerned with our own research with *Datura*, this material seemed to be of sufficient interest to be included. Dr. Jean Cummings participated for several years in the studies at Smith College on the effects of radiation. We are indebted to her for preparing a large part of Chapter 9.

We thank sincerely Dr. D. D. Keck, Dr. H. W. Rickett, and J. V. Monachino of the New York Botanical Garden, who have been very helpful in the preparation of Chapter 2. We are particularly grateful to Dr. F. R. Fosberg of the U. S. Geological Survey, Washington, D. C., and Miss Marie-Hélène Sachet of the Pacific Science Board, National Research Council. To them we are greatly indebted for much valuable criticism and advice and for assistance in assembling and writing this chapter on the historical review of the taxonomy of *Datura*—a field quite unfamiliar to us.

To Dr. E. W. Sinnott, who succeeded Dr. Blakeslee as Professor of Botany at Connecticut in 1915, the authors are extremely indebted. Between these two botanists there was a very close friendship and it is very fitting that Dr. Sinnott should have prepared the Biographical Sketch and the Foreword for this volume.

The authors are particularly appreciative of the encouragement and advice so generously given by Dr. H. H. Plough during the preparation of this material. Dr. Plough has read nearly all the manuscript and suggested many improvements, for which the authors will be ever grateful.

To the Committee of the Genetics Society of America the authors are deeply indebted. With the support of that committee and with the material assistance, herewith gratefully acknowledged, of the National Science Foundation and Smith College, this volume has become a reality. We hope that in a limited way it will serve as a memorial to Dr. Blakeslee, our leader and teacher for so many years, and to whom this volume is dedicated.

AMOS G. AVERY
SOPHIE SATINA
JACOB RIETSEMA

June, 1959

# Contents

# *Illustrations*

# Tables

# Albert Francis Blakeslee

## A Biographical Sketch

## By Edmund W. Sinnott

Albert Francis Blakeslee, whose major scientific work is reported and summarized in the present volume, was one of the leading geneticists of his time and a remarkable man in many ways.

He was born in Geneseo, New York, on November 9, 1874, and died at Northampton, Massachusetts, on November 16, 1954, a few days after his eightieth birthday. Both his father and his paternal grandfather were Methodist ministers. His education began at the East Greenwich (Rhode Island) Academy, of which his father was principal, and continued at Wesleyan University, where he graduated, *cum laude,* in 1896. After teaching in secondary schools for three years, he went to Harvard for graduate work, receiving the Master's degree there in 1900 and the doctorate in 1904.

It was at Harvard that Blakeslee first distinguished himself in research by discovering the surprising fact of heterothallism, the beginnings of sex, in the bread molds (Mucoraceae). As a result of this he received a grant that enabled him to spend two years in Germany for further study. Here he not only worked with molds and met many German botanists but also became acquainted with some of the wealth of art and music that Europe had to offer and that he so much enjoyed for the rest of his life.

On returning to the United States he spent another year at Harvard and then went to the Connecticut Agricultural College at Storrs as Professor of Botany. In his eight years there Blakeslee made an enviable record as a teacher. His work outside the classroom then turned away from the molds and in other directions. He was Director of the Summer School. He developed an agricultural botanical garden. He wrote (with C. D. Jarvis) a notable book, still one of the best, on New England trees in winter. He developed a method for distinguishing laying from nonlaying hens by the color of their beaks and feet. He studied mutations in *Rudbeckia.* At Storrs he organized what was probably the first undergraduate course in genetics in the country. He spent a year (1912–1913) in research at the Station for Experimental Evolution at Cold Spring Harbor. In all these activities he showed the remarkable versatility, originality, powers of observation, and tireless enthusiasm that always distinguished him.

These years at Storrs were pleasant ones, and he greatly enjoyed not only his teaching but his life in the small academic community. When the offer came to join the staff at Cold Spring Harbor, he was undecided whether to accept or not but finally promised to go for two years. He remained there for twenty-seven years (1915–1942). Soon after going to Cold Spring Harbor he married (1919) Margaret Dickson Bridges; and the marriage proved to be a very happy one, for these two people were ideally suited to each other.

In connection with his teaching of genetics, Blakeslee became acquainted with *Datura,* and this acquaintance ripened into lifelong devotion. At Storrs there appeared the first of those remarkable mutants upon which he worked so long. He took the Jimson weeds with him to Cold Spring Harbor and the several species of this genus soon became the center of his research.

Blakeslee's name is closely associated with *Datura,* and the present volume is concerned with his work and that of his colleagues on this interesting plant. We should not forget, however, that his interests were never restricted to any one species. He continued, from time to time, to work on the MUCORACEAE and was concerned especially with the biochemical basis of sexual differentiation here and in the higher plants. He was the first to demonstrate in detail and publish the effect of colchicine in causing chromosome doubling and early appreciated the possibilities this chemical offered. With the use of this drug he produced tetraploid races of his highly selected strains of *Rudbeckia hirta.* After Blakeslee's death seeds of these were bought by a commercial seed company and have been featured as outstanding new varieties.

The subject of sensory thresholds and of genetic differences between individuals in their ability to taste and smell greatly intrigued him. He gave the phenyl-thiocarbamide (PTC) test countless times and wrote a considerable series of papers in this field, which was so far removed from *Datura* genetics. What interested him in it, perhaps, was not so much the genetic significance of this work as the demonstration it so dramatically made that people are not turned out of the same hereditary mold but are individually *different,* a conception that still needs to be continually stressed.

This emphasizes one of Blakeslee's conspicuous traits, his interest in people and his concern with human problems. He knew the vital importance of good teaching and recognized the necessity in it for demonstrations as well as for words. He was always a good showman, and his little paper—"Teachers Talk Too Much"—written after he went to Smith College, is worth reading by everyone who deals with education at any level.

Blakeslee's interest in problems outside research was shown in many other ways. For a number of years he was Director of the Carnegie Station at Cold Spring Harbor and made an excellent administrator. He took his responsibilities as an officer of various organizations very seriously and not as perfunctory duties. He continually sought to better their policies and practices—as witness the list of thirty proposals for the improvement of Sigma Xi at Smith College given in his talk as retiring president of the Chapter.

A few days before his death, in a letter to a friend, he remarked with the touch of humor present in so much of what he said, that as a clergyman's son he had acquired both through heredity and environment a sensitive conscience which he had not always succeeded in keeping under control! This social conscience was active throughout his life.

One of the aspects of the *Datura* program in which he took great satisfaction was the opportunity of bringing to it a group of collaborators, young and old. He enjoyed sharing with others the labor and adventure of research. Blakeslee did not dominate these people but cooperated with them. He scrupulously gave credit to everyone for what they did; on most of his many papers the names of others appear besides his own and in joint papers his name is often placed last.

The atmosphere of the *Datura* laboratory, particularly in the busy summer season, was always exciting. Discoveries were being made, ideas were hatched, and all were interested in the progress of the work. No one could help feeling, too, the genuine personal interest that he took in everyone's welfare. This was warmly shared by Mrs. Blakeslee, and the generous hospitality of their home is gratefully remembered by all alumni of the *Datura* group.

When Blakeslee reached the age of retirement at Cold Spring Harbor, he was fortunate in being invited to Smith College as the William Allan Neilson Professor of Botany for the year 1942–43, and in 1943 he was appointed Visiting Professor of Botany. Here he spent twelve fruitful years. At Smith College he organized the Smith College Genetics Experiment Station, which he directed until his death. In addition to the support from Smith College he sought and received assistance and financial backing from many other sources. He obtained funds to build a large modern greenhouse, which is a valuable addition to the permanent facilities of the College.

The same friendly spirit was evident in the *Datura* group there as well. He delighted in the opportunity to teach once more. His concern with the problems of college and community was also close, as shown by his activity in the Smith College Faculty Club and in town-and-gown affairs. His contacts with the three neighboring colleges ( Mt. Holyoke College, University of Massachusetts, and Amherst College) led to his organization of the Four College Genetics Conference. As his birthdays accumulated, he formed the O.B.N.D. Club (Out But Not Down) for senior citizens. The latter part of his life at Northampton was clouded by the tragedy of Mrs. Blakeslee's sudden death in 1947.

Blakeslee was an active or honorary member of many scientific societies both here and abroad. From 1916, when he served as secretary of Section G of the American Association for the Advancement of Science, until his death, he held many important offices in these societies, as: Vice President (1916) and President (1930), American Society of Naturalists; Vice President (1924) and President (1950), Botanical Society of America; Vice President (1953), Human Genetics Society; President (1933), Torrey Botanical Club; President (1946), Society for Study of Development and Growth. He was also a member of the American Philosophical Society, Genetics Society of America, National Academy of Sciences, Phi Beta Kappa, Sigma Xi, Phi Sigma, and others. In 1940 he served as President of the American Association for the Advancement of Science, one of the few botanists to hold this high office.

Among the scientific societies of foreign countries to which he had been elected a member (honorary, associate, or corresponding) were those of India, Japan, France, London, Moscow, Leningrad, Belgium, Denmark, Sweden, and the Netherlands. During his numerous trips abroad Blakeslee always made an effort to visit as many of his correspondents in their laboratories as possible. His keen interest in biological research of all kinds made him welcome in laboratories in many lands.

His achievements were given recognition during his active years by the awarding of honorary degrees to him by several universities here and abroad: University of San Marcos, D.Sc. (1925); University of Delhi, D.Sc. (1947); Yale University, D.Sc. (1947); Smith College, D.Sc. (1952); Wesleyan University, D.Sc. (1931); University of Paris, D.Sc. (1951); University of Arkansas, L.L.D. (1947). It was characteristic of him that his reception of these honors was often not known to his immediate colleagues for some time. He was also the recipient of numerous medals and prizes for specific achievements or projects.

Close to his heart through all these years was always that same homely, rank-smelling weed to which so much of his life was given. When Edna St. Vincent Millay wrote rather disparagingly of this thorn apple in one of her poems and asked "who would plant this by his dwelling?" he rose to its defense and wrote her "*I* would plant this by my dwelling and have done so for the last thirty years." It is most appropriate that the present volume should be devoted to a presentation of the rich fruits of the research upon *Datura* which Blakeslee and his colleagues gathered through the years. It is the memorial that he would most have valued.

# Datura Bibliography[*]

## A. F. Blakeslee and Associates

## 1910–1956

The figures in italics between parentheses throughout this book refer to this numbered list of papers.

### 1910

*1.* Blakeslee, A. F.  The botanic garden as a field museum of agriculture.  Science 31: 684–688.

### 1916

*2. Datura* investigations.  Carnegie Inst. Wash. Yearbook 15: 131.

### 1917

*3.* Blakeslee, A. F., and B. T. Avery, Jr.  Adzuki beans and Jimson weeds.  Jour. Hered. 8: 125–131.
*4. Datura* investigations.  Carnegie Inst. Wash. Yearbook 16: 125–127.

### 1918

*5. Datura* investigations.  Carnegie Inst. Wash. Yearbook 17: 116.

### 1919

*6.* Blakeslee, A. F., and B. T. Avery, Jr.  Mutations in the Jimson weed.  Jour. Hered. 10: 111–120.
*7. Datura* investigations.  Carnegie Inst. Wash. Yearbook 18: 138.

### 1920

*8.* Blakeslee, A. F., J. Belling, and M. E. Farnham.  Chromosomal duplication and Mendelian phenomena in *Datura* mutants.  Science 52: 388–390.
*9. Datura* investigations.  Carnegie Inst. Wash. Yearbook 19: 110, 130–131.

### 1921

*10.* Belling, J.  Counting chromosomes in pollen mother cells.  Amer. Nat. 55: 573–574.
*11.* Blakeslee, A. F.  A graft-infectious disease of *Datura* resembling a vegetative mutation.  Jour. Genetics 11: 17–36.

[*] References other than those of Blakeslee and Associates may be found on page 263.

12. BLAKESLEE, A. F. The globe mutant in the Jimson weed (*Datura stramonium*). Genetics 6: 241–264.
13. BLAKESLEE, A. F. Types of mutations and their possible significance in evolution. Amer. Nat. 55: 254–267.
14. BLAKESLEE, A. F. An apparent case of non-Mendelian inheritance in *Datura* due to a disease. Proc. Nat. Acad. Sci. 7: 116–118.
15. BLAKESLEE, A. F. The Globe, a simple trisomic mutant in *Datura*. Proc. Nat. Acad. Sci. 7: 148–152.
16. *Datura* investigations. Carnegie Inst. Wash. Yearbook 20: 103–109.

### 1922

17. BELLING, J., and A. F. BLAKESLEE. The assortment of chromosomes in triploid Daturas. Amer. Nat. 56: 339–346.
18. BLAKESLEE, A. F. Variations in *Datura* due to changes in chromosome number. Amer. Nat. 56: 16–31.
19. BLAKESLEE, A. F., J. BELLING, M. E. FARNHAM, and A. D. BERGNER. A haploid mutant in the Jimson weed, *Datura stramonium*. Science 55: 646–647.
20. BLAKESLEE, A. F., J. BELLING, and J. A. HARRIS. The probability established by a culture of given size that a mating is capable of producing only dominant individuals. Amer. Nat. 56: 458–461.
21. BUCHHOLZ, J. T., and A. F. BLAKESLEE. Studies of the pollen tubes and abortive ovules of the Globe mutant of *Datura*. Science 55: 597–599.
22. SINNOTT, E. W., and A. F. BLAKESLEE. Structural changes associated with factor mutations and with chromosome mutations in *Datura*. Proc. Nat. Acad. Sci. 8: 17–19.
23. *Datura* investigations. Carnegie Inst. Wash. Yearbook 21: 95–100.

### 1923

24. BELLING, J. The attraction between homologous chromosomes. Eugenics, Genetics and the Family I: 84–85.
25. BELLING, J. Microscopic methods used in examining chromosomes in iron-aceto-carmine. Amer. Nat. 57: 92–96.
26. BELLING, J., and A. F. BLAKESLEE. The reduction division in haploid, diploid, triploid and tetraploid Daturas. Proc. Nat. Acad. Sci. 9: 106–111.
27. BLAKESLEE, A. F. Variations in the Jimson weed (*Datura stramonium*) caused by differences in the number of chromosomes. Eugenics, Genetics and the Family 1: 82–83.
28. BLAKESLEE, A. F., J. BELLING, and M. E. FARNHAM. Inheritance in tetraploid Daturas. Bot. Gaz. 76: 329–373.
29. BLAKESLEE, A. F., and M. E. FARNHAM. Bottle grafting. Jour. Hered. 14: 171–173.
30. BLAKESLEE, A. F., and M. E. FARNHAM. Trisomic inheritance in the Poinsettia mutant of *Datura*. Amer. Nat. 57: 481–495.
31. *Datura* investigations. Carnegie Inst. Wash. Yearbook 22: 88–96.

### 1924

32. BELLING, J., and A. F. BLAKESLEE. The distribution of chromosomes in tetraploid Daturas. Amer. Nat. 58: 60–70.
33. BELLING, J., and A. F. BLAKESLEE. The configurations and sizes of the chromosomes in the trivalents of 25-chromosome Daturas. Proc. Nat. Acad. Sci. 10: 116–120.
34. BLAKESLEE, A. F. Distinction between primary and secondary chromosomal mutants in *Datura*. Proc. Nat. Acad. Sci. 10: 109–116.
35. BLAKESLEE, A. F. Bottle grafting again. Jour. Hered. 15: 54.
36. BLAKESLEE, A. F., and J. BELLING. Chromosomal chimeras in the Jimson weed. Science 60: 19–20.

37. BLAKESLEE, A. F., and J. BELLING.  Chromosomal mutations in the Jimson weed, *Datura stramonium.* Jour. Hered. 15: 195–206.
38. *Datura* investigations. Carnegie Inst. Wash. Yearbook 23: 24–31.

### 1925

39. *Datura* investigations. Carnegie Inst. Wash. Yearbook 24: 22–26.

### 1926

40. BELLING, J., and A. F. BLAKESLEE.  On the attachment of non-homologous chromosomes at the reduction division in certain 25-chromosome Daturas. Proc. Nat. Acad. Sci. 12: 7–11.
41. BLAKESLEE, A. F., and J. L. CARTLEDGE.  Pollen abortion in chromosomal types of *Datura.* Proc. Nat. Acad. Sci. 12: 315–323.
42. *Datura* investigations. Carnegie Inst. Wash. Yearbook 25: 40–46.

### 1927

43. BELLING, J., and A. F. BLAKESLEE.  The assortment of chromosomes in haploid Daturas. La Cellule 37: 355–365.
44. BLAKESLEE, A. F.  The chromosomal constitution of Nubbin, a compound ($2n + 1$) type in *Datura.* Proc. Nat. Acad. Sci. 13: 79–85.
45. BLAKESLEE, A. F.  Nubbin, a compound chromosomal type in *Datura.* Annals N.Y. Acad. Sci. 30: 1–29.
46. BLAKESLEE, A. F.  Irregularities of chromosome behavior in relation to plant and animal improvement. Anat. Rec. 37: 105.
47. BLAKESLEE, A. F., and J. L. CARTLEDGE.  Sterility of pollen in *Datura.* Mem. Hort. Soc. N.Y. 3: 305–312.
48. BLAKESLEE, A. F., G. MORRISON, and A. G. AVERY.  Mutations in a haploid *Datura.* Jour. Hered. 18: 193–199.
49. BUCHHOLZ, J. T., and A. F. BLAKESLEE.  Abnormalities in pollen-tube growth in *Datura* due to the gene "tricarpel." Proc. Nat. Acad. Sci. 13: 242–249.
50. BUCHHOLZ, J. T., and A. F. BLAKESLEE.  Pollen-tube growth at various temperatures. Amer. Jour. Bot. 14: 358–369.
51. BUCHHOLZ, J. T., and A. F. BLAKESLEE.  Pollen-tube behavior with reference to sterility in *Datura.* Mem. Hort. Soc. N.Y. 3: 245–260.
52. GAGER, C. S., and A. F. BLAKESLEE.  Chromosome and gene mutations in *Datura* following exposure to radium rays. Proc. Nat. Acad. Sci. 13: 75–79.
53. *Datura* investigations. Carnegie Inst. Wash. Yearbook 26: 36–39.

### 1928

54. BLAKESLEE, A. F. Genetics of *Datura.* Verh. d. 5tes Inter. Kongresses für Vererbungswissenschaft 1: 117–130.
55. *Datura* investigations. Carnegie Inst. Wash. Yearbook 27: 41–49.

### 1929

56. BLAKESLEE, A. F.  Cryptic types in *Datura* due to chromosomal interchange and their geographical distribution. Jour. Hered. 20: 177–190.
57. BLAKESLEE, A. F.  An attempt to analyze the composition of Nb, a compound ($2n + 1$) chromosomal type in *Datura.* Proc. Intern. Congress Plant Sci. 1: 831–832.
58. BUCHHOLZ, J. T., and A. F. BLAKESLEE.  Pollen-tube growth in crosses between balanced chromosomal types of *Datura stramonium.* Genetics 14: 538–568.
59. *Datura* investigations. Carnegie Inst. Wash. Yearbook 28: 40–45.

### 1930

60. BERGNER, A. D., and A. F. BLAKESLEE.  Chromosome configurations in intra- and inter-specific hybrids of *Datura.* Proc. 5th Intern. Bot. Congress: 126–127.
61. BLAKESLEE, A. F.  Genetics at Storrs. Storrs Agric. Exp. Sta. Bull. 168: 225–231.

62. BLAKESLEE, A. F., A. D. BERGNER, and A. G. AVERY. Compensating extra chromosomal types in *Datura* and their use as testers. Science 71: 516.
63. BLAKESLEE, A. F., and R. E. CLELAND. Circle formation in *Datura* and *Oenothera*. Proc. Nat. Acad. Sci. 16: 177–183.
64. BUCHHOLZ, J. T., and A. F. BLAKESLEE.. Pollen-tube growth of the primary mutant of *Datura*, Rolled, and its two secondaries. Proc. Nat. Acad. Sci. 16: 190–195.
65. BUCHHOLZ, J. T., and A. F. BLAKESLEE. Radium experiments with *Datura*. I. The identification and transmission of lethals of pollen-tube growth in $F_1$'s from radium-treated parents. Jour. Hered. 21: 119–129.
66. BUCHHOLZ, J. T., and A. F. BLAKESLEE. Pollen-tube growth and control of gametophytic selection in Cocklebur, a 25-chromosome *Datura*. Bot. Gaz. 90: 366–383.
67. CLELAND, R. E., and A. F. BLAKESLEE. Interaction between complexes as evidence for segmental interchange in *Oenothera*. Proc. Nat. Acad. Sci. 16: 183–189.
68. *Datura* investigations. Carnegie Inst. Wash. Yearbook 29: 35–44.

1931

69. BLAKESLEE, A. F. The genetic viewpoint. Science 73: 571–577.
70. BLAKESLEE, A. F. Extra chromosomes, a source of variations in the Jimson weed. Smithsonian Report 3096 (1930): 431–450.
71. BLAKESLEE, A. F. New methods for locating genes in particular chromosomes. Science 73: 508.
72. BUCHHOLZ, J. T. The dissection, staining and mounting of styles in the study of pollen-tube distribution. Stain Tech. 6: 13–24.
73. CLELAND, R. E., and A. F. BLAKESLEE. Segmental interchange, the basis of chromosomal attachments in *Oenothera*. Cytologia 2: 175–233.
74. *Datura* investigations. Carnegie Inst. Wash. Yearbook 30: 40–45.

1932

75. BERGNER, A. D., and A. F. BLAKESLEE. Cytology of the *Ferox-quercifolia-stramonium* triangle in *Datura*. Proc. Nat. Acad. Sci. 18: 151–159.
76. BLAKESLEE, A. F. The species problem in *Datura*. Proc. 6th Intern. Congr. Genetics 1: 104–120.
77. BLAKESLEE, A. F., and A. D. BERGNER. Methods of synthesizing pure-breeding types with predicted characters in the Jimson weed. Science 76:571.
78. BUCHHOLZ, J. T., and A. F. BLAKESLEE. Pollen-tube growth in primary and secondary $2n + 1$ Daturas. Amer. Jour. Bot. 19: 604–626.
79. BUCHHOLZ, J. T., C. C. DOAK, and A. F. BLAKESLEE. Control of gametophytic selection in *Datura* through shortening and splicing of styles. Bull. Torrey Bot. Club: 59: 109–118.
80. *Datura* investigations. Carnegie Inst. Wash. Yearbook 31: 40–44.

1933

81. BERGNER, A. D., S. SATINA, and A. F. BLAKESLEE. Prime types in *Datura*. Proc. Nat. Acad. Sci. 19: 103–115.
82. BLAKESLEE, A. F., A. D. BERGNER, and A. G. AVERY. Methods of synthesizing pure-breeding types in the Jimson weed, *Datura stramonium*. Proc. Nat. Acad. Sci. 19: 115–122.
83. *Datura* investigations. Carnegie Inst. Wash. Yearbook 32: 35–39.

1934

84. BERGNER, A. D., and A. F. BLAKESLEE. Cytology of a translocation of the 1·2 chromosome in *Datura*. Bull. Torrey Bot. Club: 61: 197–209.
85. BERGNER, A. D., J. L. CARTLEDGE, and A. F. BLAKESLEE. Chromosome behaviour due to a gene which prevents metaphase pairing in *Datura*. Cytologia 6: 19–37.

86. BLAKESLEE, A. F. New Jimson weeds from old chromosomes. Jour. Hered. 25: 80–108.

87. BLAKESLEE, A. F. Genes in *Datura* classified as to effects on gametophyte and sporophyte. Amer. Nat. 68: 468.

88. BLAKESLEE, A. F., and A. G. AVERY. Three genes located in the 21 · 22 chromosome of the Jimson weed. Jour. Hered. 25: 393–404.

89. BLAKESLEE, A. F., and A. G. AVERY. Summary of 10 years records of breeding behavior of primary and secondary $2n + 1$ types in *Datura*. Amer. Nat. 68: 83.

90. BLAKESLEE, A. F., and A. G. AVERY. Visible genes from aged seeds. Amer. Nat. 68: 466.

91. BLAKESLEE, A. F., and S. SATINA. Les plantes diffèrent-elles des animaux par des gamètes léthals? Compt. Rend. Acad. Sci. Paris V. 198 No. 8, 768–770.

92. BUCHHOLZ, J. T., and A. F. BLAKESLEE. Location of genes responsible for pollen tube abnormalities. Collect. Net 9: 181.

93. BUCHHOLZ, J. T., C. C. DOAK, and A. F. BLAKESLEE. Results obtained from spliced styles. Amer. Nat. 68: 162.

94. CARTLEDGE, J. L., and A. F. BLAKESLEE. Mutation rate increased by aging seeds as shown by pollen abortion. Proc. Nat. Acad. Sci. 20: 103–110.

95. CARTLEDGE, J. L., and A. F. BLAKESLEE. Inheritance of a number of mutations resulting from aging seed. Collect. Net 9: 182.

96. CARTLEDGE, J. L., and A. F. BLAKESLEE. Types of mutations affecting pollen grains which have been induced by x-raying and aging seeds of *Datura*. Amer. Nat. 68: 163.

97. SATINA, S., A. F. BLAKESLEE, and A. G. AVERY. Twins in the Jimson weed, *Datura stramonium*. Amer. Nat. 68: 162.

98. SINNOTT, E. W., A. F. BLAKESLEE, and H. HOUGHTALING. The relation of nuclear content to cell size in the polyploid series of *Datura stramonium*. Amer. Nat. 68: 67.

99. SINNOTT, E. W., H. HOUGHTALING, and A. F. BLAKESLEE. The comparative anatomy of extra-chromosomal types in *Datura stramonium*. Carnegie Inst. Wash. Publ. 451.

100. *Datura* investigations. Carnegie Inst. Wash. Yearbook 33: 36–39.

## 1935

101. BERGNER, A. D., and A. F. BLAKESLEE. Chromosome ends in *Datura discolor*. Proc. Nat. Acad. Sci. 21: 369–374.

102. BLAKESLEE, A. F., A. G. AVERY, and A. D. BERGNER. A type in *Datura* with extra-chromosomal material which in inheritance resembles a recessive. Science 81: 463–464.

103. BLAKESLEE, A. F., M. J. MURRAY, and S. SATINA. Crossability in relation to taxonomic classification in the genus *Datura*. Amer. Nat. 69: 57.

104. BUCHHOLZ, J. T., A. F. BLAKESLEE, and A. G. AVERY. Pollen-tube growth of a translocation of the 1 · 2 chromosome in *Datura*. Proc. Nat. Acad. Sci. 21: 208–213.

105. BUCHHOLZ, J. T., L. F. WILLIAMS, and A. F. BLAKESLEE. Pollen-tube growth of ten species of *Datura* in interspecific pollinations. Proc. Nat. Acad. Sci. 21: 651–656.

106. CARTLEDGE, J. L., and A. F. BLAKESLEE. Mutation rate from old *Datura* seeds. Science 81: 492–493.

107. CARTLEDGE, J. L., M. J. MURRAY, and A. F. BLAKESLEE. Increased mutation rate from aged *Datura* pollen. Proc. Nat. Acad. Sci. 21: 597–600.

108. SATINA, S., and A. F. BLAKESLEE. Cytological effects of a gene in *Datura* which causes dyad formation in sporogenesis. Bot. Gaz. 96: 521–523.

109. SATINA, S., and A. F. BLAKESLEE. Fertilization in the incompatible cross *Datura stramonium* x *D. metel*. Bull. Torrey Bot. Club 62: 301–312.

110. *Datura* investigations. Carnegie Inst. Wash. Yearbook 34: 37–40.

## 1936

111. BLAKESLEE, A. F. Twenty-five years of genetics, 1910–1935. Brooklyn Bot. Garden Mem. 4: 29–40.
112. BLAKESLEE, A. F., A. G. AVERY, and A. D. BERGNER. A method of isolating tertiary $2n + 1$ forms in *Datura* from prime types by use of double half chromosomes. Science 83: 486.
113. BLAKESLEE, A. F., A. D. BERGNER, and A. G. AVERY. A new method of synthesizing pure-breeding types with extra chromosomal material in *Datura*. Amer. Nat. 70: 255–257.
114. BUCHHOLZ, J. T., and A. F. BLAKESLEE. Genes from radium treatment affecting pollen-tube growth in *Datura*. Genetics 21: 731–751.
115. CARTLEDGE, J. L., L. V. BARTON, and A. F. BLAKESLEE. Heat and moisture as factors in the increased mutation rate from *Datura* seeds. Proc. Amer. Phil. Soc. 76: 663–685.
116. *Datura* investigations. Carnegie Inst. Wash. Yearbook 35: 37–40.

## 1937

117. BLAKESLEE, A. F. Dédoublement du nombre de chromosomes chez les plantes par traitement chimique. Compt. Rend. Acad. Sci. 205: 476–479.
118. BLAKESLEE, A. F., and A. G. AVERY. Methods of inducing doubling of chromosomes in plants. Jour. Hered. 28: 393–411.
119. BLAKESLEE, A. F., and A. G. AVERY. Methods of inducing chromosome doubling in plants by treatment with colchicine. Science 86: 408.
120. BLAKESLEE, A. F., A. G. AVERY, and A. D. BERGNER. Bud sports in *Datura* due to elimination of specific chromosomes. Science 85: 442–443.
121. BLAKESLEE, A. F., A. D. BERGNER, and A. G. AVERY. Geographical distribution of chromosomal prime types in *Datura stramonium*. Cytologia, Fujii jub. 1070–1093.
122. SATINA, S., and A. F. BLAKESLEE. Chromosome behavior in triploids of *Datura stramonium*. I. The male gametophyte. Amer. Jour. Bot. 24: 518–527.
123. SATINA, S., and A. F. BLAKESLEE. Chromosome behavior in triploid *Datura*. II. The female gametophyte. Amer. Jour. Bot. 24: 621–627.
124. SATINA, S., A. F. BLAKESLEE, and A. G. AVERY. Balanced and unbalanced haploids in *Datura*. Jour. Hered. 28: 192–202.
125. *Datura* investigations. Carnegie Inst. Wash. Yearbook 36: 38–44.

## 1938

126. BLAKESLEE, A. F. Colchicine. Teaching Biologist 7: 52.
127. BLAKESLEE, A. F. Studies in the behavior of chromosomes. USDA Yearbook Separate No. 1605, 1–35.
128. BLAKESLEE, A. F., and A. G. AVERY. Fifteen-year breeding records of $2n + 1$ types in *D. stramonium*. Cooperation in Research, Carnegie Inst. Wash. Publ. 501, 315–351.
129. BUCHHOLZ, J. T., and A. F. BLAKESLEE. Direct demonstration in the male gametophyte of the result of crossing-over in *Datura*. Collect. Net 13: 150.
130. INMAN, O. L., and A. F. BLAKESLEE. New or modified chlorophylls resulting from a recessive pale mutation in *Datura*. Science 87: 428–429.
131. SATINA, S., A. F. BLAKESLEE, and A. G. AVERY. Chromosome behavior in triploid *Datura*. III. The seed. Amer. Jour. Bot. 25: 595–602.
132. *Datura* investigations. Carnegie Inst. Wash. Yearbook 37: 35–40.

## 1939

133. BLAKESLEE, A. F. The present and potential service of chemistry to plant breeding. Amer. Jour. Bot. 26: 163–172.
134. *Datura* investigations. Carnegie Inst. Wash. Yearbook 38: 176–185.

**1940**

135. BERGNER, A. D., A. G. AVERY, and A. F. BLAKESLEE. Chromosomal deficiencies in *Datura stramonium* induced by colchicine treatment. Amer. Jour. Bot. 27: 676–683.

136. BLAKESLEE, A. F., A. G. AVERY, and A. D. BERGNER. Genes associated with prime types in *Datura* and their possible relation to the hypothesis of position effect. Genetics 25: 111.

137. SATINA, S., A. F. BLAKESLEE, and A. G. AVERY. Demonstration of the three germ layers in the shoot apex of *Datura* by means of induced polyploidy in periclinal chimeras. Amer. Jour. Bot. 27: 895–905.

138. *Datura* investigations. Carnegie Inst. Wash. Yearbook 39: 201–211.

**1941**

139. AVERY, A. G., and A. F. BLAKESLEE. A white-flowered race of *Datura* which is genetically distinct from similar white races in nature. Proc. Nat. Acad. Sci. 27: 512–518.

140. BERGNER, A. D. Chromosome association in *Datura*. Proc. 7th Intern. Congr. Genetics: 63–64.

141. BLAKESLEE, A. F. The induction of polyploids and their genetic significance. Proc. 7th Intern. Congr. Genetics: 65–72.

142. BLAKESLEE, A. F. Effect of induced polyploidy in plants. Amer. Nat. 75: 117–135.

143. BLAKESLEE, A. F. Chromosomal interchanges. Cytology, genetics, and evolution. Univ. of Penn. Bicentennial Conference: 37–46.

144. BLAKESLEE, A. F. Growth patterns in plants. Growth, 5. Suppl. 77–88.

145. BLAKESLEE, A. F., and A. G. AVERY. Classification and location of genes in *Datura*. Genetics 26: 138–139.

146. BLAKESLEE, A. F., and A. G. AVERY. Genes in *Datura* which induce morphological effects resembling those due to environment. Science 93: 436–437.

147. BUCHHOLZ, J. T., and A. F. BLAKESLEE. Pollen-tube growth in intra- and interspecific pollinations between balanced polyploids of *Datura*. Genetics 26: 142–143.

148. SATINA, S., A. D. BERGNER, and A. F. BLAKESLEE. Morphological differentiation in chromosomes of *Datura stramonium*. Amer. Jour. Bot. 28: 383–390.

149. SATINA, S., and A. F. BLAKESLEE. Periclinal chimeras in *Datura stramonium* in relation to development of leaf and flower. Amer. Jour. Bot. 28: 862–871.

150. VAN OVERBEEK, J., M. E. CONKLIN, and A. F. BLAKESLEE. Factors in coconut milk essential for growth and development of very young *Datura* embryos. Science 94: 350–351.

151. VAN OVERBEEK, J., M. E. CONKLIN, and A. F. BLAKESLEE. Chemical stimulation of ovule development and its possible relation to parthenogenesis. Amer. Jour. Bot. 28: 647–656.

152. *Datura* investigations. Carnegie Inst. Wash. Yearbook 40: 211–225.

**1942**

153. BLAKESLEE, A. F. Induced evolution in plants through chromosome changes. Proc. 8th Amer. Sc. Congress. III. Biol. Sc.: 173. Dept. State.

154. BLAKESLEE, A. F. Determination of the factors involved in chemical regulation of embryo development in plants with possibility of their ultimate control. Amer. Phil. Soc. Year Book: 158–159.

155. SANSOME, E. R., S. SATINA, and A. F. BLAKESLEE. Disintegration of ovules in tetraploid-diploid and in incompatible species crosses in *Datura*. Bull. Torrey Bot. Club 69: 405–420.

156. VAN OVERBEEK, J., M. E. CONKLIN, and A. F. BLAKESLEE. Cultivation in vitro of small *Datura* embryos. Amer. Jour. Bot. 29: 472–477.

157. *Datura* investigations. Carnegie Inst. Wash. Yearbook 41: 176–180.

**1943**

158. BERGNER, A. D. Geographical distribution of chromosomal types in *Datura metel*. Amer. Jour. Bot. 30: 222–230.
159. BERGNER, A. D. Chromosomal interchange among six species of *Datura* in nature. Amer. Jour. Bot. 30: 431–440.
160. BERGNER, A. D., and A. F. BLAKESLEE. Chromosome ends in *Datura pruinosa*. Proc. Nat. Acad. Sci. 29: 1–7.
161. SATINA, S., and A. F. BLAKESLEE. Periclinal chimeras in *Datura* in relation to the development of the carpel. Amer. Jour. Bot. 30: 453–462.

**1944**

162. BERGNER, A. D. Chromosome associations in tetraploid hybrids between prime type 1 and prime type 2 in *Datura stramonium*. Proc. Nat. Acad. Sci. 30: 302–308.
163. BLAKESLEE, A. F. Smith College conference on plant embryo culture. Science 100: 497–498.
164. BLAKESLEE, A. F., and S. SATINA. New hybrids from incompatible crosses in *Datura* through culture of excised embryos on malt media. Science 99: 331–334.
165. SATINA, S. Periclinal chimeras in *Datura* in relation to development and structure (A) of the style and stigma, (B) of calyx and corolla. Amer. Jour. Bot. 31: 493–502.

**1945**

166. BLAKESLEE, A. F. Removing some of the barriers to crossability in plants. Proc. Amer. Phil. Soc. 89: 561–574.
167. CARSON, G. L. A. The crossability of *Datura quercifolia* with seven species of the genus. B. A study of the hybrids from the cross between *Datura inoxia* and *Brugmansia suaveolens*. Unpublished thesis, Smith College.
168. SANZ, C. Pollen-tube growth in intergeneric pollinations on *Datura stramonium*. Proc. Nat. Acad. Sci. 31: 361–367.
169. SATINA, S. Periclinal chimeras in *Datura* in relation to the development and structure of the ovule. Amer. Jour. Bot. 32: 72–81.

**1946**

170. BLAKESLEE, A. F., S. SATINA, and A. G. AVERY. Genetic evidence suggesting that egg cells in *Datura* may sometimes develop from the epidermal layer. Amer. Jour. Bot. 33: 818.
171. LEAVENWORTH, M. M. Barriers to embryo formation in interspecific pollinations of *Datura*. Unpublished thesis, Smith College.
172. McLEAN, S. Interspecific crosses involving *Datura ceratocaula* obtained by embryo dissection. Amer. Jour. Bot. 33: 630–638.
173. SATINA, S., A. F. BLAKESLEE, and A. G. AVERY. Periclinal chimeras in *Datura*. Amer. Jour. Bot. 33: 826.

**1947**

174. BLAKESLEE, A. F., and S. SATINA. Further study of crossability in *Datura*. Amer. Jour. Bot. 34: 580.
175. DOERPINGHAUS, L. S. Differences between species in *Datura* in utilization of five carbohydrates. Amer. Jour. Bot. 34: 583.

**1948**

176. AVERY, A. G., and A. F. BLAKESLEE. Effect of extra chromosomes on the shape of stigmas of *Datura stramonium*. Genetics 33: 603.
177. CUMMINGS, J. M. Chromosome end arrangement in *Datura ceratocaula*. Amer. Jour. Bot. 35: 444–454.

178. DOERPINGHAUS, L. S. The effect of various sugars on the growth of excised embryos in ten species of *Datura*. Unpublished thesis, Smith College.
179. GARDELLA, C. Relative times of mitosis in pollen tubes of ten species of *Datura*. Amer. Jour. Bot. 35: 792.
180. HANDLER, H. S. Triploid hybrids of three species of *Datura*. Amer. Jour. Bot. 35: 793.
181. SACHET, M. H. Fertilization in six incompatible species crosses of *Datura*. Amer. Jour. Bot. 35: 302–309.
182. SANDERS, M. E. Embryo development in four *Datura* species following self and hybrid pollination. Amer. Jour. Bot. 35: 525–532.

### 1949

183. BLAKESLEE, A. F. Control of evolution and life processes in plants. Year Book of United Hortic. 30–33.
184. BLAKESLEE, A. F. Chromosomes, chemical stimulators, and inhibitors of normal and abnormal plant growth. Proc. First Nat. Cancer Conference: 42–49.
185. BLAKESLEE, A. F., and S. SATINA. Differences in crossability between species of *Datura* due to individual races used in the cross. Amer. Jour. Bot. 36: 795.
186. GARDELLA, C. Relative times of mitosis in the ten species of *Datura*. Unpublished thesis, Smith College.
187. JOSHI, P. C. A comparative study of two intergeneric hybrids, *Datura inoxia* × *Brugmansia suaveolens* and *Datura inoxia* × *Brugmansia rosei*, and their parents. Unpublished thesis, Smith College.
188. SAWYER, M. A colchicine-induced chimera in a *Datura* hybrid, 2n for one species and 4n for another. Amer. Jour. Bot. 36: 802.

### 1950

189. BLAKESLEE, A. F. New hybrids in *Datura* from cultures of excised embryos. Proc. 7th Intern. Congress of Bot.: 324–325.
190. GARDELLA, C. Overcoming barriers to crossability due to style length. Amer. Jour. Bot. 37: 219–224.
191. RAPPAPORT, J. A comparison of effects of nucleic acids and extracts of ovular tumors on the development of *Datura* embryos. Amer. Jour. Bot. 37: 682.
192. RAPPAPORT, J., S. SATINA, and A. F. BLAKESLEE. Ovular tumors and inhibition of embryo growth in incompatible crosses of *Datura*. Science 111: 276–277.
193. RAPPAPORT, J., S. SATINA, and A. F. BLAKESLEE. Extracts of ovular tumors and their inhibition of embryo growth in *Datura*. Amer. Jour. Bot. 37: 586–595.
194. SANDERS, M. E. Development of self and hybrid *Datura* embryos in artificial culture. Amer. Jour. Bot. 37: 6–15.
195. SATINA, S. Preferential functioning of 2n pollen grain in certain species crosses of *Datura*. Amer. Jour. Bot. 37: 666–667.
196. SATINA, S., and A. F. BLAKESLEE. Chromosomal end arrangements due to segmental interchanges in ten species of *Datura*. Proc. 7th Intern. Congress of Bot.: 223.
197. SATINA, S., and A. F. BLAKESLEE. Periclinal chimeras as a tool in determining the contribution of germ layers to floral organs in *Datura*. Proc. 7th Intern. Congress of Bot.: 351.
198. SATINA, S., J. RAPPAPORT, and A. F. BLAKESLEE. Ovular tumors connected with incompatible crosses in *Datura*. Amer. Jour. Bot. 37: 576–586.
199. SAWYER, M. The effects of colchicine on sterile numerical triploid hybrids in *Datura*. Unpublished thesis, Smith College.
200. SOLOMON, B. Inhibiting effect of autoclaved malt preventing the in vitro growth of *Datura* embryos. Amer. Jour. Bot. 37: 1–5.

### 1951

201. BLAKESLEE, A. F. "Control of evolution and life processes in plants." Plant growth substances, Univ. of Wisconsin, 57–66.

202. Brugge, P. Pollen germination and pollen-tube growth in ten species of *Datura* on artificial media. Unpublished thesis, Smith College.

## 1952

203. Cole, K. The primary and secondary trisomics of *Datura stramonium* and the influence of their extra chromosomes on interspecific crossability. Unpublished thesis, Smith College.

204. Rietsema, J. The presence of indole-3-acetic acid in ovular tumors of incompatible *Datura* crosses and its possible role as an embryo inhibitor. Rec. Gen. Soc. Amer. 21: 62.

## 1953

205. Paris, D., J. Rietsema, S. Satina, and A. F. Blakeslee. Effect of amino acids, especially aspartic acid and glutamic acid and their amides, on the growth of *Datura stramonium* embryos in vitro. Proc. Nat. Acad. Sci. 39: 1205–1212.

206. Rietsema, J., S. Satina, and A. F. Blakeslee. The effect of sucrose on the growth of *Datura stramonium* embryos in vitro. Amer. Jour. Bot. 40: 538–545.

207. Rietsema, J., S. Satina, and A. F. Blakeslee. The effect of indole-3-acetic acid on *Datura* embryos. Proc. Nat. Acad. Sci. 39: 924–933.

208. Satina, S. Chromosome end arrangements in *Datura inoxia, D. meteloides* and *D. metel*. Amer. Jour. Bot. 40: 638–646.

209. Spencer, J. L., W. R. Singleton, and A. F. Blakeslee. Induced pollen lethals from seeds of *Datura stramonium* treated with thermal neutrons. Proc. Nat. Acad. Sci. 39: 288–292.

210. Yost, H. T. Jr., W. R. Singleton, and A. F. Blakeslee. The effect of thermal neutron radiation on the chromosomes of *Datura*. Proc. Nat. Acad. Sci. 39: 292–297.

## 1954

211. Blakeslee, A. F. The aging of seeds and mutation rates. Ann. N.Y. Acad. Sci. 57: 488–490.

212. Blakeslee, A. F. Seventy-five years of progress in genetics. Northern India Science Assoc. Everyday Science 2: 129–152.

213. Rietsema, J. Physiologische Isolatie bij planten. Vakblad voor Biologen 34: 106–115.

214. Rietsema, J. The composition of the internal atmosphere of developing fruits of *Datura stramonium*. Program Amer. Soc. Plant Physiol.: 36.

215. Rietsema, J., B. Blondel, and A. F. Blakeslee. Chemical changes in embryonic development of *Datura stramonium* and the incompatible cross *D. inoxia* x *D. discolor*. 8th Intern. Bot. Congress Sect. 9–10: 209–210.

216. Rietsema, J., S. Satina, and A. F. Blakeslee. On the nature of the embryo inhibitor in ovular tumors of *Datura*. Proc. Nat. Acad. Sci. 40: 424–431.

217. Satina, S., and A. F. Blakeslee. Differences in embryonic development in selfs and incompatible crosses of ten species of *Datura*. 8th Intern. Bot. Congress, Sect. 9–10: 208–209.

218. Spencer, J. L., and A. F. Blakeslee. Induced pollen lethals from seeds of *Datura stramonium* exposed to radiation from nuclear detonation. Proc. Nat. Acad. Sci. 40: 441–446.

219. Yost, H. T. Jr., J. M. Cummings, and A. F. Blakeslee. The effects of fast-neutron radiation from a nuclear detonation on chromosome aberration in *Datura*. Proc. Nat. Acad. Sci. 40: 447–451.

## 1955

220. Blondel, B., J. Rietsema, and A. F. Blakeslee. Studies on ovule and embryo development in *Datura*. Proteins and free amino acids in ovules of *Datura stramonium*. (Unpublished.)

221. CUMMINGS, J. M., L. GOLDSTEIN, and A. F. BLAKESLEE. Chromosome aberrations in *Datura* due to various kinds of irradiation. Proc. Nat. Acad. Sci. 41: 355–358.

222. KUHN, E. Incompatibility and fertility in diploid and tetraploid crosses of *Datura metel*. Unpublished thesis, Smith College.

223. RIETSEMA, J., and B. BLONDEL. Studies on ovule and embryo development in *Datura*. Free amino acids in ovules of *Datura innoxia* and the incompatible cross *D. innoxia* x *D. discolor*. (Unpublished).

224. RIETSEMA, J., B. BLONDEL, S. SATINA, and A. F. BLAKESLEE. Studies on ovule and embryo growth in *Datura*. I. A growth analysis. Amer. Jour. Bot. 42: 449–455.

225. SPENCER, J. L., and A. F. BLAKESLEE. Induced pollen lethals from seeds of *Datura stramonium* exposed to different radiations. Proc. Nat. Acad. Sci. 41: 307–312.

## 1956

226. COLE, K. The effect of various trisomic conditions in *Datura stramonium* on crossability with other species. Amer. Jour. Bot. 43: 794–801.

227. SATINA, S. Seed development in selfs of ten *Datura* species. In preparation.

228. SATINA, S. Seed development in incompatible crosses of *Datura*. In preparation.

# BLAKESLEE:

# THE GENUS DATURA

# Continuation of Research on Datura

[*The American Naturalist* 90: 394, 1956]

*Datura* is almost an ideal plant for research. It is easy to grow either in the greenhouse or field; selfing and crossing is simple and a large number of seed is produced. As many as four generations a year have been obtained in special instances although two or three are usual. It is also readily propagated by cuttings or grafting.

Seed of all the species and of most of the races and types have been grown and placed in controlled cold storage. These are available to any investigator who desires to continue some phase of the *Datura* research. Application should be made to Dr. H. H. Plough, Amherst College, Amherst, Massachusetts, indicating the seeds desired and the general nature of the investigation planned. Seeds will be mailed promptly.

Committee of the Genetics Society
of America for the Preservation of
A. F. Blakeslee's *Datura* material

H. H. Plough, *Chairman*
R. E. Cleland
M. Demerec
P. C. Mangelsdorf
E. W. Sinnott

# 1

# Historical Review

A. G. AVERY

The use of narcotic plants goes back to times before recorded history. Classical Greek writings frequently mention the use of concoctions made from various plants. The Odyssey relates that Helen of Troy gave Telemachus wine to which she had added nepenthe to help him forget his sorrows. Early Sanscrit and Chinese accounts tell of a magic narcotic plant used as a hypnotic that is probably identical with the metelnut, dhatura, or unmata, which Christoval Acosta described in an account of the drug plants of the East Indies and which is certainly a species of *Datura*.

What is perhaps the earliest mention of a plant of this genus is given by the Arab Avicenna in the eleventh century in his account of medicinal plants used by the Arabs. Avicenna's account was translated by Dioscorides and the so-called "nut" was recognized by early botanists as the fruit of the solanaceous plant that many years later was called *Datura metel*. The Arabs knew that a small dose would bring intoxication and that a large dose was fatal. This plant was known under the name dhustura, or unmata in Sanscrit, and called jous-mathel, datora, tatorah by the Arabs, and dhatura, unmata, or unmeta by the East Indians. It was known in Japan as chosen-asagao or Korean morning-glory. The early Greeks called it nux-methal, neura, or neurada (Kilmer, 1930). According to Chinese legend the flower of this plant was given the name of a star. The generic name *Datura* was derived from the East Indian Dhatura, or Dutra, or from the Arabic Tatorah (Chapter 2).

The genus *Datura* belongs to the solanum family, which includes a great many other plants noted for their narcotic properties, such as *Mandragora* (mandrake), *Atropa* (belladonna), *Hyoscyamus* (henbane), *Scopolia*, and *Nicotiana* (tobacco). This family also includes several important food plants such as the potato and the tomato, which have long been in cultivation or commonly used.

**The Hypnotic Effect and Narcotic Use of *Datura*.** The hypnotic effects following the ingestion of almost any part of the plant of any *Datura*

3

species has long been known and regarded with dread. These effects have been utilized both in the Old World and in America in religious ceremonies, in oracular divination, or in the forecasting of future events. All species of the genus seem to have the same properties in this respect. Concoctions made with ground seed have been especially potent, as has an essence prepared by distilling the seeds with water. The powdered seed may be easily mixed with particles of food or with tobacco. Other parts of the plant give effects similar to that of the seed.

In Asia, and especially in India, the natives have long been familiar with the narcotic and intoxicating properties of *Datura*, particularly of *D. metel,* which is a common species in most parts of India. The drug obtained from *Datura* has been used in India by thugs to stupefy their victims. A concoction made from the leaves of *D. stramonium* is reported to have been used in India as a treatment for hydrophobia. In Russia thieves have been known to add extracts from seeds of *D. stramonium* to drinks that they offer their victims to make them dazed and stupefied.

In the New World several species of *Datura* have been used in religious and ceremonial rituals by many scattered primitive peoples. In western South America the wild and cultivated species (principally species of *Brugmansia*) were used by the natives to induce partial intoxication, to control unruly children, and were given in large doses with tobacco to women and slaves to deaden their senses before burial alive with their dead husbands or masters. Extracts from the bark, leaves, and seed of these plants have been used in shamanistic rites and practices (Cooper, 1949).

The Aztec Indians used *D. meteloides* and probably other native species, which they called "the magic plant" or ololiuhqui. The plant was used in the fresh or dry state. The entire plant—leaves, roots, flowers, and seeds—was used by the Aztecs against all diseases, applied as an ointment to cuts or wounds, used in cases of paralysis, and for its narcotic effect. Drinks prepared from these plants were also used in various ceremonies as well as by priests or medicine men to enable them to communicate with the spirits. The drug provokes various effects, depending probably on the dose taken. It commonly causes phantasmic visions or stimulates people to dance, or laugh, weep, sleep, or tell oracular prophecies. The Aztecs considered the seeds of this plant sacred, made sacrificial offerings to them, and kept them on their altars or in secret boxes.

The respect and veneration accorded the plant among Indian tribes extended through Mexico to the southern and western parts of what is now the United States, and many legends and unusual customs were developed. *Datura,* known as "toloache," was probably the most universally used drug by the Indians of this region. It was employed, both therapeutically and ritually, for nearly all diseases. The hypnotic effect was utilized by some tribes to relieve pain in the setting of broken bones. Concoctions of the herb were also used in ceremonies following the death of members of the tribe. The attitude of the tribes toward this plant varied. Some tribes had no special reverence for it but may have used it to give immunity from snake or animal bites. Other tribes, such as the Yokuts and the Luiseños, accorded the plant supernatural powers and used it in rituals and ceremonies at the initiation of their boys into manhood (Kroeber, 1925; Culley, 1936).

The Indians of the eastern United States practiced ceremonies similar to those of some of the southwestern tribes, in initiating boys into manhood. An amazing account of this ceremony is given by Beverly (1705) in his history of Virginia. The boys were kept in confinement and away from the rest of the village for several months. They were fed nothing but concoctions of some poisonous or intoxicating roots (probably including *D. stramonium*) until they became raving mad, in which condition they were kept for 18 or 20 days. They were gradually restored to their senses by reducing the intoxicating ingredients in their diet. Many interesting details of such ceremonial usages of *Datura* are given by Safford (1921b, 1922), Youngken (1924, 1925), and Kroeber (1925).

An incident in the history of the early settlement of this country as related by Beverly gives us a dramatic account of the effect that *Datura* had on British soldiers sent to Jamestown, Virginia, to quell the uprising there known as Bacon's Rebellion in 1676. This account is also of considerable interest as it gives the probable origin of the common name of *D. stramonium:* James Town Weed, or Jimson Weed, to which the name has been shortened.

The James-Town Weed, which resembles the Thorny Apple of Peru, . . . is supposed to be one of the greatest Coolers in the World. This being an early Plant, was gathered very young for a boiled salad, by some of the soldiers . . . and some of them ate plentifully of it, the Effect of which was a very pleasant Comedy; for they turn'd natural Fools upon it for several days: One would blow up a Feather in the Air; another would dart Straws at it with much Fury; and another stark naked was sitting up in a Corner, like a Monkey, grinning and making Mows at them; a Fourth would fondly kiss, and paw his Companions, and snear in their Faces, with a Countenance more antick, than any in a Dutch Droll. In this frantick Condition they were confined, lest they should in their Folly destroy themselves; though it was observed, that all their Actions were full of Innocence and good Nature. Indeed, they were not very cleanly; for they would have wallow'd in their own Excrements, if they had not been prevented. A Thousand such simple Tricks they play'd, and after Eleven Days, return'd to themselves again, not remembring anything that had pass'd.

Apparently all the species of *Datura* are plentifully supplied with the narcotic properties that cause the effects described above. The species which have been principally used by various peoples are those that grow most commonly in their neighborhoods. The smaller growing species (*D. leichhardtii, D. pruinosa*), as also those which never seem to be abundant (*D. ferox* and *D. quercifolia*), have not been used for these purposes as extensively as the other six species. The several species of the *Brugmansia* section (or genus) apparently have similar narcotic properties. The chemistry and the identification of the several alkaloids that have been found in *Datura* are related in Chapter 3.

**Early Breeding Experiments. 1760–1890.** The fitness or adaptability of the *Datura* species as subjects for plant breeding has long been recognized. The relatively large size and simplicity of the flowers of *Datura*, its easy culture, the large number of seed produced, and other natural characteristics make it a very suitable plant for breeding experiments. Many of the early plant hybridizers have reported on experiments with plants of this genus. Quite complete accounts of some of this early experimental work in hybridization may be found in the excellent book, *Plant Hybridization Before Mendel*, by Roberts (1929) and also in an early review by Focke (1881).

In 1760 Joseph Koelreuter in Germany had grown the first plant hybrid ever obtained in a planned scientific experiment. This hybrid was between two species of *Nicotiana*, a genus closely related to *Datura*. In Koelreuter's second "*Fortsetzung*" (1764) to the *Vorläufige Nachricht*, he reported on reciprocal crosses between purple- and white-flowered forms (*D.* "*tatula*" and *D.* "*stramonium*") of *D. stramonium*. He found that the hybrids from the reciprocal crosses were alike in form but described the color of the flowers of the hybrids as distinctly paler than that of the purple parent. He apparently did not attempt to grow $F_2$ generations. Among crosses between other species and genera reported by Koelreuter in his third "*Fortsetzung*" (1765) is one between *D.* "*ferox*" with white flowers and *D.* "*tatula*" with violet-colored flowers. The hybrids were described as having pale violet flowers. He also noted that there was much seed abortion in the capsules of the hybrids and reasoned that this was proof that the parents were two distinct species. From the flower colors reported and from the seed abortion found in the hybrids it now seems evident that Koelreuter had actually obtained a hybrid between *D. ferox* and a purple-flowered race of *D. stramonium*. Koelreuter's original papers have not been available; the references given here were taken from Roberts' book.

In 1830 the Dutch Academy of Sciences offered a prize for work on artificial fertilization (pollination) and the production of new plants by that method. In 1837 Carl F. von Gaertner was awarded the prize. Gaertner's report was a summary of many years of hybridization experiments with some 700 species representing 80 genera. In an earlier paper, he reported on efforts begun in 1825 to produce hybrids and gave the results of attempted crosses between 16 genera, including *Datura*. Most of his crosses were between species of different genera. It was only between closely related species (of the same genus) that he was able to obtain crosses. He worked especially with *D.* "*laevis*" (*D. stramonium*) and *D. metel* and reported successful crosses (capsules) between these two species as well as between the white and inermis forms *D.* "*stramonium*" and *D.* "*laevis*" (Gaertner, 1827).

The two chief contenders for a prize offered in 1861 by the Paris Academy of Sciences for research on the general problem of plant hybrids were Charles Naudin of the Museum of Natural History at Paris and D. A. Godron of the University of Nancy. The papers of both appeared

in 1863 in the *Annales des Sciences Naturelles,* the prize being awarded
to Naudin. In this and an earlier paper, Naudin reported on considerable
work with *Datura.* His first report had to do with what he called "hy-
bridité disjointe" in the cross of *D.* *"laevis"* (smooth capsules) with *D.*
*stramonium.* Of 40 hybrid plants, 37 resembled *D. stramonium.* The
other three had capsules that were partly spiny and partly smooth in
varying proportions. Naudin believed this to be an indication of the
retarded influence of the female parent. He also reported that seeds
from the smooth parts of these capsules produced only plants with smooth
capsules. From the results of certain phases of our work, first published
in 1921 (*11, 14*),[1] and from extensive unpublished records since, it is
clear that Naudin's stock was infected with a virus disease, "quercina,"
which causes smooth or partly smooth capsules to appear on plants that
genetically should have spiny capsules. In spite of the disturbance
caused by this virus, he was able to demonstrate the reappearance of the
parental forms among offspring of the hybrids.

Naudin also reported on crosses between purple- and white-flowered
forms, as well as on certain species crosses. In 1863 he crossed reciprocally *D. "laevis"* with *D. ferox.* The hybrids from either cross were
uniform and like those of the reciprocal. These hybrids had purple
stems and flowers and spiny capsules. This is in agreement with what
would be expected from a cross of *D. ferox* with a white-flowered *D.*
*stramonium.*[2] His description of the second generation of this cross also
agrees with what we have obtained: ". . . there succeeded the most
astonishing diversity of forms, . . . of the forty-five plants . . . one
would not find two which exactly resembled each other" (Roberts, 1929).

Naudin also reported the results of crosses of *D. metel* x *D. metel-*
*oides, D. quercifolia* x *D. stramonium,* and *D. stramonium* x *D. "cera-*
*tocaula."* With the exception of the last cross, his results were, in general,
as would be expected. He described the hybrid from the cross of *D.*
*stramonium* x *D. "ceratocaula"* as resembling the female (*D. stra-*
*monium*) parent. We have been able to obtain hybrids between *D.*
*stramonium* and *D. ceratocaula* only by the dissection of very young
embryos, as described in Chapter 12. Since hybrids thus obtained between these species are actually very distinct from *D. stramonium,* it is
likely that either the plant Naudin called *D. "ceratocaula"* was incorrectly
identified or that selfing had occurred in producing the supposed hybrid.
Extensive reviews of Naudin's experiments have been published by
Blaringhem (1911) and by Roberts.

D. A. Godron was chiefly interested in demonstrating differences between species and varieties and in determining whether hybrids would
return to the form of their parents in later generations or whether they

---

[1] The figures in italics between parentheses throughout this book refer to the
numbered list of *Datura* papers by Dr. Blakeslee and his associates on pp. xxxi to xli.
[2] *D. ferox* appears as green-stemmed and white-flowered, although it is genetically
purple, with the purple coloring restricted to that part of the plant below the cotyledons.

would establish new races. Included in the list of species with which he worked are forms of *D. stramonium* and closely related species. He made two classes of crosses: first, between what he considered as races or varieties of a species and, second, between forms that he believed to be true species. The plants obtained from crosses between races resembled one or the other parent and never gave intermediate forms. The hybrids between what he considered to be species were uniform but of a type intermediate between the two parents. Later generations of the species hybrids displayed a wide variety of forms. Some of his work paralleled that of Naudin. An $F_2$ generation from the cross of *D. "bertolonii"* (*D. stramonium*—white flowers and smooth capsules) with *D. "tatula"* (*D. stramonium*—purple flowers and spiny capsules) produced 16 plants with purple flowers and spiny capsules, 11 plants with purple flowers and smooth capsules, and 2 plants with white flowers and spiny capsules. These numbers are too small to demonstrate a 9:3:3:1 segregation, and the double recessive class did not appear at all (Godron, 1873).

**Other Independent Researches. 1890–1928.** Before Hugo de Vries of the University of Amsterdam settled on *Oenothera* as the most suitable plant for his investigations, he had made preliminary experiments with many other species. In the paper announcing the rediscovery of Mendel's work, de Vries (1900) gave accounts of his own work conducted before he had learned of Mendel's paper. In 1897 he crossed reciprocally *D. "tatula"* (purple, spiny) with *D. "stramonium"* (white, inermis). He found that the hybrids had purple flowers and spiny capsules regardless of which type was the female or male parent. Progeny from selfing these hybrids were grown in 1899 and found to segregate for plants like the original parents and for two new types: purple flowers with smooth capsules and white flowers with spiny capsules. The proportions of the four types are given as 9:3:3:1.

In a report to the Evolution Committee of the Royal Society, W. Bateson and E. R. Saunders (1902) of the John Innes Horticultural Institution gave lengthy accounts with detailed tables of their experiments with the purple *vs.* white and spiny *vs.* inermis forms of *D. stramonium*. With fairly large numbers of individuals represented in their $F_2$ and backcross generations close approximations to the 3:1, 9:3:3:1, 1:1, and 1:1:1:1 ratios were obtained.

These accounts summarize the principal experiments concerning the crossing and breeding of *Datura* from the time of Koelreuter (1765) to the date (1917) of the first of the many papers of A. F. Blakeslee and his colleagues. To complete the record of *Datura* investigations, brief mention of certain independent genetic researches conducted since 1917 will be made.

In November, 1919, C. M. Woodworth of the University of Wisconsin published a short paper on the application of the principles of breeding to drug plants with special reference to *Datura*. The results of crosses made over a period of several years confirmed the findings reported by earlier workers and are in agreement with our own later work. Also reported here is a new "mutation" in *D. stramonium*, which is described as being "much taller" than the type plant (Woodworth, 1919). From pictures presented and from the description given, this type would seem to be similar to the "many-noded" or "few-noded" type found in our own cultures and pictured and described in March of the same year (6).

In 1926 and 1928 M. J. Sirks of the Instituut voor Plantenveredeling * published a series of three papers on Mendelian factors in *Datura* (Sirks, 1926a, b; 1928). His conclusions were based on experiments conducted from 1922 to 1927 and dealt especially with abnormal ratios in $F_2$ generations. The Daturas he used in his breeding work were obtained from botanical gardens under the names of *D.* "*tatula*," *D.* "*stramonium*," *D.* "*laevis*," and *D.* "*inermis*." It is unfortunate that he did not have inbred standardized strains available. Among $F_2$'s segregating for purple and white flowers and spiny and smooth capsules, either alone or in combination, Sirks demonstrated that the number of individuals in the several $F_2$ classes seemed to differ consistently from that expected from random assortment. This variance he attributed to one or more factors for differential pollen-tube growth or "certation," as he called it. He concluded that this factor for "certation" is linked to the factors for spiny capsules. He recognized the complex and varying nature of his results and in his final paper concluded that the factor(s) for "certation" probably had "different values or intensities." He also stated that it was possible "that the strains used in these experiments, differ in the number of multiple factors for certation." From our records of many thousands of $F_2$ or backcross individuals from crosses involving these characters, purple *vs.* white and spiny *vs.* smooth, in several highly inbred races of *D. stramonium* we have not observed any similar and consistent deviation from that expected from random assortment.

In the second paper of the above series, Sirks reported a new character, "the fourth known in *Datura*," which he found to be dominant to the normal condition. This type, which he called "Bronze" ("B"), is described as having a deep purple coloration in the young leaves. Records are given to show that it is inherited independently of the factors for purple flowers and spiny capsules. The Bronze condition was found to be "cryptomeric" in individuals lacking the dominant purple factor. The description and breeding records given by Sirks indicate that the Bronze character that he reported presumably was the same as the "Bronze" found in our own cultures and that, in 1925, had been located by trisomic ratios in a specific $(3 \cdot 4)$ chromosome (44).

**Work of A. F. Blakeslee and Associates. 1912–1955.** To complete this review of the history of *Datura* breeding work it seems useful to give a brief outline of the beginnings and trends of the *Datura* investigations conducted by Blakeslee and his many co-workers. Many phases of this work

---

* Located in Wageningen, The Netherlands.

will be discussed in greater detail in later chapters and much of it has been published in full elsewhere (see: *Datura* Bibliography, pp. xxxi to xli). While Blakeslee had *Datura* growing in the systematic section of the botanic garden of the Connecticut Agricultural College at Storrs as early as 1909, it was not until after a quantity of *Datura* seed was obtained from the United States Department of Agriculture in 1912 or 1913 that any definite breeding program was attempted (*1*). The *Datura* breeding work was carried on from 1913 to 1954 by Blakeslee with the assistance of B. T. Avery, Jr. (1914–1918); M. E. Farnham (1919–1923); G. Morrison (1923–1926); and A. G. Avery, brother of the first named (1926–1954).

The seed received from the U. S. Department of Agriculture was found to segregate for the form having green stems and white flowers, the recessive of the normal purple-stemmed and purple-flowered type. This pair of characters (purple *vs.* white) was found to be very suitable for the demonstration of Mendelian principles to college classes in genetics. In 1914 a second recessive type (inermis capsules) was obtained from Germany. With these two independent pairs of contrasting factors it was possible to demonstrate all combinations of ratios to be expected from hybrid or dihybrid $F_1$'s. The suitability of *Datura* for class work was shown by Blakeslee and Avery in a paper in the *Journal of Heredity* for March, 1917, the first of many papers on the various aspects of the *Datura* research. Tables giving results with several hundred individuals obtained in $F_2$'s and backcrosses show how close the actual ratios were to those expected from random assortment (*3*).

At Storrs, during the summer of 1915, an unusual plant was observed among a culture grown from selfed seed of the race obtained from the U. S. Department of Agriculture. This plant had relatively broad leaves and globose fruits. It was called "Globe" from the shape of its capsules and was for several seasons treated as a recessive type, despite the fact that a homozygous race could not be obtained. This was the first of the many $2n + 1$ types to be found in *Datura*, although the cytological explanation for it was only established by J. Belling at Cold Spring Harbor in 1920, by which time all the twelve $2n + 1$ primary types had been identified and described (*8, 12,* Chapter 6).

In the latter part of 1915 Blakeslee joined the staff of the Department of Experimental Evolution (later the Department of Genetics) of the Carnegie Institution of Washington, at Cold Spring Harbor, Long Island, New York, where the work with *Datura* was continued until 1942. In June, 1916, B. T. Avery, Jr., a former student at Storrs, became his first full-time associate. Among the cultures of *Datura* which were grown in 1916, there was discovered a plant that was called "New Species" (N.S.), since, besides being distinct and highly self-fertile, it was found to be sterile, or nearly so, in crosses with normals (*4*). Later cytological investigation by Belling demonstrated this to be a tetraploid. During the years of World War I (1917–1918) work with *Datura* was considerably curtailed and facilities were devoted to increasing the food value and yield of the Adzuki bean as a war measure.

The years 1918 to 1921 were largely devoted to establishing several fundamental principles of *Datura* cytology and breeding behavior. Work was completed on the transmission of "quercina," a virus disease carried by both seed and pollen. It was shown that in certain instances the peculiar inheritance of "inermis" reported by Naudin, Godron, and other early hybridizers could be explained by the effects of this disease (*11, 14*). Extensive experiments were conducted in the study of the inheritance of the recessive factor for white flowers. Abnormal ratios were obtained in $F_2$'s and backcrosses with one of the 12 mutant types. After the discovery by Belling that these types were due to the presence of a single, and specific, extra chromosome, the principle of "trisomic" inheritance was established and amply demonstrated in the case of the $2n + 1$ type called Poinsettia when heterozygous for the recessive white-flower color. Also during this period the cytology and breeding behavior of tetraploids was worked out and published (*28, 30*).

In November, 1921, an unusual plant in a culture of the inbred Line 1 of *D. stramonium* was observed and was determined cytologically to be a haploid by A. D. Bergner, then an assistant of Belling. This plant, the first haploid reported among flowering plants, became the single ancestor of our standard race known as Line 1A (L 1A). *Datura* haploids by nondisjunction occasionally form normal sex cells with 12 chromosomes and thus a few seeds are produced when such a plant is self-pollinated. These seeds are diploid and give rise to normal diploid plants, which, barring new mutations, must be homozygous (*19*).

By 1921 an extensive program of *Datura* research was well under way with the complete support of the Department of Genetics. Several new and important techniques had been devised and put into use, which greatly facilitated research. One of the most valuable of these was the iron-acetocarmine technique developed by Belling for the study of chromosomes. This method greatly reduced the time needed for cytological investigations. Belling was soon able to classify the 12 pairs of chromosomes in *Datura* by sizes and to relate each of the 12 primary mutant types to a particular chromosome (*25, 37*).

To develop efficiently the expanded program of *Datura* research, a number of special investigators were attracted to Cold Spring Harbor for intensive work in some particular phase. Many found it especially convenient to carry on their research during the summer months. E. W. Sinnott began a study of differences in morphology and histology between chromosomal types. J. T. Buchholz perfected a method of observing pollen-tubes and of studying their growth in the style (*72*). Buchholz's studies were continued until 1941 and added considerably to the understanding of incompatibilities between types and species. J. L. Cartledge began the study of pollen sterility, which has been most valuable in all later researches. Pollen sterility has been found to be an

indicator of chromosomal constitution as well as a reliable measure of
the mutation rate induced by any treatment (*41, 115*). In 1921, with
the cooperation of C. S. Gager of the Brooklyn Botanic Garden, the first
radiation treatments were begun (*52*). These resulted in the first experimentally induced chromosomal and gene mutations reported in flowering plants and led to further radiation research, as related in Chapter 9.

In 1922 very abnormal ratios of the recessive character white flowers
were observed in certain $F_2$'s or backcrosses when the white was derived
from particular "B" races. To determine the cause of these results considerable breeding and cytological work was carried on. From this,
Belling proposed the hypothesis of segmental interchange between nonhomologous chromosomes (*40*). The correctness of the hypothesis, not
only in regard to the constitution of the "B" races but for other cryptic
types (later called prime types), was soon apparent. An understanding
of segmental interchange between nonhomologous chromosomes has
been of immense value in the study of differences between *Datura* races
and species (Chapter 4).

The first sectorial chimera was observed in 1922. This proved to be a
$2n - 1$ sector on a normal $2n$ plant (*23*). The following year a $2n + 1$
sector was found on a $2n$ plant. In 1922 the first species hybrid was
obtained. This was a cross between *D. stramonium* and *D. ferox*, which
was made with the expectation of extracting, in later generations, a number of Mendelian characters. New Mendelian factors as tags for chromosomes, or parts of chromosomes, were being sought from various
sources. Several genes had already been located in specific chromosomes, and for the group located in the Poinsettia ($17 \cdot 18$) chromosome,
a few linkage figures had been compiled. By 1930 eighteen genes had
been studied and located in nine different chromosomes (*68*). New
genes were appearing frequently after radiation treatments. One recessive gene (swollen) was found to mutate occasionally to normal when
in a heterozygous condition, but only then (*53*).

Buchholz demonstrated that the pollen tubes of certain $2n + 1$ types
and a number of Mendelian types, when heterozygous, exhibited a
bimodal growth curve. By cutting and splicing styles at the proper times
after pollination, he was able to increase or decrease the number of
$n + 1$ or recessive gene gametes taking part in fertilization (*79*).

All of the known secondaries had been identified by 1930, and from
prime types derived from segmental interchange following various radiation (x-ray and radium) treatments many tertiaries and compensating
types had also been obtained. The constitution of Nubbin, the first compensating type found in *Datura*, had been determined in 1926. Compensating types were proving to be of considerable practical value for
determining the location of new genes in particular chromosomes (Chapter 7). New compensating types could readily be obtained from crosses
involving appropriate prime types (*45, 74*).

In 1927 Belling retired as cytologist and from then until 1942 the extensive cytological investigations were carried on under the supervision

of A. D. Bergner, who had earlier worked with Belling. A systematic study of the comparison of the chromosomal constitution of races found in nature with the standard Line 1A was undertaken, and by 1930 hybrids between L 1A and some 500 races had been studied cytologically. During this period a study of the chromosomal differences between species was also commenced. This last has been one of the major problems since. In 1928 and 1929 methods were devised whereby pure breeding types with extra chromosomal material could be synthesized. Several such types, with a fragment of the largest chromosome in excess, were so developed. In 1930 the number system was devised to simplify the designation of chromosomes and their parts (63, 68, 82).

The years after 1931 were particularly devoted to a more intensive study of the chromosomal differences between the ten herbaceous species of *Datura*. Investigations were undertaken to determine what caused the barriers to crossability between certain species and not between others. It was found that *D. leichhardtii* could be successfully used as a female with other species and could thus be used as a "bridging" species (74).

For use as testers, the collection of prime types and Mendelian genes was being steadily increased from collections from the wild, from rare spontaneous mutations, and especially from the results of radiation, x-ray and radium, and from the aging of seed and pollen. About 90 prime types (PT's), the chromosomal constitutions of which were known, were in use. Nearly 300 types were recognized that showed simple Mendelian inheritance. About 70 of these had been located in specific chromosomes. In addition to the methods usually used for the location of genes, several new ones were devised that were found to be especially valuable in the *Datura* work (Chapter 7).

In 1937 the discovery was made that the treatment of seeds, or growing parts of the plant, with the alkaloid colchicine would bring about a doubling of the number of chromosomes. Colchicine was also found to be an effective agent to cause doubling of chromosome numbers in species from many other genera and families. By this new method it was found possible to produce diploid branches on haploids, octoploid branches from treatment of tetraploids, and hexaploid branches on $3n$ plants. One important result of this discovery was the demonstration that certain sterile hybrids ("mule plants") could be made fertile by doubling their chromosome number (117, 118). It was found that colchicine sometimes caused a doubling of a single layer of cells of the plant affected. By the use of the resulting periclinal chimeras, it was possible to identify individual germ layers as $2n$, $4n$, or $8n$ and so trace the development of various plant organs. The important results and conclusions gained from the study of such periclinal chimeras are discussed in Chapter 8.

From 1938 until the removal of the *Datura* research to Smith College in 1942, the further study of the effect of colchicine on cell division and chromosome doubling received special attention. Extensive tests were made to discover other chemicals causing similar effects. Studies on colchicine-induced periclinal chimeras were continued and a great deal of material collected for later study. The existence of the three "germ layers" in *Datura* and their part in the development of the plant were established (*134*).

The successes attained from the use of colchicine to increase the number of chromosomes suggested that it might be possible to reverse the process. A number of substances, growth-promoting hormones, and many other chemicals were tested by J. van Overbeek in an effort to induce parthenogenesis—producing haploids from diploids or diploids from tetraploids. Although the original object of these experiments was not realized, the knowledge he obtained of the development of the young embryo led to further intensive studies and to perfecting the method of growing in culture excised embryos of many otherwise incompatible species crosses (*138, 150*).

Meanwhile the study of the chromosomal differences between the species was continued. The chromosomal constitution, in terms of Line 1A of *D. stramonium,* of many of the species had been determined by 1942 (*157, 159*). This work was continued at Smith College (Chapter 13).

In September, 1942, all *Datura* material and research problems were moved from Cold Spring Harbor to the Smith College Genetics Experiment Station, Northampton, Massachusetts, newly organized with Blakeslee as Director. Two members of the Cold Spring Harbor staff, S. Satina and A. G. Avery, continued their individual parts of the *Datura* work at Smith College. Many of the major problems were continued and others were commenced. The study of the differences between races and species continued to be an important problem. Many other questions of lesser scope related to this wide subject were also investigated.

The methods of dissection of immature embryos and their culture in artificial media, as initiated by van Overbeek in 1940, have been improved and expanded. Some crosses give good fertilization, but the embryos develop only to the sixth or eighth cell stage and others deteriorate in later stages. The abnormal growth of cells surrounding, and soon invading, the embryo sac seemed to be tumorous in nature. Elaborate studies of these ovular tumors, their cause and nature, were undertaken by J. Rappaport and extended by J. Rietsema. It became evident that this tissue is not the cause of seed abortion but accompanies it. The effect of extracts from these tumors on embryos growing on nutrient media has been studied in detail by Rietsema.

Since the work of van Overbeek, much attention has been given to the physiological aspects of embryo growth. The subsequent discovery that isolated embryos are capable of further growth and development into mature plants stimulated investigation into the nature of seed abortion. At first the studies were mainly descriptive, with the principal emphasis on histological features, but during the last ten years the physiological and biochemical aspects have received more and more attention. Although far from completed, these investigations have contributed to a better understanding of the processes leading to seed abortion in *Datura*. A study of the barriers to crossability between races and species has been approached from several directions. The possible factors favoring or hindering hybridization between species has been constantly under investigation. These factors have been classified as prefertilization or postfertilization barriers (*166*). Among the prefertilization barriers are the bursting of pollen tubes, which can be partly overcome by the cutting and splicing of styles. The presence of certain extra chromosomes in plants of *D. stramonium* used as females has been found to increase the crossability with other species. In certain successful crosses, the hybrids were found to be numerical triploids, being diploid for one of the parents and haploid for the other.

With the support of the Atomic Energy Commission further studies were begun in 1952 to determine the effect of different forms of radiation on the mutation rate. Seed of the standard Line 1A were exposed to varying dosages of radiation from thermal neutrons and nuclear detonations. The resulting gene and chromosomal mutations were studied in comparison with the effects brought about by x-rays and gamma rays (Chapter 9).

Many of the lines of research so briefly mentioned here are fully discussed in later chapters. Other phases of the work have been presented in published accounts listed in the bibliography of *Datura* papers. Many of the important problems encountered in the years of *Datura* research were still incomplete at the closing of the Genetics Experiment Station at the end of 1955. Plans had been outlined for the continued study of interspecific crosses between the ten herbaceous species. This would have involved a study of racial differences, differences between the $2n + 1$ types on crossability, and a study of the condition of growth of the female parent as it affects the degree of incompatibility. Studies on the cause and nature of ovular tumors and the deterioration of embryo and endosperm were to have been continued.

# 2

# A Review of the Taxonomic History of Datura

SOPHIE SATINA AND A. G. AVERY

In recent years taxonomy, in common with other branches of biological science, has become closely allied with various other lines of investigation. It is the result of descriptive and comparative morphological studies of species combined with evidence obtained from experimental biology, genetics, cytology, and other branches of science which have been found useful in determining relationships in modern studies on speciation and taxonomy.

The work on *Datura* conducted for years by Blakeslee and his associates did not include specific studies on the taxonomy of this genus. However, the large collection of races of all species, particularly of *D. stramonium*, together with the results obtained from numerous experiments, observations on inherited characters, on mutations that affect the size, shape, or color of the plant, the analysis of cryptic or prime types in species found in nature, and the result of species crosses greatly amplify the knowledge about the *Datura* species and certainly offer valuable information that could be used by taxonomists. Many of these problems are discussed in later chapters of this volume. The present chapter is a brief review of the taxonomic history of the species. It is not intended as a complete taxonomic study. No attempts are made to evaluate definitively or to revise the accepted classification of the species within the genus.

The present review is based on the morphological descriptions given by a number of authors who were the first to introduce and to name the several species of the genus. A number of contradictory statements have been made as to the origin and identity of some of the species and there has been uncertainty about other types as to whether they are distinct species or varieties. There are cases in which two obviously different species have been given the same specific name and there is disagreement as to whether a group of species (*Brugmansia*), more distantly related

16

to the typical *Datura*, should be included or placed in an independent genus. Some of these misleading statements, which appeared years ago as a result of incorrect interpretation or misunderstanding, have been corrected by later taxonomists; some errors have been traced back to the original sources and other statements have been disproved experimentally by breeding work. But there are still many taxonomic problems that remain unsettled and need thorough taxonomic study.

The status of many names remains uncertain, since the authors were in some cases unable to study authentic material of the plants represented. For a few the original literature was not available for consultation. For others the descriptions are so meager that no final disposition can be made without reference to the type specimens, certain of which are apparently no longer extant, and most of which were not available for study during the preparation of this chapter. Some names are clearly illegitimate for nomenclatural reasons. Others are now referred to genera other than *Datura*. The synonyms given under each of the accepted species names include only such names as have been in common use and which we can interpret with confidence. At the end of this chapter is given a list of names published, to date, in *Datura*, plus those published originally in other genera which are now referred to *Datura*.

The revised descriptions given in this chapter are compiled from published accounts supplemented by our own observations of all the species grown for many years under comparable conditions.

As will be shown later, the taxonomy of *Brugmansia* is not clear and taxonomists disagree on the relation of those species to the herbaceous *Datura*. However, the results of experiments carried on by Blakeslee and his associates for many years and observations of both the herbaceous and woody species have led us to believe that there is some justification in treating the latter group as a separate genus, as has been done by some authors. We do not, however, attempt to settle this question here, nor to give a complete account of the species of Sect. *Brugmansia*. The attention of the reader is therefore called to the fact that whenever *Datura* is mentioned in later chapters of this volume, only the ten herbaceous species are implied. Experiments with the woody species, Tree Daturas or *Brugmansia*, were limited to a few crosses made between *D. innoxia* and two species of *Brugmansia*.

## *Datura* L. 1754. Genera Pl., ed. 5, p. 83.

*Datura* belongs to the Solanaceae. This family was named Solaneae by Jussieu. The present name was adopted by Bartling (Milne Edwards, 1864). The generic name of *Datura* was first used by Linnaeus (1737) in his *Hortus Cliffortianus*. According to Safford (1922), Linnaeus Latinized the East Indian name Dhatura or Dutra. According to Asa Gray (1848), the name *Datura* is from the Arabic name Tatorah.

The genus *Datura* belongs to the tribe Datureae. Flowers perfect, gamopetalous, solitary and pediceled, rather small in some species and very large in others. Calyx elongated and tubular, evenly or unevenly five-lobed or spathe-like, splitting lengthwise, or circumscissile with the base and breaking away after flowering, or forming an enlarged and subtended disk, or cup, under the capsule. Corolla funnel-shaped or tubular. The tube long and slender, the limb either five-lobed or forming a ten-toothed and plaited border. The five stamens, alternating with the corolla lobes, are attached to the inner surface of the tube near the base. Stigma two-lobed, style filiform. Ovary superior, two-celled at the top and often four-celled below because of the presence of a false septum. Fruit a capsule, globose, fusiform, or ovoid, four-valved or bursting irregularly, spiny or smooth. Leaves and stem glabrous or pubescent. Annual or occasionally perennial herbs, bushes, or small trees.

The genus *Datura* is divided by Bernhardi (1833) into four sections: I. *Brugmansia*. II. *Stramonium*. III. *Dutra*. IV. *Ceratocaulis*. Because of the uncertain taxonomic position of *Brugmansia*, we prefer to use Safford's (1921a) order of sections and are taking *Stramonium* as Section I, *Dutra* as Section II, *Ceratocaulis* as Section III, and *Brugmansia* as Section IV.

**Section I.** *Stramonium* [Tournefort] Bernhardi.

The species belonging to this section, *D. stramonium, D. ferox,* and *D. quercifolia* have erect flowers and capsules, which, when ripe, break regularly into four valves. Calyx evenly five-toothed, circumscissile. Seeds black. Each fork of the dichotomous stem has a flower bud. These species are erect, annual, terrestrial herbs.

1. *D. stramonium* L. 1753. Sp. Pl. 1: 179.

> *D. tatula* L. 1762. Sp. Pl., ed. 2: 256.
> *D. inermis* Jacq. 1776. Hort. Vindob. 3: 44, Pl. 82.
> *D. laevis* L.f. 1781. Suppl. Pl: 146.
> *D. bertolonii* Parl. ex. Guss. 1842. Fl. Sic. Syn. 1: 267.

Corolla five-lobed, white or lavender, 6 to 10 cm long, 3 to 4 cm wide. Calyx half, or slightly more, as long as the corolla, dropping with the corolla shortly after the withering of the latter. Anthers purple in the purple-flowered types and white in the white types. Style shorter than the corolla tube. Capsule ovoid, 5 to 7 cm long, 3 to 5 cm wide, spiny or smooth. Stem 0.5 to 2 meters high, purple or green. Leaves 5 to 15 cm long, ovate, sinuately dentate. Stems and leaves glabrous or nearly so (Figs. 1, 2a, 3a, 24).

*D. stramonium* with white flowers and *D. tatula* with purple flowers, both with spiny capsules, were proposed by Linnaeus in 1753 and 1762, respectively, as two distinct species. In 1781 Linnaeus filius in the Supplementum described another species, *D. laevis*, with white flowers and smooth capsules, which has been identified with *D. inermis* Jacquin (1776). These forms, *D. stramonium, D. tatula,* and *D. inermis* Jacq. (*D. laevis* L.f. and *D. bertolonii* Parl.), have been considered for years by many botanists to be different species (Bernhardi, 1833; Wettstein, 1895; Souèges, 1907). However, other botanists were inclined to regard them rather as varieties (Torrey, 1824; Clarke, 1885). The breeding experiments of Bateson and Saunders (1902), of Safford (1921b), and our own work have proved without doubt that the white-flowered *D.*

*stramonium* L. and the purple-flowered *D. tatula* L. differ only by a single pair of genes and that they belong to a single species. The gene responsible for the purple form is dominant to that for white flowers. It has also been established that *D. inermis* Jacq. with smooth capsules has the recessive gene inermis and that *D. stramonium* L. and *D. tatula* L., both with armed or spiny capsules, have the dominant allelomorph. We have, therefore, considered these forms as a single species and used the name *D. stramonium* L. since it preceded the other two names (*3, 139*).

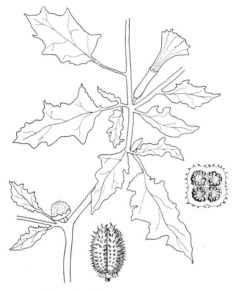

Fig. 1. *Datura stramonium.*

The origin of the species name *stramonium* is not known. Asa Gray stated that the name was supposed to be from *struma* or *strama*, meaning a swelling. The species is well known under the common names of "raving night shade" or "thorn apple" in England and the United States or as "stink weed" or Jimson weed in this country, where the latter name is a corruption of Jamestown, Virginia (Chapter 1). In France it is called "pomme épineuse" or "herbe aux sorciers," the Dutch call it "doornappel," and the Germans "Dornapfel" (Kilmer, 1930). The Russian name means "stinking stupefier" because of its peculiar and unpleasant odor and its narcotic properties.

Linnaeus gave the habitat of *D. stramonium* as America. He did not indicate the origin of *D. tatula*. *D. laevis* came from Abyssinia. Some botanists consider the origin of *D. stramonium* to be South America or Europe; others attribute it to Asia. It might be of some interest to mention here that the common name used in Japan for *D. stramonium* is "yoshu," which means "foreign" (Safford, 1921b, 1922).

(a)

(b)

FIG. 2. (a) *D. stramonium* L. (b) *D. leichhardtii* Muell.

FIG. 3. Capsules of the ten herbaceous species of *Datura*.

The present distribution of *D. stramonium* is extensive. It has undoubtedly accompanied the migration of man from early times throughout most parts of the temperate regions of the world. Seeds of the eleven
cryptic or prime types of *D. stramonium* found in nature and used in the
experiments reported in this volume were collected from all six continents.

2. *D. ferox* L. 1756. Amoen. Acad. 3: 403.

> *Stramonium ferox* Boccone. 1674. Ic. Descript. Rar. Pl. 50–52.

This species, described by Boccone under the name of *Stramonium ferox* and
later named by Linnaeus *Datura ferox* L., can be easily recognized by the large
and very stout spines covering the capsules. Corolla five-toothed, white, 4 to 6
cm long, 2 to 3 cm wide. Calyx slightly less than half the length of the corolla.
Anthers white. Capsule ovoid, 5 to 8 cm long, 4 to 6 cm wide, including
spines. Spines relatively few, of unequal size, very heavy with thick conical
bases and slightly acuminate, often slightly recurved points, reaching a length

of 2.5 cm. Upper spines larger than the lower. Leaves angular and sinuate. Stem erect, 0.5 to 1.5 meters high; green, except the hypocotyl, which is purplish. Leaves and stem glabrous (Figs. 3b, 4).

The type locality of *D. ferox* L. is China. It is distributed widely in warm regions throughout the world. The seeds of the two chromosomal types in our collection came from Egypt, Abyssinia, Pretoria, Argentina, Brazil, Chile, Uruguay, Italy, and Australia.

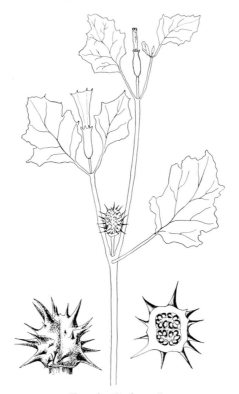

FIG. 4.  *D. ferox* L.

3. *D. quercifolia* H.B.K.  1818.  Nov. Gen. and Sp. 3: 6.

   *D. villosa* Fernald.  1900.  Proc. Amer. Acad. 35: 571.

This species was described by Humboldt, Bonpland, and Kunth in 1818. Corolla pale lavender, 4 to 7 cm long and about 2 cm wide. Calyx half as long as the five-toothed corolla. Anthers purple. Capsule ovoid, 6 to 7 cm long, 4 to 6 cm wide, including spines. Spines very unequal in size, larger at the top of capsule, and less stout than in *D. ferox*. Leaves deeply pinnately lobed. Stem purple, erect, 0.5 to 1.5 meters high. Stem and leaves slightly downy or pubescent (Figs. 3c, 5).

*D. quercifolia* was first found in Mexico. Its range of distribution is not extensive. It is found in the southwestern regions of the United

States and Mexico. The three chromosomal types in our collection were found in Texas, Arizona, and Mexico.

The description of *D. villosa* given by Fernald (1900), and the isotype of the species, seen in the U. S. National Herbarium, correspond well with our plants of *D. quercifolia.* The type locality is Bolaños, Jalisco, Mexico.

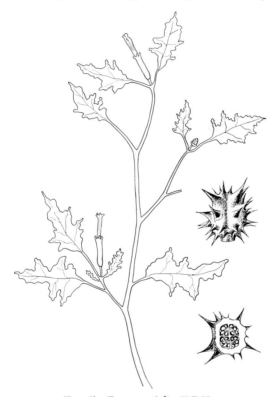

Fig. 5. *D. quercifolia* H.B.K.

**Section II.** *Dutra* Bernhardi.

Six species belong to this section: *D. pruinosa, D. leichhardtii, D. meteloides, D. innoxia, D. discolor,* and *D. metel.* Flowers erect, small or very large, five-lobed or ten-angled, white or colored, with simple or double corolla. Calyx usually dropping with the withered corolla, circumscissile. Capsules nodding or inclined, breaking irregularly at maturity, spiny or tuberculate. Seeds brown or black with strophiole attached to the hilum. Annual herbs, occasionally forming perennial roots.

4. *D. pruinosa* Greenm. 1898. Proc. Am. Acad. 33: 486.

Corolla white, small, 3.5 to 4.5 cm long, 1 to 1.5 cm wide. Calyx densely pubescent, more than half to three-fourths the length of the corolla. Capsule nodding, nearly globular, 3 to 4 cm in diameter, covered with short slender spines. Seeds small, brown. Leaves dark green, ovate, slightly dentate, 3 to

8 cm long, unequal at the base. Stem slightly spreading, usually less than 0.5 meter tall. Leaves and stem strongly pubescent.

This species was first found in Oaxaca, Mexico, by Rev. L. Smith in 1894. He again collected it in 1895, and in 1897 it was collected by C. G. Pringle. It was named *D. pruinosa* by Greenman in 1898. Its distribution is very limited. Seeds have been sent to us from Oaxaca and from the adjacent state of Puebla (Figs. 3d, 6).

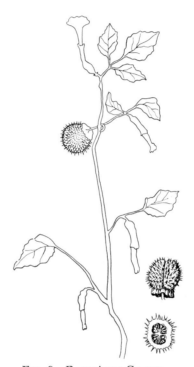

FIG. 6.  *D. pruinosa* Greenm.

5. *D. leichhardtii* Muell. 1869. Benth. and Muell. Fl. Austral. 4: 468.

This species, like the preceding, differs from other species in the *Dutra* section by the smaller size of its flowers, leaves, capsules, and general habit. Corolla white, about 3.5 cm long. Calyx about three-fourths of the length of the corolla. Capsule nodding, globose, 3 to 4 cm in diameter, covered with short slender spines. Seeds small, brown, with the strophiole attached when fresh. Leaves ovate, slightly dentate. Stem about 0.5 meter tall. Leaves and stem only slightly pubescent (Figs. 2b, 3e, 7).

The type locality is Australia. The range of distribution is apparently limited to that continent. The seeds of the two chromosomal types that we have studied came from Queensland and Central Australia.

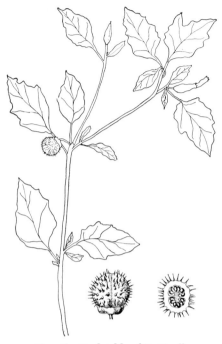

Fig. 7.  *D. leichhardtii* Muell.

6.  *D. meteloides* DC. in Dunal.  1852.  DC. Prodr. 13. 1: 544.

  *D. wrightii* Regel.  1859.  Gartenfl. 8: 193. T. 260.
  *D. metel* var.? *quinquecuspida* Torr.  1856.  Pac. R. R. Rept. Vol. 7, part III:
    18.

Corolla white, ten-toothed, faintly suffused with violet, 17 to 19 cm long, 15 cm wide.  Calyx about half as long as corolla, with unequal lobes, weakly persistent at the base of the capsule.  Style 17 to 18 cm long; stigma frequently protrudes from the corolla in buds.  Anthers white.  Capsule globose, nodding, 4 to 5.5 cm in diameter, covered with slender, subangular spines.  Seeds brown, strophiole large.  Leaves unequally dentate, asymmetrical at the base, nearly entire.  Stem to 1 meter tall, widely branching and spreading.  Leaves and stem pubescent.  In its native habitat and occasionally in our experimental plots, this species forms perennial thickened roots from which new annual growth will start (Figs. 3f, 8, 9a).

The type locality is Mexico. The range of distribution is western Texas to California and Mexico.  Seeds of the four chromosomal types used in our studies were collected in Arizona, Utah, Oklahoma, Nevada, New Mexico, California, and Mexico.

Differences in characters between the description of this species given by Dunal in DC. Prodromus XIII and plants grown in Zürich from seeds received from California were first pointed out by Regel (1859) and led

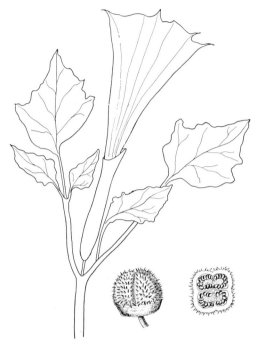

Fig. 8.  *D. meteloides* DC.

him to propose the name *D. wrightii* for the living plants.  These discrepancies have been noted by later authors who studied the plants from California, the southwestern United States and Mexico, and also those found in our own collections.  The differences, as listed by Ewan (1944), are as follows:

| Datura meteloides (As described by De Candolle) | Datura meteloides (As known from wild plants in the field) |
|---|---|
| *Calyx lobes* very unequal | *Calyx lobes* equal or nearly so |
| *Fruiting calyx* deciduous | *Fruiting calyx* persistent |
| *Leaf blades* sinuate to strictly entire, equilateral at base | *Leaf blades* coarsely sinuate-dentate, usually equilateral at base |
| *Corolla limb* short, scarcely flaring | *Corolla limb* ample, distinctly trumpet-flaring |
| *Capsule* thinly spinose | *Capsule* closely beset with slender subacicular spines |

It will be noted that Ewan regards the calyx lobes of the wild plants as equal or nearly so, while we describe them as unequal.

A specimen collected by Palmer in Mexico in 1907 and preserved in the Kew Herbarium appears, according to Timmerman (1927a), to be the only plant which agrees with the original description and illustration of *D. meteloides.* She described it as having "small glaucescent, lanceolate leaves, acute at both ends."

The problems connected with the nomenclature of this species have been discussed in great detail by Ewan (1944). He indicates that the name *D. meteloides* DC. in Dunal was not based on fresh or herbarium material but on "a hastily executed copy of a Sessé and Mociño drawing" which serves as the "type." He explains that "no other species of *Datura* has been found in Central Mexico which agrees with the original description and drawings." He gives a detailed tabulation (quoted above) of the discrepancies between the description of *D. meteloides* and wild plants, and recommends in conclusion that the name *D.*

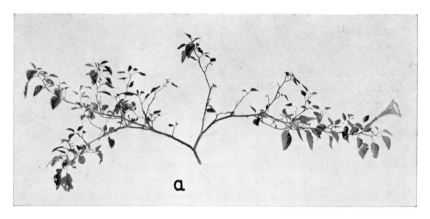

Fig. 9.   (a) *D. meteloides* DC.   (b) *D. innoxia* Mill.

*meteloides* DC. in Dunal be accepted but its diagnosis amended. The next available name would be *D. wrightii* Regel.

The plant of "Toloachi" described by Torrey (1856) as *D. metel* var.? *quinquecuspida* from a southern California specimen collected by Anticell in 1855 is undoubtedly *D. meteloides* as understood by Ewan and others.

7. *D. inoxia* Mill. 1768. Gard. Dict., ed. 8. *Datura* No. 5 (spelled *innoxia* in de Chazelles and Holandre's translation of Miller's ed. 8, 1787, vol. 3, and by most subsequent authors).

    *D. metel sensu* Sims. 1812. Curtis's Bot. Mag. 35: Pl. 1440.
    *D. guayaquilensis* H. B. K. 1818. Nov. Gen. and Sp. 3: 6.
    *D. metel sensu* Dunal. 1852. DC. Prodr. 13: 543.

Corolla white, ten-toothed, 15 to 18 cm long, limb 10 to 12 cm wide. Calyx with uneven lobes as in *D. meteloides*. Anthers about 2 cm long, white. Style 13 to 17 cm long. Capsule ovoid, nodding, 6 to 6.5 cm in diameter; covered with long, slender spines. Seeds brown. Leaves ovate, entire. Stem to 2 meters tall. Leaves and stem covered with soft hairs.

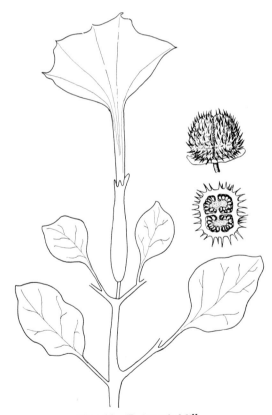

Fig. 10. *D. innoxia* Mill.

This species is often confused with *D. meteloides* DC.  The more erect habit of *D. innoxia* and its smaller *white* flowers are characters by which it can be distinguished.  The stigmas of *D. innoxia* are larger and are carried on somewhat shorter styles (Figs. 3g, 9b, 10).

The type locality of *D. innoxia* is Vera Cruz.  The present range is wide.  The seeds of the three chromosomal types studied came from Asia, South America, Central America, Italy, Spain, Mexico, and the southwestern part of the United States.  This species is frequently cultivated in gardens, and may be occasionally found as an apparent escape in parts of the eastern and southeastern United States.

The taxonomic history of this species also is complicated.  It was named *D. "inoxia"* (*innoxia*) by Miller in 1768.  His description was based on a plant grown from seed received from Mexico.  Sims (1812), according to Timmerman (1927a), erroneously described and identified as *D. metel* L. a plant grown in London from seed obtained in America.  Sims admitted, however, that this "downy thorn apple" might be the species described earlier by Miller as *D. innoxia*.  A few years later another specimen was described by Humboldt, Bonpland, and Kunth

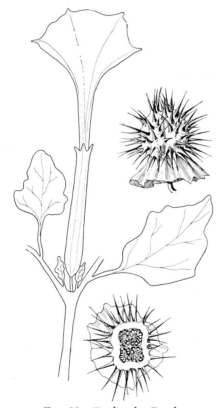

Fig. 11.  *D. discolor* Bernh.

(1818) as a new species. They named this *D. guayaquilensis*. More confusion was caused later by Dunal (1852). He applied to *D. innoxia* Mill., i.e., to a species native to America, the name of the Asiatic metel-nut, *D. metel* L. This error was made in spite of the distinct character-istics that distinguish *D. innoxia* Mill.: its pubescent and soft stem, calyx and leaves, its spiny capsules and the ten-toothed corolla. Many botanists did not correct Dunal's error and incorrectly used the name *D. metel* L. instead of *D. innoxia* Mill. (Timmerman, 1927a).

In a number of reports of our experimental work published previously in several journals, the name of this species was spelled *D. inoxia*, as it was by Miller (1768).

8. *D. discolor* Bernh. 1833. Trommsdorf N. Jour. Pharm. 26: 149; 1833.
    Linnaea 8: Lit. Ber. 138.

Corolla nearly white with violet striped throat, trumpet-shaped, ten-toothed, about 14 to 16 cm long. Calyx sharp-angled, 4 to 6 cm long, dropping with the corolla, leaving at the base of the capsule a large frill. Capsule ovoid, 6 to 7 cm long, 4 to 6 cm wide, covered with long slender spines. Seed black. Leaves ovate, large, dentate or almost entire. Stem to about 1.5 meters tall. Stems and leaves slightly pubescent. Habit spreading (Figs. 3h, 11, 12a).

The type locality is the West Indies. The range of distribution is the West Indies, Mexico, and the southwestern parts of the United States. The races in our collection came from Mexico, Arizona, and New Mexico.

Fig. 12. (a) *D. discolor* Bernh.

There is considerable doubt that the name *Datura discolor* is correctly applied to the species here described, but there seems to be no other available name for it, unless the much smaller-flowered *D. thomasii* Torrey (1857) can be shown to be merely a depauperate collection of this species. Both Bernhardi and Dunal place *D. discolor* in Sect. *Stramonium* without apparent hesitation, while the plant to which this name is generally applied is in Sect. *Dutra.* There is nothing in the description of Bernhardi nor in the amplified one of Dunal to suggest that their plant is not correctly placed in Sect. *Stramonium* and both mention that the leaves are incanous beneath, from which the epithet *discolor* undoubtedly comes. The plants generally called *D. discolor* do not show this char-

FIG. 12.  (b) *D. metel* L.

acter nor do they have the dehiscence into four valves of Sect. *Stramonium*. The dehiscence is not specifically mentioned by either Bernhardi or Dunal, but, in one of the pre-Linnaean references cited by Bernhardi, *Stramonium curassavica humilior Hyoscyamifolio* (Hermann, 1698, pp. 233–234), the fruit is said to dehisce into four parts. In none of the early references to this species do the capsules correspond well with the plant here called *D. discolor*, for they are described as muricate-aculeate. Neither does this characterization fit those of any of the species of Sect. *Stramonium*. Hence it is not possible to associate this name very satisfactorily with any known species. It is with considerable misgiving that, for lack of an available name that can be applied with certainty to the species under discussion, we continue to use *Datura discolor* Bernh. for it.

9. *D. metel* L.  1753.  Spec. Pl. 1: 179.

> *D. fastuosa* L.  1759.  Syst. Nat., ed. 10. 2: 932.
> *D. alba* Rumph. ex Nees.  1837.  Trans. Linn. Soc. 17: 73.
> *D. cornucopaea* Hort. ex. W. W.  1894.  The Garden. 46: 224, pl. 978.

This species includes several distinct types. Flowers white, yellow, purple, or purple outside and white inside. Corolla trumpet-shaped, simple, double, or triple by the irregular petaloid outgrowth of the stamens and inner corolla surfaces; about 14 to 15 cm long. Calyx regular, 5 to 7 cm long, evenly five-lobed, less than half as long as the corolla. Style 11 to 13 cm long. Capsule globose, inclined, 4 to 6 cm in diameter, covered with very short spines or tubercles. Leaves ovate, nearly entire or with a few teeth. Stems green in forms with white or yellow flowers, and purple in those with purple flowers. Leaf scars conspicuous on the stems. Stem erect, about 0.3 meter in some varieties, reaching to 1.5 meters in others. Stem and leaves glabrous. The very short spines or tubercles on the capsules and the glabrous condition of the stem and leaves are the main characters that distinguish this species from the other large species of the *Dutra* section (Figs. 3i, 12b, 13).

The type locality of *D. metel* L. is Asia. The range of distribution includes tropical and subtropical Asia, Africa, and America. The plant is often cultivated throughout warm regions of the world. The races used in our studies came from seed from various countries in Asia, Africa, and southern Europe as well as from Mexico, the West Indies, and South America. This species is so frequently cultivated that it is impossible to determine if any of these collections represent native habitats or are merely cultivated races.

Linnaeus (1737) first described this species in Hortus Cliffortianus, p. 55, as *Datura pericarpiis nutantibus globosis*, with references to earlier names, including *Stramonia multis dicta sive Pomum spinosum* of J. Bauhin (1651), Historia Pl. 3: 624, *Solanum pomo spinoso rotundo longo flore* of C. Bauhin (1623), Pinax, p. 168, and *Hummatu* of Rheede (1679), Hortus Malabaricus 2, p. 47, t. 28. He also cited a species and several varieties named by Tournefort (1700). These varieties were plants with simple or double, white or colored corollas. Safford (1922) points out that one of J. Bauhin's figures (Safford, Fig. 2) is a reduced copy of that of Fuchsius (1542). The species has also been identified with the metel-nut (nux methel) of the Arab writer Avicenna, which was known in the eleventh century as a plant used by the Arabs for its narcotic properties.

The name *D. metel* for this species was first validly published by Linnaeus in 1753, in his first edition of Species Plantarum. It is based on the Hortus Cliffortianus name. The habitat is given as Asia and Africa.

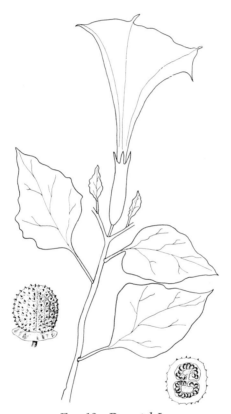

FIG. 13. *D. metel* L.

Linnaeus, on p. 932 of the tenth edition of the Systema Naturae (1759), established *Datura fastuosa* L. with the diagnosis "D. pericarp. tuberculatis nutantibus globosis" contrasted with the "D. pericarp. spinosis nutantibus globosis" of *D. metel* L. For *D. fastuosa* he gave, here, no reference to a previous publication, but later, on p. 256 of the second edition of the Species Plantarum (1762), he added references to Rumphius' *Datura rubra*, to *Solanum foetidum, fructu spinoso rotundo, femine pallido* of Bauhin, and to *Nux Metella* of Camerarius, the second of these negating what would have seemed to be the essential character of the species as understood in the Systema. He also added *"foliis laevibus"* to his own diagnosis and provided a description of the corolla which showed that here he included forms with corolla externally purple and often double. He also included here a variety *beta* to which he did not give a varietal epithet. Safford's interpretation that Linnaeus had regarded *fastuosa* as a variety of *D. metel* may have been based on a careless reading of this or on a misinterpretation of the "B" which preceded the diagnosis of *D. fastuosa* in the Systema and which really only indicated that this species was one of the two inserted in addition to those listed in Species Plantarum ed. 1.

To the treatment of *D. metel* as given in Species Plantarum ed. 1 Linnaeus added in the second edition (1762) the form with a simple white corolla called by Rumphius *D. alba,* and added to the diagnosis that the leaves of *D. metel* are pubescent. This incorrect additional statement has led to much confusion. A number of botanists overlooked Linnaeus' original treatment in the first edition of Species Plantarum and based their conclusions only on the second edition. Thus, for example, the actual *D. metel* L. with smooth stems and leaves was renamed *D. alba* by Nees von Esenbeck (1837), who kept the name of *D. metel* L. for a pubescent form.

Further confusion was added by Dunal (1852) who, working on De Candolle's herbarium, took the smooth Asiatic specimens to be identical with the Mexican pubescent species named earlier by Miller as *D. innoxia.* The latter species cannot be identified with *D. alba* Nees as suggested by Dunal since Nees von Esenbeck's species is the real *D. metel* L. Dunal made another mistake by stating that *D. metel* came from Central America. Clarke (1885) repeated Dunal's mistake. He mistook *D. innoxia* Mill. for *D. metel* L. and instead of the illustrations cited by Linnaeus (Bauhin and Rumphius) copied an incorrectly identified illustration published by Sims (1812).

Timmerman (1927a) states that she studied the specimens of Hortus Cliffortianus preserved in the British Museum and saw the actual specimen on which Linnaeus' description is based and which is the type of *D. metel.* This plant is not pubescent, has smooth stems and leaves, a single white corolla and globose capsules. This corresponds to the plant described as *D. alba* Nees which must, therefore, be placed in the synonymy of *D. metel* L.

In the Linnaean herbarium kept in London by the Linnaean Society, Timmerman saw another specimen of significance in this discussion. The name of this distinctly pubescent specimen, which had been first labeled *"D. toxica,"* had later been changed by some unknown person to *"D. metel."* Timmerman adds that this may possibly account for Linnaeus' added statement in the second edition of the Species Plantarum that *D. metel* L. has pubescent stems and leaves.

The taxonomy of *D. metel* is obviously very confused and should be revised. A comparative study needs to be made of the several varieties (forms) that the species displays. However, it should not in any way be confused with the American species *D. innoxia* Mill. or *D. meteloides* DC.

**Section III.**  *Ceratocaulis* (Spach.) Bernhardi.

Plants of the single species of this section differ from other herbaceous forms of *Datura* by having pendant, smooth, berrylike capsules.  Flowers large, erect, trumpet-shaped; corolla tube long and narrow, ten-toothed.  Calyx spathelike. Stems smooth.

10.  *D. ceratocaula* Ort.  1797.  Decas. 1: 11.

> *Apemon crassicaule* Raf.    1836.  Fl. Tell. Part II. Cent. I, No. 8: 11.
> *D. sinuata* Sessé & Moc.  1893.  Pl. Nov. Hisp., ed. 2: 24.
> *D. macrocaulos* Roth.  1802.  Neue Beytr: 159.

Corolla funnel- or trumpet-shaped, pale lavender, darker along the veins, 16 to 18 cm long, 10 to 12 cm wide, limb ten-toothed.  Calyx 8 to 9 cm long, splitting on one side.  Capsule ovoid, fleshy, smooth, 3 to 4 cm long, glabrous. Leaves pinnately lobed, slender, farinose beneath.  Seeds black, smooth, shiny. Stem erect, hollow in older stages.  Although this species grows in shallow water or marshes in its native range, it has grown well in our experimental plots and in pots in greenhouses (Figs. 3j, 14, 57).

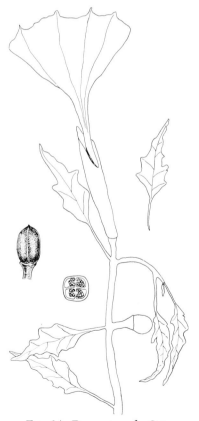

Fig. 14. *D. ceratocaula* Ort.

Type locality given as Cuba. The range of this species is probably limited to Mexico but may include some of the West Indies. The plant first described and named as a *Datura* species by Ortega grew in the Royal Botanic Garden in Madrid, Spain, from seed said to be collected in Cuba. An excellent colored illustration of this species is given in Plate 339, pp. 48–49 of Jacquin (1798). Seeds of the two chromosomal types of this species in our collection were collected from plants growing in shallow ponds in the states of Michoacan and Durango, Mexico, and from two botanical gardens. The original sources of the latter plants are unknown.

There is a suggestion of a discrepancy between the description by Roth of the fruit of *Datura macrocaulos* and that of *D. ceratocaula* as observed in the garden. Roth described the fruit as dehiscing elastically in four caducous valves, while the fruits of our plants open irregularly into parts that curl back and break up but without any suggestion of four valves. Roth's original material should be examined if it can be found, to see if these two names are really synonymous.

**Section IV.** *Brugmansia* (Persoon) Bernhardi.

Flowers large, pendulous, white or colored, single or double. Calyx spathe-like or toothed, not circumscissile at the base, falling off entirely or persisting as a husk about the base of the fruit. Fruit unarmed, spheroid, oblong, lemon-shaped, or long and slender, opening irregularly. Seeds large, covered by a thick corky layer. Stems woody; shrubs or small trees of tropical America, especially Colombia, Ecuador, Peru, and Brazil (Fig. 15).

The type for the section is *D. candida* (Persoon) Safford. The type locality is Peru. Its range of distribution is widely spread in tropical and subtropical regions, where it is often in cultivation.

The species forming the section *Brugmansia* were first placed in a distinct genus by Persoon (1805). He named the first two species *Brugmansia candida* Pers. and *B. bicolor* Pers. However, a number of botanists did not accept the generic rank given to *Brugmansia* but considered these plants to be so closely connected with other species of the genus as to form a section of *Datura:* the Tree Datura or *Brugmansia.* For example, Bernhardi (1833) indicated that some of the *Brugmansia* properties mentioned by Persoon are also present in *D. ceratocaula:* the smooth capsules and their irregular opening and the arrangement of the anthers. Bernhardi thought that Persoon's *Brugmansia* species needed closer study and preferred to consider them, at least temporarily, as a section subordinated to the genus *Datura.*

Safford did not accept the generic rank for the *Brugmansia* group of species. He considered them as forming a section of *Datura* and indicated that *D. ceratocaula* has a number of characteristics common with *Brugmansia:* nodding and irregularly dehiscent capsules with smooth epidermis and fleshy tissues. *Datura's* Section III, *Ceratocaulis,* according to Safford, connects the Section II, *Dutra,* with *Brugmansia,* which

Fig. 15. Tree *Datura* or *Brugmansia* (sp. ?).

forms Section IV. Safford described fourteen species, seven with white and seven with colored flowers. Some of these species were new: *D. pittieri* Safford, *D. rosea* Safford, *D. rubella* Safford (Safford, 1921a, 1922).

On the other hand, Lagerheim (1895) accepted Persoon's view and considered peculiarities of *Datura* and *Brugmansia* so striking and numerous that they should be separated into two genera. He also re-established the name of *Brugmansia*, which had erroneously been given by the botanist Blume to a group of *Rafflesiaceae* species, and insisted that the name given the latter species must be changed.

According to van Steenis (1931), van Zijp also had agreed in 1920 that *Brugmansia* must be given a generic name and suggested the name *Pseudodatura*. This was rejected by van Steenis, who insisted that the name *Brugmansia* offered by Persoon must be kept for the genus of the SOLANACEAE and that the differences between *Datura* and *Brugmansia* are so numerous that they justify a generic separation.

The question whether *Brugmansia* should be considered as a genus or as a section of *Datura* is not within the sphere of this chapter. However, the reader is again reminded that the cytogenetical and physiological experiments reported in this volume are concerned only with the ten herbaceous species of *Datura*.

**Conclusion.** It is obvious from this brief review that more studies are needed to clarify the taxonomy of the genus *Datura*. This is particularly true concerning the species *D. meteloides* DC. and *D. metel* L. But without doubt the most confusing and unsettled problem in the taxonomy of *Datura* is its relationship to the *Brugmansia* group of species. This problem remains unsolved and needs a thorough and complete study. A fresh approach with new criteria and data might be of help. A classification based almost exclusively on morphological descriptions and on phenotypical resemblances and differences is apparently insufficient and inadequate for the proper determination of these solanaceous species.

As indicated by Turrill (1938), the species problem is not a single problem; it includes a whole series of problems. The proper criteria for species must be based on the synthesis of all available facts. On such criteria are founded the new, and still developing, taxonomic methods. These methods include, among others, experimental taxonomy in which studies are made on living plants. The work on individual plants as well as on plants grown in clones under uniform and various environments allows one to see hereditary diversities within a species. Cytogenetic analysis should accompany all such studies (Clausen *et al.*, 1940). Another important approach includes observations on the range of variations in a population of species under natural conditions in the field (Stebbins, 1950). The importance and value in taxonomic work of geographical distribution and of ecological studies, and particularly of genetics, as well as of plant anatomy, ontogeny, paleontology, biophysical and biochemical studies, were stressed by Babcock (1942) and by Turrill (1942). Such studies permit one to select and to evaluate the characters common to groups of species, to learn and to compare their origin, distribution, habitats, and relationships. Such improved methods applied to *Datura* and *Brugmansia* would undoubtedly help taxonomists to make proper conclusions about their relationship and would indicate whether *Brugmansia* should be considered a separate genus, a subgenus, or kept as one of the sections of *Datura*.

# Summary of Datura Nomenclature, 1753-1958.

## Marie-Hélène Sachet

Reference to the original place of publication is given for those names that are neither accepted in this chapter nor included in the lists of synonymy of accepted species. Names thus included in the text are indicated by a page reference to the text with the accepted species in bold-faced italics. In this list a comment is offered for each dubious name as to the reason for uncertainty. For each illegitimate or invalid name the reason for its rejection is indicated. Present disposition is indicated for names now referred to other genera, but no attempt is made to assign them to species. Likewise, names applied to species of section *Brugmansia,* which is not treated in detail here, are indicated as belonging to section *Brugmansia* but without attempting to place them in the proper species. Trinomials that are the result of transfers or changes in status of names already in this list are not included. Misapplications of names are not listed, even though many of these have found their way into Index Kewensis or are listed in synonymy by various authors. It is entirely possible that certain names which really apply to *Datura* but which were published under other generic names have been inadvertently omitted.*

## Generic Names

*Datura* L.  See p. 17.

*Apemon* Rafinesque.  1836.  Flora telluriana, Part II. Cent. I, No. 8: 11.
  If Sect. *Ceratocaulis* is regarded as a genus, this will be its correct name.

*Brugmansia* Persoon.  1805.  Synopsis Plant. 1: 216.

*Ceratocaulos* Spach.  1840.  Hist. Nat. Veg. Phan., vol. 9: 69.
  This name is a superfluous one for *Apemon* Raf., as *Datura ceratocaula* Ort. is cited in the synonymy of the type species of both, making them equivalent nomenclaturally.

*Pseudodatura* Van Zijp.  1920.  Natuurk. Tijdschrift Ned.-Indië 80: 24.
  Substitute name for *Brugmansia,* therefore superfluous.

*Stramonium* [Tourn.] Scopoli.  1772.  Flora Carniolica, ed. 2, 1: 157.
  This name, taken from Tournefort, with Tournefort's diagnosis is substituted in ed. 2 for *Datura* L. used in ed. 1. In it is included only S. *foetidum,* which is nomenclaturally equivalent to *Datura stramonium,* the type species of *Datura* L. Therefore, *Stramonium* Scop. is a superfluous name for *Datura* L. and is illegitimate.

## Specific Names and Names of Lower Ranks

*Apemon crassicaule* Rafinesque.  1836.  Fl. tellur. Part II. Cent. I, No. 8: 11.
  This name is illegitimate, for *Datura ceratocaula* Ortega is cited in synonymy.  See p. 35.

* See footnote on p. 47.

*Brugmansia aurantiaca* Hort. ex Walpers. 1844–45. Repert. Bot. Syst. 3: 934.
Listed by Walpers as a synonym of *Juanulloa parasitica* Ruiz & Pavon.

*B. aurea* Lagerheim. 1893. Gartenflora 42: 33.
See *Datura aurea.*

*B. bicolor* Persoon. 1805. Synopsis 1: 216.
Illegitimate as citing *D. sanguinea* Ruiz & Pavon in synonymy.

*B. candida* Persoon. 1805. Synopsis 1: 216.
See *Datura candida.*

*B. coccinea* Hort. ex Siebert & Voss. 1895. Vilmorin's Blumengärtnerei, ed. 3, 1: 734.
Listed by Sieb. and Voss in synonymy of *Juanulloa aurantiaca.*

*B. dolichocarpa* Lagerheim. 1895. Bot. Jahrb. 20: 665.
See *Datura dolichocarpa.*

*B. floribunda* Paxton. 1842. Paxt. Mag. of Bot. 9: 3.
Referred to *Juanulloa* by Ind. Kew.

*B. longifolia* Lagerheim. 1895. Bot. Jahrb. 20: 666.
See *Datura longifolia.*

*B. lutea* Hort. ex Gardeners, Chronicle. 1888. III, 3: 268, 404, Fig. 42.
Mentioned in unsigned note accompanying drawing of fruiting twig with some casual descriptive information, partly quoted from a letter from Mr. O. Thomas who sent the plant figured. Probably yellow-flowered form of *Datura sanguinea* (*D. sanguinea* R. & P. var. *flava* Dunal). The name is also mentioned by Paxton, 1842, *l.c.*, but without descriptive information.

*B. parviflora* Paxton. 1842. Paxt. Mag. of Bot. 9: 3.
Published as a synonym of *B. floribunda,* hence invalid.

*B. versicolor* Lagerheim. 1895. Bot. Jahrb. 20: 666.
See *Datura versicolor.*

*B. waymannii* Paxton. 1838. Paxt. Mag. of Bot. 4: 421.
Probably *D. metel,* for it has erect double flowers, but calyx is cylindric and irregularly lobed at top. Definitely spelled with *y*, transferred to *Datura* by Steudel but spelled *wagmanni.*

*Ceratocaulos daturoides* Spach. 1840. Hist. Nat. Veg. Phan. 9: 69.
Cites *Datura ceratocaula* Ort. in synonymy, also *D. macrocaulis* [*sic*] Roth, therefore superfluous when published, since Roth's epithet was available, even though the binomial using the epithet *ceratocaula* might be considered a tautonym.

*Datura acaulis* Pavon ex Dunal. 1852. DC. Prodr. 13(1): 481.
Referred to *Jaborosa* by Dunal.

*D. affinis* Safford. 1921. Jour. Wash. Acad. Sci. 11: 186.
Belongs in Sect. *Brugmansia.*

*D. alba* Rumph. ex Nees.
Synonym of *D. metel;* see p. 32.

*D. albido-flava* Lemaire. 1854. Jardin Fleur. 4: Misc. 16.
Referred to *Dyssochroma* by Ind. Kew.

*D. arborea* L. 1753. Species Pl. 1: 179.
Belongs in Sect. *Brugmansia.*

*D. arborescens* Gubb.  1909.  Flora of Algeria, pl. 66.

A plant with white flowers and a long narrow fusiform fruit, possibly *D. suaveolens* in Sect. *Brugmansia*. The name is probably an error for *D. arborea*, as there is no mention of its being new and very little descriptive information is given.

*D. aurea* (Lagerh.) Safford.  1921.  Jour. Wash. Acad. Sci. 11: 186.

Belongs in Sect. *Brugmansia*.

*D. bernhardii* Lundström.  1914.  Acta Hort. Berg. 5(3): 89.

Described at great length apparently from a garden plant, but no type specimen mentioned; possibly one preserved in Stockholm. Probably a variant of *D. stramonium*.

*D. bertolonii* Parlatore ex Gussone.  1842.  Florae siculae synopsis 1: 267.

Synonym of *D. stramonium*, see p. 18.

*D. bojeri* Raffeneau-Delile.  1836?  Semina anni 1836 quae Hortus botanicus regius monspeliensis . . . , p. 23.  Reviewed and quoted in Ann. Sci. Nat. Bot. 1837.  II, 7: 286.

Validly published and legitimate name, probably to be referred to *D. metel*.

*D.* × *cabanesi* P. Fournier.  1934.  Le Monde des Plantes 35: 14.

Original publication not seen.

*D. candida* (Pers.) Safford.  1921.  Jour. Wash. Acad. Sci. 11: 186.

Belongs in Sect. *Brugmansia*.

*D. capensis* Hort. ex Bernhardi.  1833.  Trommsdorf N. Jour. f. Pharm. 26: 151; Linnaea.  1833.  8 Lit. Ber.: 139.

Listed by Bernh. in synonymy of *D. stramonium*. The original publication was not seen; pages and date obtained from Ind. Kew. The article was reproduced in the Litteratur Bericht section of vol. 8 of Linnaea. These references will be abbreviated below.

*D. cathaginensis* Hort. ex Siebert & Voss.  1895.  Vilmorin's Blumengärtnerei, ed. 3, 1: 728.

Listed by Sieb. and Voss as a synonym of *D. metel;* not described.

**D. ceratocaula** Ort.

See p. 35.

*D. chlorantha* Hooker.  1859.  Curtis Bot. Mag. 85: pl. 5128.

Referred by Hooker to Sect. *Brugmansia* on the basis of its arborescent habit and presumably because of the pendant flowers. No mention is made of the fruit. Safford (*l.c.*, p. 187) thinks that it is a form of *D. metel fastuosa* and that the illustration is inverted. However, Hooker does say that the flowers are pendant.

*D. cornigera* Hooker.  1846.  Curtis Bot. Mag. 72: pl. 4252.

Belongs in Sect. *Brugmansia*.

*D. cornucopaea* Hort. ex W. W.  1894.  The Garden 46: 294, pl. 978.

Synonym of *D. metel*, see p. 32. Since the abbreviation "fl.-pl." is appended to this name, it may be disqualified as a polynomial.

*D. de-noteri* Sollier ex Noter.  1912.  Le Jardin 26: 238.

Described informally, but apparently validly published, by de Noter, quoting at length from a letter from Sollier who sent him the seeds from the Cape region of Africa. Described as annual, flowers bright red. Evidently not a *Datura*.

**D. discolor** Bernh.
See p. 30.

D. *dolichocarpa* (Lagerh.) Saff. 1921. Jour. Wash. Acad. Sci. 11: 186.
Belongs in Sect. *Brugmansia*.

D. *dubia* Persoon. 1805. Synopsis 1: 216.
Obscure species in Persoon's work. Very briefly characterized. Described as a species but said to be perhaps a cultural variety of D. *fastuosa*.

D. *erinacea* Velloso. 1825. Flora fluminensis, Text vol. p. 70; plate vol. 2: pl. 46, dated 1827.
Plate appears to be of a species of *Allamanda* but text says "*caulis arboreus,*" c.f. Dunal, DC. Prodr. 13(1): 546.

D. *eximia* Lemaire. 1859. Illustr. Hortic. 6: Misc. 23.
Referred to *Dyssochroma* by Ind. Kew.

**D. fastuosa** L.
Synonym of D. *metel*, see p. 32.

D. *fastuosa* L. var. δ *alba* Bernhardi. 1827. N. Gart. Mag. II, 4: 163.
Based on *Dutra alba* Rumph. and an extensive synonymy, mostly polynomial, except for D. *muricata* Bernh., D. *dubia* Pers., D. *tatula* β Poir. Synonym of D. *metel*.

D. *fastuosa* L. var. *flaviflora* O. E. Schulz ex O. C. Schmidt. 1933. Fedde Repert. Spec. Nov. 32: 89.
Apparently a yellow variety of D. *metel*.

D. *fastuosa* L. var. α *glabra* Bernh. 1827. L.c.
A form of D. *metel*.

D. *fastuosa* L. var. β *parviflora* Nees. 1837. Trans. Linn. Soc. 17: 74.
Not nomenclaturally equivalent to D. *parviflora* Salisb. nor to *Brugmansia parviflora* Paxt.; could be identified only by examination of the type specimen.

D. *fastucsa* L. var. γ *rubra* Bernh. 1827. L.c.
Based on *Dutra rubra* Rumph.

D. *fastuosa* L. var. β *tuberculosa* Bernh. 1827. L.c.
A form of D. *metel*.

D. × *ferocissima* Cabanès & P. Fournier. 1934. Le Monde des Pl. 35: 14.
Original publication not seen.

**D. ferox** L.
See p. 21.

D. *floribunda* (Paxt.) Dunal. 1852. DC. Prodr. 13(1): 546.
Published as *Brugmansia floribunda*, which see.

D. *frutescens* Hort. ex Siebert & Voss. 1895. Vilmorin's Blumengärtn. 1: 727.
Listed by Sieb. and Voss as synonym of D. *knightii*.

D. *fruticosa* Hornemann. 1813. Hortus Reg. Bot. Hafniensis 1: 212.
Briefly described as a new species; probably not recognizable from description alone.

D. *gardneri* Hook. 1846. Curtis Bot. Mag. 72: pl. 4252.
Belongs in Sect. *Brugmansia*.

D. *gigantea* Hort. ex [Avebury] Lubbock. 1892. Contribution to . . . seedlings. 2: 297.
Description of a seedling with nothing on which to base identification.

*D. guayaquilensis* HBK.
Synonym of *D. innoxia,* see p. 28.

*D. huberiana* Hort. 1891. Wien. Ill. Gart.-Zeit. 16: 157, fig. 34.
The name is applied to the illustration, which is mentioned in the text; but the descriptive remarks in the text do not refer specifically to the plant called by this name. The binomial, then, applies only to the illustration, which is of a double-flowered plant, probably a form of *D. metel,* but this would be hard to prove.

*D. humilis* Desfontaines. 1829. Catalogus pl. hort. reg. Parisiensis, ed. 3: 396. Apparently validly published and legitimate. Probably a variant of *D. metel.*

*D. hummatu* Bernhardi. 1833. Trommsd., *l.c.,* p. 153; Linnaea, *l.c.,* p. 141. Illegitimate, for various available earlier names cited in synonymy, including *D. dubia* Pers. as basis for the var. a *dubia.*

*D. hummatu* Bernh. var. c *rubra* Bernh., *l.c.*
Varietal name illegitimate, since it was published under an illegitimate specific name. Bernhardi makes no reference here to his earlier *D. fastuosa* var. *rubra.*

*D. hybrida* Tenore. 1823. Fl. Neap. Prodr. App. 4: 34.
Name listed in Tenore, Cat. Pl. Horti Regii Neapolitani, 1813, p. 34, but as a *nomen nudum.* Plant briefly described in 1823 and said to be "*D. metel* affinis," but reported to be "glauco-pubescens; perennis." Cannot be positively identified without examination of type specimen if extant. May be *D. meteloides* or *D. innoxia.*

*D. inermis* Jacq.
Synonym of *D. stramonium,* see p. 18.

**D. inoxia** Mill.
See p. 28.

*D. insignis* Barbosa Rodrigues. 1888. Vellosia, ed. 1, vol. 1. 1891. Ed. 2, 1: 62. (Ed. 2 an improved reissue of ed. 1, which is unavailable generally.)
Described as arborescent, 2–3 meters tall; probably belongs in Sect. *Brugmansia.* It is not absolutely clear that the 1888 edition is the original place of publication.

*D. knightii* Siebert & Voss. 1895. Vilmorin's Blumengärtnerei, ed. 3, 1: 727. Superfluous name for *D. cornigera* Hook., which is in Sect. *Brugmansia.*

*D. laevis* L. f.
Synonym of *D. stramonium,* see p. 18.

*D. laevis* Schkuhr. 1791. Botanisches Handbuch . . . 1: 140.
Described briefly as a garden variety "Abart" of *D. fastuosa,* but given a binomial. Illegitimate because a later homonym of *D. laevis* L. f.

**D. leichhardtii** Muell.
See p. 24.

*D. longifolia* (Lagerh.) Safford. 1921. Jour. Wash. Acad. Sci. 11: 186.
Belongs in Sect. *Brugmansia.*

*D. loricata* Sieber. Coll. Sem. ex Bernh. 1833. Trommsd. p. 151, Linnaea, *l.c.* p. 139.
Listed as a synonym of *D. stramonium* by Bernhardi,

*D. lurida* Salisbury. 1796. Prodromus stirpium . . . , p. 131.
Illegitimate, substitute name for *D. stramonium* L.

*D. macrocaulos* Roth.
Synonym of *D. ceratocaula*, see p. 35.

*D. maxima* Sessé & Mociño. 1893. Plant. Nov. Hisp., ed. 2: 23.
Referred to *Solandra* by Ind. Kew.

*D. metel* L.
See p. 32.

*D. metel sensu* Dunal.
Synonym of *D. innoxia*, see p. 28.

*D. metel sensu* Sims.
Synonym of *D. innoxia*, see p. 28.

*D. metel* L. var. *fastuosa* (L.) Safford. 1921. Jour. Wash. Acad. Sci. 11: 187.
This combination, probably varietal, made here casually in discussion of *D. chlorantha* Hook.

*D. metel* L. forma *pleniflora* Degener. 1934. Flora hawaiiensis: family 318, D.m.
A form of *D. metel* with triple yellow flower.

*D. metel* L. var.? *quinquecuspida* Torrey.
Synonym of *D. meteloides*, see p. 25.

*D. meteloides* DC. in Dunal.
See p. 25.

*D. microcarpa* Godron. 1873. Mém. Acad. Stanisl. IV, 5: 202.
Well-described new species, probably actually a form of *D. stramonium*.

*D. mollis* Safford. 1921. Jour. Wash. Acad. Sci. 11: 183.
Belongs in Sect. *Brugmansia*.

*D. muricata* Bernh. Cat. sem. Hort. Erfurt. a 1818. 1827. N. Allg. Garten-Mag. II, 4: 159.
Original publication not seen, date unknown. In 1827 paper, text illustrated with a colored plate of a dark purple double (?) corolla greatly exceeding the calyx, which, with the capsule, are those of *D. metel*. On p. 163, Bernhardi reduces *D. muricata* to synonymy of *D. fastuosa* L. var. δ *alba*. He also regards his earlier *D. muricata* and that of Link as the same, which they probably are not.

*D. muricata* Link. 1821. Enumeratio Hort. Berolinensis 1: 177.
Link is clearly enough describing a new species, though he nowhere says so. There is little to go on from the description other than glabrous, repand leaves, long white corolla. Perhaps a form of *D. stramonium*. In any event, a later homonym of *D. muricata* Bernh. if that is described in the catalogue for 1818.

*D. nigra* Rumph. in Hasskarl. 1844. Catal. Hort. Bogoriensis alter, p. 142.
Based on the Rumphian description and illustration in Herbarium Amboinense, therefore validly published. Merrill (1917) in his Interpretation of Rumphius's Herbarium Amboinense, p. 465, refers this to *D. fastuosa* L. var. *alba* (Nees) C.B. Cl., which is *D. metel* L.

*D. nilhummatu* Dunal. 1852. DC. Prodr. 13(1): 542.
Dunal cites "*D. tatula dubia* Pers. Syn. p. 216" in synonymy of var. *α*, but

Persoon's plant was not described as a variety, so *D. nilhummatu* is illegitimate. Probably synonymous with *D. metel.*

*D. parviflora* Salisbury. 1796. Prodr., p. 131.
Illegitimate, substitute name for *D. tatula* L.

*D. pittieri* Safford. 1921. Jour. Wash. Acad. Sci. 11: 187.
Belongs in Sect. *Brugmansia.*

*D. praecox* Godron. 1873. Mém. Acad. Stanisl. IV, 5: 199.
Well-described new species, probably a form of *D. stramonium.*

**D. pruinosa** Greenm.
See p. 23.

*D. pseudo-stramonium* Sieber. Herb. Mart. 286 ex Bernh. 1833. Trommsd., *l.c.*, p. 151; Linnaea, *l.c.*, p. 139.
Listed by Bernhardi as synonym of *D. stramonium.*

*D. pubescens* Roques. 1808. Plantes Usuelles Indig. & Exot. 2: 187, pl. 47, fig. 188.
An inadequately described, poorly illustrated plant, from Asia and Africa, the description corresponding best with that of *D. innoxia* Mill. but the capsule shown in the plate most resembles that of *D. metel*, which is not pubescent. This cannot be identified with any confidence without examination of the original material, which, if it exists, may be either in the herbarium at Montpellier or that at Paris.

**D. quercifolia** HBK.
See p. 22.

*D. rosei* Safford. 1921. Jour. Wash. Acad. Sci. 11: 188.
Belongs in Sect. *Brugmansia.*

*D. rubella* Safford. 1921. *L.c.*, p. 185.
Belongs in Sect. *Brugmansia.*

*D. sanguinea* Ruiz & Pavon. 1799. Flora peruviana 2: 15.
Belongs in Sect. *Brugmansia.*

*D. sanguinea* Ruiz & Pavon var. *β flava* Dunal. 1852. DC. Prodr. 13(1): 545.
Belongs in Sect. *Brugmansia.* The plant was mentioned, but not named, by Bentham, 1846, in his Plantae Hartwegianae, p. 239.

*D. sarmentosa* Lamarck. 1793. Tableau Encycl. 2: 9.
Based on *Solandra grandiflora* Sw. (1787), which is cited in synonymy; therefore the name is illegitimate. The plant is a *Solandra*, not a *Datura.*

*D. scandens* Velloso. 1825. Flora fluminensis Text vol. p. 70; plate vol. 2: pl. 45, dated 1827.
Certainly a species of *Solandra* is illustrated in the plate.

*D. sinuata* Sessé & Mociño.
Synonym of *D. ceratocaula*, see p. 35.

*D. speciosa* Salisbury. 1796. Prodr., p. 131.
Illegitimate, substitute name for *D. arborea* L.

**D. stramonium** L.
See p. 18.

*D. stramonium* L. var. *β canescens* Wallich in Roxburgh. 1824. Flora Indica 2: 239.
Described in detail by Wallich, probably a form of *D. stramonium.*

*D. stramonium* L. var. β *chalybea* Koch. 1837. Synopsis Fl. Germ. Helvet., p. 510.

Illustrated by Reichenbach, Ic. Fl. Germ. 20: pl. 1624, 1861. Equals *D. tatula* L., hence belongs in synonymy of *D. stramonium* L. Illegitimate, since *D. tatula* is cited in synonymy and has been used earlier in varietal rank by Torrey, 1824, Fl. north and mid. U.S. 1: 232.

*D. suaveolens* Humb. & Bonpl. ex Willd. 1809. Enum. plant. Hort. Berol., p. 227.

Belongs in Section *Brugmansia*.

*D. suaveolens* Humb. & Bonpl. f. *macrocalyx* Sendin.

Listed, with description, by Siebert and Voss, 1895, Vilmorin's Blumen-gärtnerei, ed. 3, 1: 726. No earlier publication of this name was located, but one may exist.

*D. tarapacana* Philippi. 1891. Anales Mus. Nac. Chile Sect. 2 Bot. [Entrega 8]: 62.

Rather amply described, but lacking information on dehiscence of fruit; scarcely to be finally identified without reference to authentic specimens.

*D. tatula* L.

· Synonym of *D. stramonium*, see p. 18.

*D. thomasii* Torrey. 1857. Pacific R. R. Repts., vol. 7, appendix, art. 7: 362–363.

Usually referred to *D. discolor,* but the type must be examined for satisfactory interpretation.

*D. timoriensis* Zipp. ex Spanoghe. 1841. Linnaea 15: 337.

Apparently published in synonymy, therefore invalid. Probably *D. metel.*

*D. trapezia* Nees. 1837. Trans. Linn. Soc. 17: 74.

Validly published, but could only be disposed of by reference to the type specimen.

*D. versicolor* (Lagerh.) Safford. 1921. Jour. Wash. Acad. Sci. 11: 183.

Belongs in Sect. *Brugmansia*.

*D. villosa* Fernald.

Synonym of *D. quercifolia*, see p. 22.

*D. wagmannii* Steudel. 1840. Nomenclator botanicus, ed. 2, 1: 484.

Orthographic error for *waymannii*, which Steudel transfers from *Brugmansia*.

*D. wallichii* Dunal. 1852. DC. Prodr. 13(1): 539.

Based on *D. stramonium* L. var. β *canescens* Wall. in Roxb., which probably belongs in *D. stramonium*.

*D. waymannii* (Paxton) Steud. 1840. Nomencl., ed. 2, 1: 484.

See discussion under *Brugmansia waymannii*.

*D. wrightii* Regel.

Synonym of *D. meteloides*, see p. 25.

*Solandra herbacea* Mordant de Launay. 1819. Herb. de l'Amat. 3: pl. 207.

This is a transfer of *Datura ceratocaula* Ort. to *Solandra* with substitution of the epithet *herbacea* for *ceratocaula*. The binomial is superfluous and illegitimate, since two legitimate names, *D. ceratocaula* Ort. and *D. macrocaulis* [*sic*] Roth, are cited as synonyms.

*Stramonium foetidum* Scopoli. 1772.  Flora Carniolica, ed. 2, 1: 157.

In ed. 1, 1760, of Flora Carniolica, p. 290, the genus *Datura* L. is adopted, with one species, not described anew nor given a binomial but referred to by the Hort. Cliff. polynomial, as in Spec. Pl., ed. 1.  In Scopoli's ed. 2, the genus is referred to as *Stramonium* Tourn. with Tournefort's diagnosis. *Stramonium foetidum* is described, but to it are referred both the poly-nomial or diagnosis of Syst. Nat., p. 170, and *Datura stramonium* of Spec. Pl., ed. 1, p. 179.  *S. foetidum* is superfluous and illegitimate because its equivalent, *Datura stramonium* L., should have been adopted.

*S. spinosum* Lamarck. 1778.  Flore françoise 2: 256.

Illegitimate name, for *D. stramonium* L. is cited in synonymy and should have been adopted.

*S. vulgare* Moench. 1794.  Methodus pl. hort. bot. Marburgensis, p. 456.

Illegitimate name, for *D. stramonium* L. is cited in synonymy and should have been adopted.

*S. vulgatum* Gaertner. 1791.  De Fruct. Semin. Pl. 2: 243.

The synonymy of this name includes a reference to *Datura pericarpiis spino-sis erectis ovatis, foliis ovatis glabris* Linn. syst. veg. 220 [ed. 14, 1784, Murray], which is exactly the Hortus Cliffortianus polynomial on which *Datura stramonium* L. is founded; therefore, Gaertner's name is superfluous and illegitimate, because the generic name *Datura* and the specific name *Datura stramonium* should have been adopted.

EDITOR'S NOTE: For a more extended discussion, see FOSBERG, F. R., *Taxon* 8: 52–57, 1959. For a clarification of the status of some names, including *D. meteloides* DC., see BARCLAY, A. S., *Bot. Mus. Leaflets Harvard Univ.* 18: 245–272, 1959. Both of these papers appeared while this text was in press.

# 3

# The Alkaloids of Datura

EDWARD LEETE

Extracts or powdered portions of *Datura* plants show complex physiological actions when taken internally in toxic doses. Some of the effects of these drugs when taken for medicinal or ceremonial purposes by primitive peoples are reviewed in Chapter 1. The therapeutical use and value of these drugs have been recognized in modern medicine. Various pharmacopoeias list one or more species as being acceptable. The United States Pharmacopoeia has listed only *D. stramonium*, thereby excluding other species of equal or greater value for medicinal use. It has also excluded all parts of the plant except the leaf, in spite of the fact that it has been shown that the leaves may contain smaller proportions of the effective alkaloids than do some other parts of the plant. Several alkaloids of medicinal importance have been identified in *Datura* although their extraction from other sources has usually been found to be more economical.

During the two world wars *Datura* was brought to some prominence as a possible source of these alkaloids when other solanaceous plants, especially belladonna (*Atropa*), became scarce. Certain large drug companies in this country commenced the cultivation of several species of *Datura*. Tests were made of many of the different geographical races, as well as of the $2n + 1$ and polyploid forms, which had been assembled by Blakeslee to determine if any showed significantly higher proportions of alkaloids. It was found that environmental factors caused as wide variations as were found between specific races.

Atropine, hyoscyamine, and hyoscine are the only three alkaloids of *Datura* that are used to any considerable extent in medicine. The first of these rarely, if ever, occurs as such in these plants. Atropine is principally used in medicine on account of its property of causing dilation of the pupil of the eye. The dilation can be induced by internal administration as well as by application of solutions directly to the eye. The potency of the plant juices in this respect has often been demonstrated to those of us who have handled *Datura* plants and then happened to rub our eyes with fingers carrying the alkaloid-laden juices.

48

All the species of *Datura* that have been examined chemically have been shown to contain alkaloids of the tropane class.  The same alkaloids are also found in related solanaceous plants such as *Atropa belladonna* and *Duboisia leichhardtii*.  Nothing is known about the function of these alkaloids in the *Datura* plant, but recently some work has been carried out on their mode of formation.  In this chapter the chemistry, pharmacology, distribution, and biogenesis of the alkaloids will be reviewed.

**Chemistry of the Alkaloids.**  Apart from cuscohygrine all the alkaloids of *Datura* are derivatives of tropane (I).  The most abundant alkaloid is hyoscyamine (II).  This alkaloid has an asymmetric carbon (denoted

by an *).  The optically active form is known as hyoscyamine and the racemic mixture is atropine.  Like most of the tropane alkaloids, hyoscyamine is an ester readily breaking at the —O—CO— bond, producing an alcohol, tropine (III), and an acid, tropic acid (IV).  Formula III represents the established stereochemical relation of the atoms in tropine.

Nor-hyoscyamine (V) is a minor alkaloid differing from hyoscyamine by absence of the methyl group attached to nitrogen.  Hyoscine (VI), also known as scopolamine, is a fairly widespread alkaloid in this genus. It is an ester of tropic acid and the alcohol scopine (VII).

V

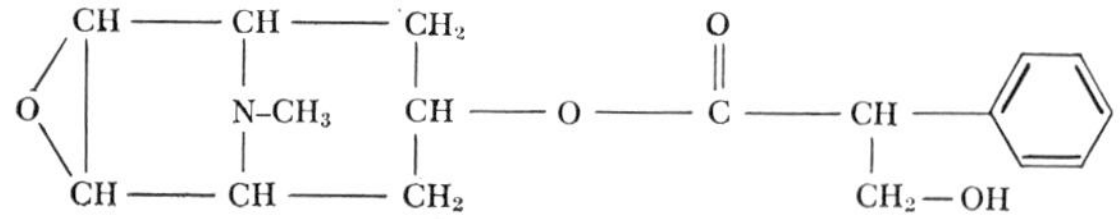

VI 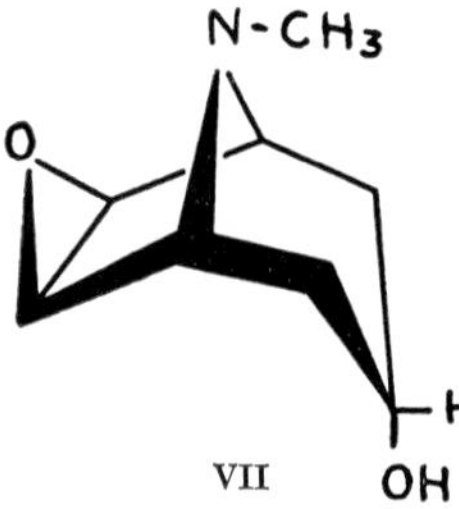          VII

Meteloidine (VIII) is found in two species of *Datura* and is an ester of tiglic acid (IX) and teloidine (X). Recently a new alkaloid has been isolated from the roots of several species. It has the structure (XI) and is 3, 6-ditiglylteloidine. Cuscohygrine (XII) has been detected in the roots of several *Datura* species. It does not contain a tropane ring, but it may be related to the other alkaloids biogenetically. The chemistry of

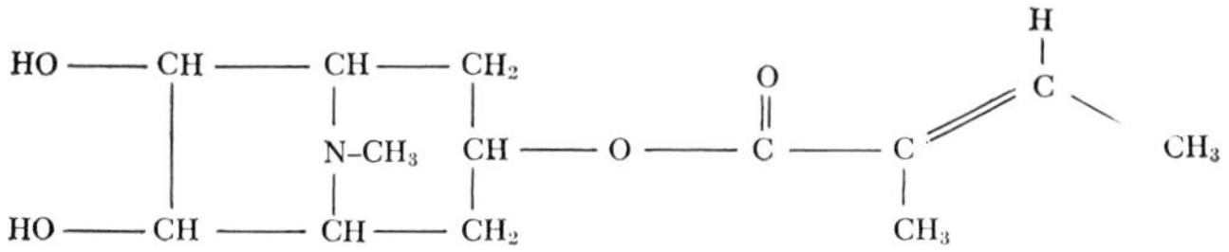

VIII

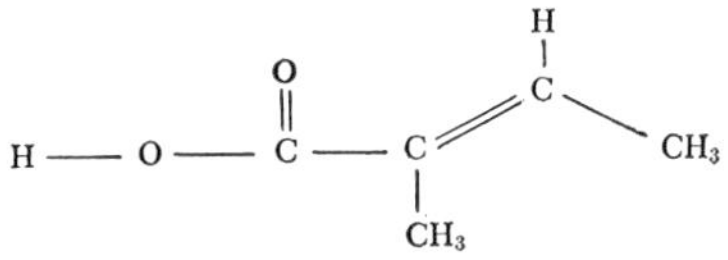

IX 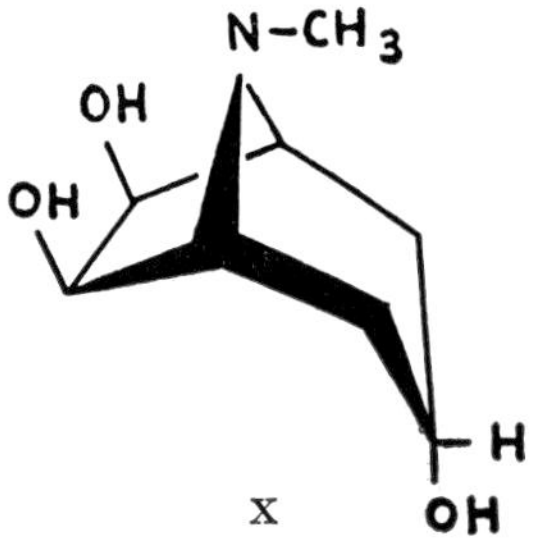          X

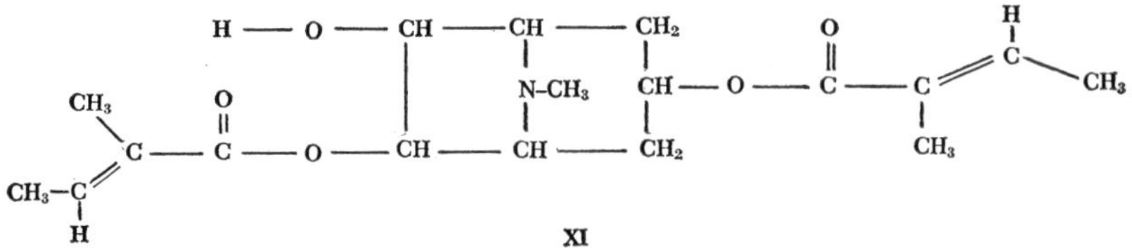

XI

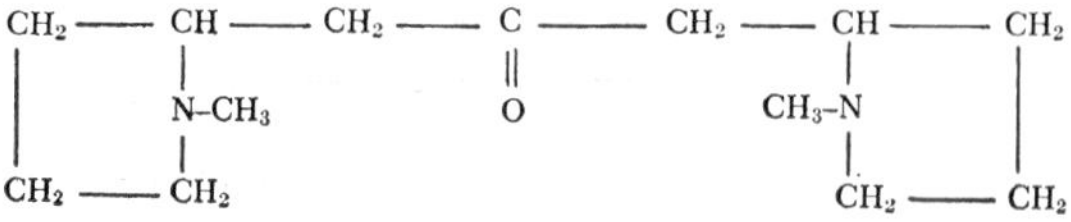

XII

these alkaloids is discussed in more detail by Henry (1949), Holmes (1950), and Fodor (1957).

**Pharmacology of the Alkaloids.** Atropine, hyoscyamine, and hyoscine are sometimes referred to as the mydriatic alkaloids, since they cause dilation of the pupil of the eye (mydriasis). They also cause paralysis of the muscles of accommodation (cycloplegia). Thus atropine is used extensively in ophthalmology for resting an inflamed eye. It is normally placed directly in the eye as a 1 per cent aqueous solution of its neutral sulfate. Mydriasis begins in about half an hour. The effect is remarkably prolonged and will often last for seven to ten days. The cycloplegic effect is slower in onset and passes off in about four days. Hyoscine produces the same effect on the eye as atropine, but its effects are weaker and of much shorter duration. It is used as the hydrochloride or hydrobromide in 1 to 2 per cent solutions.

Atropine and hyoscine also affect the central nervous system. In general atropine causes a stimulation while hyoscine acts as a depressant. Atropine has been used to counteract the depression caused by morphine. It also acts as an antidote to the highly toxic phosphate insecticides such as tetraethylpyrophosphate. It is also an antidote to the dialkylfluorophosphates, the so-called "nerve gases."

Hyoscine is an excellent preventative for motion sickness (sea or air). It is normally available in tablets mixed with a hypnotic such as sodium amytal. It is reported to be more effective than Dramamine or Benadryl. The usual tablet dose is 1/300 gram. Hyoscyamine sulfate is sometimes found in "sea sickness pills." Hyoscine is used in obstetrics along with morphine as an analgesic producing "twilight sleep." Hyoscine has also achieved some notoriety as a truth drug.

Slight changes in the structure of the alkaloids has a profound effect on their physiological action. Thus only one optical isomer of atropine (l-hyoscyamine) has mydriatic properties. However both isomers seem to have equal effect on the central nervous system. Removal of the N-methyl group as in nor-hyoscyamine reduces the mydriatic activity eight times. The ester group is essential for activity, tropine being inactive. Many esters have been synthesized from tropine and the most active drugs were obtained when the esterifying acid was an aromatic one containing an asymmetric center. Simple esters such as tropine acetate have low activity. The steric position of the OH group in tropine is important. Thus esters of pseudo tropine (XIII) have very low ac-

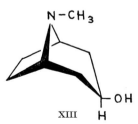

XIII

tivity. The pharmacology of the other alkaloids has not been extensively investigated. Meteloidine has been reported to be inactive. The pharmacology of the tropane alkaloids and related compounds has been discussed by Ing (1955), Dallemange and Heymans (1955), and by Gyermek and Nádor (1957).

**Distribution of the Alkaloids.** Table 1 lists the various species of *Datura* and their alkaloid content as far as they are known. The per-

TABLE 1

ALKALOID CONTENT OF DATURA SPECIES *

| Species | Alkaloids | References |
|---|---|---|
| D. stramonium | Hyoscyamine<br>  0.4 (in leaves)<br>  0.2 (in stems)<br>  0.1 (in roots)<br>Hyoscine<br>  0.01 (in leaves)<br>  0.05 (in stems)<br>  0.1  (in roots)<br>  0.2  (in very young<br>        plants)<br>3,6-ditiglylteloidine<br>  0.01 (in roots)<br>Cuscohygrine (in roots) | Andrews (1911)<br>Braun (1939)<br>Evans and Partridge (1957)<br>Feldhaus (1905)<br>Guillon (1950)<br>van Haga (1954)<br>Hegnauer (1953)<br>Hemberg and Flück (1953)<br>Jackson and Rowson (1953)<br>Johnson and Nunez-Melendez<br>  (1942)<br>Otsuka and Nagata (1953)<br>Rowson (1945)<br>Schratz and Spaning (1942)<br>Sirgo (1939)<br>Steinegger (1951, 1953a) |
| D. stramonium<br>"tatula" | Hyoscyamine 0.15<br>Hyoscine 0.07<br>3,6-ditiglylteloidine<br>  0.01 (in roots) | Beal et al. (1954)<br>Evans and Menéndez (1956)<br>Evans and Partridge (1953a,<br>  1957)<br>Jentzsch (1953)<br>Rudorf and Schwarze (1951)<br>Shibata and Imaseki (1954)<br>Shibata et al. (1951)<br>Steinegger (1953a, b) |
| D. stramonium<br>"inermis" | Hyoscine<br>  0.1 (before flowering)<br>  0.2 (after flowering)<br>Hyoscyamine<br>  0.04 (before flowering)<br>  0.07 (after flowering) | Jentzsch (1953)<br>Kurowicka-Kuleszyna (1953)<br>van Os et al. (1955) |
| D. ferox | Hyoscine 0.3<br>Meteloidine 0.1<br>  (none in seeds)<br>3,6-ditiglylteloidine<br>  0.05 (in roots)<br>Cuscohygrine<br>  (in roots)<br>An unknown alkaloid<br>$C_{15}H_{20-22}O_4N$ | Evans and Partridge (1949;<br>  1953a, b; 1957)<br>van Haga (1954)<br>Romeike and Zimmermann<br>  (1958) |

TABLE 1 (*continued*)

| Species | Alkaloids | References |
|---|---|---|
| *D. quercifolia* | Hyoscyamine<br>0.4 (in leaves)<br>0.3 (in seeds) | Kirchner (1905)<br>Starý (1952) |
| *D. metel* | Hyoscine 0.1<br>Hyoscyamine 0.04<br>(disappears after<br>flowering)<br>Nor-hyoscyamine 0.01<br>Cuscohygrine (in roots) | Andrews (1911)<br>Carr and Reynolds (1912)<br>Guha (1951)<br>van Haga (1954)<br>Jentzsch (1953)<br>Prasad (1948)<br>Shibata and Imaseki (1954) |
| *D. metel*<br>"*alba*" | Hyoscine (main alkaloid)<br>Hyoscyamine (a trace) | Pradisth and Santos (1939a, b) |
| *D. metel*<br>"*fastuosa*" | Hyoscine 0.1<br>Hyoscyamine 0.02<br>(none in seeds or roots) | Andrews (1911) |
| *D. meteloides* | Hyoscine 0.1<br>Meteloidine 0.05<br>Hyoscyamine 0.03<br>Nor-hyoscyamine 0.02 | Carr and Reynolds (1912)<br>Pyman and Reynolds (1908)<br>Shibata and Imaseki (1954) |
| *D. innoxia* | Hyoscine<br>0.3 (total plant)<br>0.04 (in seeds)<br>Hyoscyamine (with<br>meteloidine)<br>0.06 (total plant)<br>0.1 (in seeds)<br>Cuscohygrine (in roots)<br>An unknown alkaloid,<br>m.p. 44–6° C | Evans and Partridge<br>(1953a, b, c)<br>Flück and Nisoli (1954)<br>Gerlach (1948)<br>van Haga (1954)<br>James (1953)<br>Steinegger and Gessler (1955) |
| BRUGMANSIA<br>"*D. arborea*" | Hyoscine 0.4<br>Hyoscyamine (in young<br>stems and roots) | Kirchner (1905)<br>Schmidt (1906)<br>Rolando-Suárez (1952) |
| "*D. sanguinea*" | Hyoscine<br>0.35 (in aerial parts)<br>0.2 (in roots)<br>Hyoscyamine<br>0.02 (in aerial parts)<br>0.4 (in roots)<br>Several other alkaloids not<br>characterized with cer-<br>tainty | Dray and Foster (1953) |
| "*D. suaveolens*" | Hyoscyamine 0.1 | Simöes (1951) |

* The alkaloids were isolated from the aerial parts of the plant unless otherwise stated. The numbers after each alkaloid are the percentage of alkaloid by weight based on the dry weight of the plant.

No references have been found to investigations on the alkaloid content of *D. ceratocaula, leichhardtii, discolor,* or *pruinosa.*

centage weights of the alkaloids are average values, since different workers have reported varying yields of alkaloid. This is probably due in
part to changes in the environment. Thus nitrogen fertilization of the
soil increased the alkaloid yield from *D. stramonium, D. metel,* and *D.
innoxia;* however, the ratio of hyoscyamine to hyoscine in a particular
species did not change. Growth hormones such as naphthoxyacetic acid
or zinc insulin increased the alkaloid content of *D. "tatula"* (*D. stramonium*). Pruning had a beneficial effect on the alkaloid content of
*D. stramonium* and *D. metel.* A short daily exposure of *D. stramonium*
to ultraviolet light increased the alkaloid content. The alkaloid content
of *D. stramonium* was less after a rainy period than after clear weather.
A daily variation was also found to occur in the alkaloids of this species—
decreasing during the day and increasing at night. The alkaloid content
of the seeds increased rapidly during the ripening process. If the ripening was accelerated by exposure to carbon monoxide or acetylene the
alkaloid content of the seeds was less than normal. When seeds of *D.
"tatula"* (*D. stramonium*) were exposed to x-rays and then germinated,
plants were obtained with obvious morphological changes, but the nature and amount of the alkaloids was not significantly changed. However, Mothes and co-workers (1955) have produced mutants of *D. stramonium* which contain the tobacco alkaloid, nicotine. The tetraploid
races of *Datura* have in general a slightly higher alkaloid percentage
than the diploid races. Using modern techniques such as paper chromatography, new alkaloids have been found in the *Datura* genus and it
is fairly safe to predict that other new alkaloids will be detected even in
*D. stramonium,* which is the most thoroughly investigated species.

**Biogenesis of the Alkaloids.** The site of alkaloid synthesis in *Datura*
seems to vary with the species. Thus in *D. stramonium* the alkaloids are
produced in the roots. This was substantiated by the production of
hyoscyamine and hyoscine in sterile root cultures of the plant (Peacock
*et al.,* 1944; Uffelie, 1951; Stienstra, 1954). Furthermore a reduction in
alkaloid content occurred when a *D. stramonium* scion was grafted onto
an alkaloid-free rootstock such as tomato (Vincent and Dulucq-Mathou,
1946; James, 1950; Mothes and Romeike, 1951; Jackson and Rowson,
1953). Alkaloids were detected in the roots shortly after germination of
the seeds (James, 1946; Guillon, 1950).

Grafting experiments with other species of *Datura* suggest that the
leaves are able to synthesize some of the tropane alkaloids. Thus Evans
and Partridge (1953a), James (1953), and Shibata and Imaseki (1954)
have examined reciprocal grafts of *Datura* species with each other and
with *Atropa belladonna.* Their results indicated that hyoscine is produced mainly in the roots of *D. innoxia, D. metel,* and *A. belladonna;* in
the aerial parts of *D. meteloides;* and in all parts of *D. ferox.* Hyoscyamine is produced in all parts of *D. innoxia* but mainly in the roots.
Meteloidine is produced only in the aerial parts of *D. ferox.*

Cuscohygrine and 3, 6-ditiglylteloidine have been detected only in the
roots of *Datura* but the location of an alkaloid can tell us little about the

site of synthesis, since alkaloids occur in plants as water-soluble salts and are able to move in the plant either with the transpiration stream or in the phloem. It is also possible that the basic skeleton of an alkaloid is synthesized in one part of the plant and trivial changes such as N-methylation occur in another part.

Little is known of the relation of alkaloid production to other metabolic processes that occur in the plant. No one has isolated any of the enzymes responsible for alkaloid production. Work on the biogenesis of the tropane alkaloids has been strongly influenced by Robinson's (1917a, b; 1936; 1955) *in vitro* synthesis of tropinone (XVII) from succindialdehyde (XIV), methylamine (XV), and acetone (XVI) or acetone dicarboxylic acid. This reaction was carried out in aqueous solution under conditions that could well prevail in the plant.

$$
\begin{array}{ccc}
\text{CH}_2\!-\!\text{CHO} & & \text{CH}_3 \\
| & +\ \text{NH}_2\!-\!\text{CH}_3\ +\ \ \text{C}=\text{O} & \longrightarrow \\
\text{CH}_2\!-\!\text{CHO} & & \text{CH}_3 \\
\end{array}
\qquad
\begin{array}{ccc}
\text{CH}_2\!-\!\text{CH}\!-\!\text{CH}_2 \\
| \qquad | \qquad | \\
\text{NCH}_3 \qquad \text{C}=\text{O} \\
| \qquad | \qquad | \\
\text{CH}_2\!-\!\text{CH}\!-\!\text{CH}_2 \\
\end{array}
$$

|  XIV  |  XV  |  XVI  |  XVII  |

It was suggested that the succindialdehyde was derived from ornithine by oxidative deamination. The rather uncommon amino acid, ornithine, was obtained from arginine by the action of the enzyme arginase. It is of interest to note that Fuller and Gibson (1952) found that the amount of this enzyme reaches a maximum in *D. "tatula"* (*D. stramonium*) at the same time that the amount of alkaloid is at a maximum. Ornithine was conclusively shown to be a precursor of the five-membered ring of tropine by feeding radioactive ornithine to intact *D. stramonium* plants (Leete *et al.*, 1954a, b). The hyoscyamine isolated from the plant was radioactive in specific positions, showing that ornithine was a direct precursor, no randomization of activity having occurred. Putrescine has been suggested as an intermediate between ornithine and succindialdehyde. Minor increases in hyoscyamine content were noted following the injection of putrescine into the stems of *A. belladonna* (Cromwell, 1944a, b) and it was also isolated in small amounts from the same plant. However, the feeding of radioactive putrescine to *D. stramonium* did not yield radioactive alkaloids (Diaper *et al.*, 1951). It is suggested that putrescine represents an alternate pathway of ornithine metabolism not related to alkaloid synthesis. In the feeding experiment with radioactive ornithine no activity was detected in the hyoscine. Several explanations (Marion and Thomas, 1955; van Haga, 1956) have been put forward to account for this, implying that hyoscine and hyoscyamine are interconvertible. This seems unlikely on chemical grounds and attempts to prove this have failed (Hegnauer, 1951). It seems more reasonable to assume that hyoscine is derived from a different precursor, such as a hydroxy-ornithine. The results obtained with radioactive ornithine render improbable the suggestions of Mortimer (1953) that the tropane ring is derived from tryptophane.

It was thought that the 2, 3, and 4 carbons of tropine may be derived from acetate or acetoacetate; however, the writer has found that feeding these in radioactive form to *D. stramonium* did not yield radioactive alkaloids. The N-methyl group of hyoscyamine was shown to be derived from methionine by transmethylation (Marion and Thomas, 1955), but it is not known at what stage in the synthesis of the alkaloid that N-methylation takes place. Nothing is known of the origin of the tropic acid moiety of hyoscine and hyoscyamine. Trautner (1947) has suggested that it may be derived from a terpene such as limonene, but there is no experimental justification for this. Evans and Partridge (1954) obtained radioactive hyoscine and meteloidine after injecting radioactive glycine into the stems of *D. ferox*. The majority of the radioactivity was present in the tropine bases but the incorporation of radioactivity was small, suggesting that glycine is not a direct precursor of the alkaloids.

Much more work needs to be carried out before a plausible biogenetic scheme for the alkaloids of *Datura* can be formulated.

# 4

# Chromosome Number and Morphology

SOPHIE SATINA

The early years of research on *Datura* at Cold Spring Harbor were largely devoted to basic plant-breeding experiments. At this time investigators were concerned principally with the many aspects of Mendelian segregation. New types that appeared in the *Datura* cultures could be readily recognized by external appearances. Some of these showed peculiarities in heredity that could not be properly explained by the laws of inheritance known at that time. The appearance of a large number of such mutants indicated the necessity of investigating more closely the reasons for the unusual segregations and suggested the need for cytological examinations to seek a possible relation between chromosomal constitution and heredity. The first cytological studies were begun in 1920 by Belling, whose investigations not only explained the apparent discrepancies in inheritance but impelled further research on important problems of general interest in genetics.

It had been known that *D. "tatula"* (*D. stramonium*) has 12 pairs of chromosomes (Boenicke, 1911).[1] Belling found that some of the new types, the Globe, Cocklebur, and other mutants, had 25 chromosomes instead of the normal 24. His cytological examinations of one of the types, which had been temporarily named "New Species," showed a double set of chromosomes; i.e., it proved to be a tetraploid plant and counts of chromosomes of another showed that it was a haploid (8).

Belling's investigations enabled him to identify particular chromosomes by their size as being the specific extra chromosomes in certain distinguishable mutant types. These findings demonstrated the influence of

[1] Tischler (1927, 1931) reported six chromosomes in a haploid of *D. stramonium*. His error was apparently made by a misunderstanding of Blakeslee's and Belling's published papers. This incorrect report has unfortunately been quoted by other writers.

individual and specific chromosomes in producing constant and recognizable morphological characters in adult plants. Genetic and cytological investigations of the ten *Datura* species since 1920 have confirmed Belling's discoveries and have also added much new information (9, 16, 86).

By the usual methods of fixing and sectioning material, it would have been impossible to make such extensive cytological investigations of *Datura* as we have. The quick and easy iron-acetocarmine method introduced by Belling in 1921 made it possible to study many plants, to check the numbers of chromosomes, to get the necessary information about the presence of extra or deficient chromosomes in mutants, and to determine the ploidy of *Datura* plants. The same technique was also used in analyzing the ends of modified chromosomes and the various configurations formed in crosses between races and species (10, 25).

Belling's iron-acetocarmine method, which has been slightly modified in later work with *Datura*, has played such an important part in these studies that the preparation of this fixing and staining solution and its use in making slides will be given here. An excess of carmine powder is added to a 45 per cent solution of glacial acetic acid and heated (avoiding boiling) for 15 minutes. This is kept indefinitely as a stock solution. When used, 14 ml of the solution is filtered into a small bottle and three drops of ferric hydrate are added. This is used for fixing and staining pollen mother cells. When it forms a sediment, it should be discarded and a fresh mixture prepared.

Fresh immature anthers are crushed with the edge of a thick slide in two to three drops of the iron-acetocarmine solution on a clean slide. The remnants of tissues should be discarded as soon as possible and the preparation covered immediately with a No. 1 cover glass (22 × 50 mm). Air bubbles under the cover glass must be removed from the liquid. When the edges of the cover glass become dry, the latter must be sealed to the slide with a 1:1 mixture of paraffin and gum mastic, using a hot wire loop. The ingredients of this mixture must be properly mixed. This is accomplished by first melting the gum mastic in a jar over a gas flame. The jar is placed in a hot water bath and paraffin is added to the gum. Paraffin melts easily and the mixture is stirred with a glass rod. After a few minutes the mixture is poured into Petri dishes or shallow metal boxes and put on ice for immediate cooling. The quick cooling prevents the separation of the paraffin from the gum.

A 3- to 8-day-old slide is better for examination than a younger or older one. If properly prepared, the cytoplasm is slightly pink and the chromosomes dark purple. To break the walls of the pollen mother cells (p.m.c.) the cover glass is lightly pressed above the dividing p.m.c. with the point of a needle. With appropriate pressure the cytoplasm becomes flattened and thin, and the chromosomes in anaphase I, or the bivalents and configurations at metaphase I, may be clearly observed.

**Size and Morphological Differentiation of Chromosomes.** In each of the ten species of *Datura* the haploid complement of chromosomes is

12. Each of the 12 pairs of chromosomes as seen at metaphase I in meiotic divisions of pollen mother cells is joined either at one of the ends or at both ends, forming 12 bivalents, which differ in size. Belling measured and arranged the meiotic chromosomes of *D. stramonium* (Line 1) into six size groups (*17, 38*). The length of *D. stramonium* chromosomes was later measured by Lewitsky (1931). Belling's classification with some slight recent modifications is as follows: one extra large chromosome (L), two large (1), five large medium (M), two small medium (m), one small (S), and one extra small (s). The 12 pairs of diploid chromosomes are shown in Fig. 16. A numerical terminology

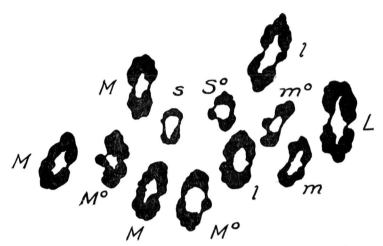

Fig. 16. *D. stramonium* chromosomes. Metaphase plate with 12 bivalents. Note the size classes: 1 extra large (L), 2 large (1), 5 large medium (M), 2 small medium (m), 1 small (S), and 1 extra small (s). M°, m°, and S° chromosomes have humps.

was adopted in 1930 for the identified chromosomes and each end of the 12 chromosomes was numbered (Fig. 17). The largest, L, is designated $1 \cdot 2$, the second largest $3 \cdot 4$, and so on until $23 \cdot 24$, which designates the smallest chromosome, s. The secondary chromosomes, composed of doubled half-chromosomes, have the same number for each of their ends: $1 \cdot 1$, $2 \cdot 2$, etc. (*63, 81*).

The different lengths of the two arms may be clearly seen in some chromosomes. The presence of terminal humps, or knobs, at meiosis in pollen mother cells (p.m.c.), at particular ends of some chromosomes, are characteristics that help to distinguish between chromosomes of the same size.

The iron-acetocarmine technique so successfully applied in most studies of *Datura* is not favorable, however, for the proper identification of structural differences in individual chromosomes. By using another technique in studies of the metaphase plates in haploid root-tips and in dividing pollen grains of $2n + 1$ types, it became possible to identify individual chromosomes. The root-tips were fixed in Lewitzky's solution and stained in iron-hematoxylin. Anthers with dividing pollen were smeared on slides, fixed in Allen's B-15 solution, and stained with crystal violet and orange G according to Newton's method (La Cour, 1931). Pollen was chosen because it contains the haploid chromosome number. The 12 chromosomes as observed in metaphase plates of haploid

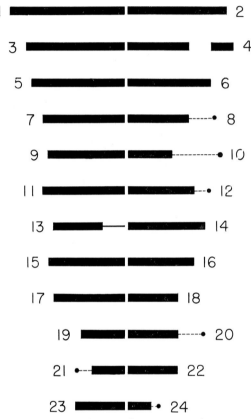

Fig. 17. Diagram of *D. stramonium* chromosomes showing relative sizes and morphological differentiation. The ends are numbered consecutively from the largest to the smallest.

root-tips are clearly divided at the insertion region into two arms of unequal size (Fig. 18a). Seven chromosomes have a secondary constriction and one of them (3·4) has an appendage that seems to be separated from the rest of the arm by an achromatic region when stained with iron-hematoxylin. In darker-stained slides the outline of the achromatic zone is visible. When dividing pollen of a diploid is stained in crystal violet (Newton's method), the connection of the appendage with the chromosome may be clearly seen (Fig. 18b). The appendage differs from satellites by having the same diameter as the chromosome to which

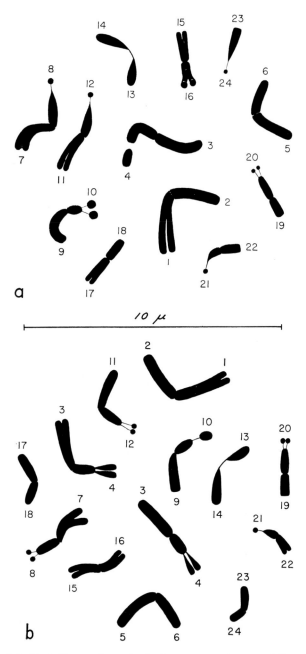

FIG. 18. (a) Haploid complement of chromosomes in a root-tip of a haploid
D. *stramonium* plant; (b) thirteen chromosomes from pollen of a $2n + 1$ plant.
Note the presence of two $3 \cdot 4$ chromosomes.

it is attached and by the absence of the thin thread which connects satellites with their chromosomes. The satellites of five chromosomes are attached to the shorter arms and in one of the chromosomes, the $19 \cdot 20$, to the longer arm. One of the 12 chromosomes, the $13 \cdot 14$, differs from the rest by lacking an internal portion of chromosomal material on the shorter arm near the insertial region. The two arms are joined by a thin chromatic region. The remaining four chromosomes, the $1 \cdot 2$, $5 \cdot 6$, $15 \cdot 16$, and $17 \cdot 18$, although differing considerably in size, have no secondary constriction. These recognizable characteristics of the chromosomes are shown in Fig. 18. Lewitzky, who studied the karyotype of *D. stramonium* $2n$ root-tips, stated that the chromosomes of this species show an "uncommon variety and fineness of differentiation." Our work has supported his important contribution and added new details about the morphological differentiation of chromosomes in *D. stramonium*. By the use of dividing pollen from $2n + 1$ types, it was possible to identify and to label each of the clearly differentiated chromosomes (*148*).

**Methods of Chromosome Analysis.** The chromosomal types called balanced types have an even number of chromosomes. The diploid or $2n$ balanced types are discussed in the present chapter. The other balanced types ($1n, 3n, 4n$, etc.) are described in Chapter 5. Details about the unbalanced types with odd numbers of chromosomes are given in Chapter 6; however, for convenience the distinction between $2n + 1$ primary and secondary trisomic types is given here, since they were used as testers for identifying the individual chromosomes and for analyzing their ends in the karyotype of diploid *D. stramonium*.

Each primary and secondary mutant has a single extra chromosome. In primaries the additional chromosome is not modified and is formed by the simple reduplication of a chromosome in a specific one of the 12 chromosomal sets. Belling (1921) found in his earlier studies on *Canna* that the like ends of homologous chromosomes are mutually attracted. In meiotic division at metaphase I the extra chromosome of primaries may be attached by one of its ends to the homologous bivalent, thus forming a trisome. The three associated chromosomes never form a closed circle. Some of the most common configurations are shown in Fig. 19a, b, c. The extra chromosome in secondaries is modified. It is made up by the duplication of a half-chromosome so that both ends are similar. The trisome in secondaries can, therefore, form a closed circle of three in addition to the open configuration found in primaries. In frequent cases the additional chromosome of secondaries may be free and so form a closed univalent by the attraction of its like ends (Fig. 19d, e).

The dividing microsposes of primaries and secondaries contain 13 as well as 12 chromosomes at metaphase I. This thirteenth chromosome is similar to one of the 12. If, for example, the pollen is taken from the primary $2n + 3 \cdot 4$, the extra chromosome is the $3 \cdot 4$ (Fig 18b). The ends of each primary chromosome have been identified and labeled by using the dividing pollen of the $2n + 1$ secondaries and by certian prime types (PT's) in cases where secondaries are unknown. For example, to identify

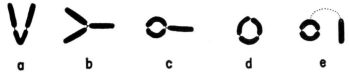

FIG. 19. Diagram showing the most common configurations in $2n + 1$ primaries and secondaries. (a) (b) (c) The configurations formed by homologous chromosomes in primaries and secondaries; (d) (e) configurations found only in secondaries.

which end of the primary $2n + 9 \cdot 10$ chromosome bears the large satellite, metaphase plates of both secondaries $2n + 9 \cdot 9$ and $2n + 10 \cdot 10$ must be compared. In one of these plates the doubled half-chromosome will be without satellites and in the other plate the extra chromosome will have satellites on both ends. Such a chromosome with satellites on both ends was found in the pollen taken from the $2n + 10 \cdot 10$ secondary (Fig. 20b). Thus the ends of the $9 \cdot 10$ chromosome can be labeled. The ends of the primary chromosome $1 \cdot 2$ can be identified by comparing the length of the arms of the chromosomes of its two secondaries, $2n + 1 \cdot 1$ and $2n + 2 \cdot 2$. The arms of the $1 \cdot 1$ are obviously longer, as is shown in Fig. 20a. The same reasoning applies to cases in which prime types were used for the identification of the ends.

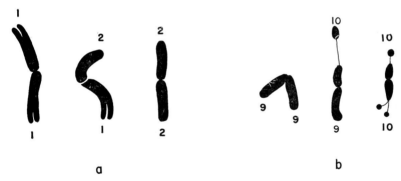

FIG. 20. Primary and secondary chromosomes of $2n + 1$ types. (a) The primary $1 \cdot 2$ chromosome and its two secondary, $1 \cdot 1$ and $2 \cdot 2$, chromosomes; (b) the primary $9 \cdot 10$ chromosome and its two secondary, $9 \cdot 9$ and $10 \cdot 10$, chromosomes with satellites attached at the $\cdot 10$ ends.

The total length of each chromosome and of its arms has been carefully measured. The average length of the largest chromosome, $1 \cdot 2$, is $4.0\mu$. The average length of the second and third largest chromosomes ($3 \cdot 4$ and $5 \cdot 6$) is $3.7\mu$ and $3.2\mu$, respectively. The average lengths of the five medium (M) size chromosomes are $3.1\mu$ to $2.6\mu$. The four smallest chromosomes are distinctly smaller, their average lengths being $2.1\mu$ to $1.5\mu$. The average length of the largest secondary chromosome, $1 \cdot 1$, is $4.5\mu$; the average length of the complementary secondary, $2 \cdot 2$, is considerably shorter, $3.6\mu$. The shortest secondary chromosome,

19 · 19, is 1.8μ. There is also a correlation between the lengths and widths of chromosomes. The difference in their diameter is best seen in some of the prime types, which will be discussed below, in which segmental interchanges have occurred between large and small chromosomes (Fig. 22).

Of the seven chromosomes with secondary constrictions only one, the 9 · 10, has given rise to secondaries by the doubling of the arm, 10 · 10, with the satellite. In all other secondaries the doubling occurred in the arm lacking a satellite. Moreover, the $2n + 10 \cdot 10$ secondary mutant has appeared spontaneously only once, while the complementary, $2n + 9 \cdot 9$, secondary has appeared five times. Various additional details of the chromosome characters helping to identify each chromosome are given in an original paper (148).

**Segmental Interchanges and Prime Types.** All the studies made on chromosome-end arrangements in *Datura* species rely upon the hypothesis of segmental interchange between nonhomologous chromosomes first proposed by Belling. This hypothesis is based on his earlier observations of the mutual attraction between homologous chromosomes and on extensive genetic evidence accumulated since 1920. The hypothesis was supported by cytological observations made on reduction divisions at M I in *D. stramonium* p.m.c. and was fully supported by later studies on *Datura* interracial hybrids and in other genera, the first of which was applied in work with *Oenothera* by Håkansson (1928). The hypothesis explained among other findings the formation of circles by four associated chromosomes, the peculiar breeding behavior of the *D. stramonium* "B-white" race, its apparent genetic relation to the $2n + 1 \cdot 2$ and $2n + 17 \cdot 18$ types, and the appearance of some new $2n + 1$ mutants called tertiaries (Chapter 6) from plants heterozygous for the B-white races (40, 86). References to segmental interchanges in many species of plants can be found in the recent review by Burnham (1956).

Reciprocal segmental interchanges, or reciprocal translocations, between nonhomologous chromosomes were observed in various crosses with plants from nature as well as with plants from experimental treatments. Such interchanges have occurred frequently in *D. stramonium* following aging or treatment with radium, x-ray, or heat, and have resulted in the so-called *prime types*. For brevity the prime types in the text are designated as PT's. They were first called "cryptic types" because most of them cannot be recognized by their appearance. However, they differ cytologically from the *D. stramonium* race, Line 1A, selected as a standard type, and which was taken as PT 1. The structure of modified chromosomes in all *Datura* studies is discussed in terms of PT 1 (56, 63, 68). Segmental interchanges and the resulting prime types that have been identified in *D. stramonium* are discussed in this chapter. Similar exchanges between chromosomes of the other nine species have also been found; these are described in Chapter 13.

The presence of modified chromosomes in races can be checked by studying cytologically the progeny of PT 1 crossed with the unknown race, $x$. The presence of a new PT is first ascertained by the appearance of a configuration in such $F_1$ plants, which proves that an interchange between modified chromosomes of $x$ and PT 1 took place. These heterozygous plants when selfed give three kinds of offspring; some are homozygous PT 1, others homozygous PT $x$. In both of these the dividing p.m.c. at M I contain 12 bivalents. The plants of the third type of offspring are heterozygous for PT $x$. In addition to a certain number of bivalents four or more chromosomes are found forming a configuration. To recover the homozygous PT $x$, the offspring with 12 bivalents are backcrossed to PT 1. The individual plants which induce only offspring with 12 bivalents are PT 1. The plants whose hybrids with PT 1 show a configuration are the homozygous PT $x$.

The analysis of modified chromosomes has been possible by means of $2n + 1$ primaries and secondaries and by means of some previously analyzed PT's, which are used as testers. Including the standard Line 1A, 97 prime types have been analyzed, purified, and propagated for further studies. The modified chromosomes (shown in boldface type) of some of these prime types and their origin, as also the configurations found in crosses with L 1A, are given in Table 2. Including the standard PT 1, only 11 PT's have been found in nature (five of these were sporadic races occurring only once) from a total of 875 races collected throughout the world and tested. The rest of the PT's were obtained from aged seed and pollen, from heat treatment, and especially from x-ray and radium treatments, which stimulate breakages and interchanges between chromosomes. Eight of the PT's found in nature, when crossed with PT 1, form circles due to the reciprocal translocations between nonhomologous chromosomes (PT's 2, 3, 4, 87, 88, 94, 96, 97). By the reciprocal interchange of humps two PT's (7 and 95), when crossed to PT 1, form a configuration in which the two bivalents become attached only by their humps. Since one of the bivalents is frequently open distally to the humps, the configuration has the appearance of a necktie and has been labeled "necktie" (63, 81). Drawings representing a circle and a necktie are given in Fig. 21a, b.

As a result of reciprocal translocations, circles were found in hybrids with the majority of the 86 PT's obtained experimentally. In some the chromosomes had exchanged humps, and so formed necktie configurations in hybrids with L 1A. But a number of the PT's obtained from the experimental treatments gave a new kind of configuration that has never been observed with *Datura* PT's found in nature. The associated chromosomes form a kitelike configuration in which a piece of chromosome seems to be attached to the end of an unbroken nonhomologous chromosome, leaving a small free fragment. The kitelike configuration (Fig. 21c) remains open and never forms a circle. Such configurations in hybrids with "simple translocations" have been reported in some other plants and in *Drosophila*. However, later studies of the early meiotic prophase in maize have suggested that the so-called simple translocation

TABLE 2

SOME REPRESENTATIVE PRIME TYPES (PT's) IN DATURA STRAMONIUM

| PT | Configuration in Crosses with L 1A | Modified Chromosomes | | Origin |
|----|----|----|----|----|
| 1 | BV | | | Nature |
| 2 | ⊙4 | L | 2 · 17 | Nature |
|   |   | m | 1 · 18 | |
| 3 | ⊙4 | M | 11 · 21 | Nature |
|   |   | S | 12 · 22 | |
| 4 | ⊙4 | l | 4 · 22 | Nature |
|   |   | S | 3 · 21 | |
| 5 | Tr. 4 | L | 2 · 11 · 12 | Radium |
| 6 | Tr. 4 | L | 2 · 11 · 12 | Radium |
|   |   | m | · 1 | |
| 7 | ⚲ 4 | M | $9 \cdot 10^{20}$ | Nature |
|   |   | m | $19 \cdot 20^{10}$ | |
| 8 | ⚲ 4 | M | $9 \cdot 10^{12}$ | Radium |
|   |   | M | $11 \cdot 12^{10}$ | |
| 9 | Tr. 4 | M | 20 · 19 · 23 | X-ray |
|   |   | s | · 24 | |
| 10 | ⊙4 | l | 1 · 13 | X-ray |
|   |   | l | 2 · 14 | |
| 11 | ⊙6 | l | 12 · 17 | Radium |
|   |   | M | 11 · 13 | |
|   |   | s | 14 · 18 | |
| 12 | ⊙4 | M | 13 · 23 | Radium |
|   |   | s | 14 · 24 | |
| 13 | ⊙4 | L | 1 · 9 | Radium |
|   |   | M | 2 · 10 | |

Key:     ⊙ = circle;     Tr. = translocation;     ⚲ = necktie

is actually a reciprocal segmental interchange in which at least one of the segments is very short (Stadler, 1932; Burnham, 1932). According to statements made by other investigators, working with other genera, the attachment of a piece of chromosome to the end of an unbroken chromosome is not possible or at least such an aberration must be considered to be very rare (Dobzhansky, 1941). A definite answer as to the nature of the kitelike configurations will be obtained only by studying the pachetene stage in meiosis. So far all attempts made to observe this in Datura have been unsuccessful. Thus, for the present, one must assume that the kitelike configurations in Datura, as in some other plants and in Drosophila, represent reciprocal translocations in which a long piece has been exchanged for a very short one.

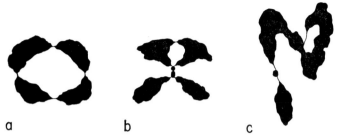

FIG. 21. Three types of chromosomal configurations. (a) A circle of four chromosomes; (b) a necktie; (c) a simple translocation forming a kitelike configuration.

Most of the 96 PT's (the 97th being the standard PT 1) have two modified chromosomes. Three chromosomes are modified in seven PT's, resulting in the formation with PT 1 of configurations with six chromosomes; four chromosomes in one PT induce the formation of two circles; and each of three other PT's has a free asymmetric bivalent. A total of 64 PT's are circle inducers; 18 PT's are inducers of the kitelike configuration; 11 PT's induce neckties; and 3 PT's induce the free asymmetric bivalents in the chromosomes $7 \cdot 8$, $9 \cdot 10$, and $17 \cdot 18$.

Each of the 12 chromosomes in *D. stramonium* is modified in a number of PT's, but with some chromosomes such changes occur more frequently than with others. For example, the largest chromosome, $1 \cdot 2$, is associated with others in 23 PT's, while another large chromosome, $5 \cdot 6$, and a small chromosome, $17 \cdot 18$, are involved in 11 and 12 PT's, respectively. Apparently there is no direct connection between the size of the chromosome and its tendency to be involved in configurations. This is also true in respect to the morphological differentiation of the chromosomes, such as the presence or absence of satellites at their ends. The $11 \cdot 12$ chromosome with a satellite is modified in 21 PT's and the $13 \cdot 14$ chromosome with no satellite is modified in 20 PT's. The modified chromosomes of some PT's are shown in Fig. 22. These PT's, among others used in the chromosome analysis, were selected for demonstration for different reasons. PT 2 was selected because of its widest distribution in nature. PT 6 was taken as representing changes in one of the largest chromosomes. Considerable increase in length of one of the arms of a chromosome is illustrated by PT 80. Prime types 17, 27, and 91 were taken to show the shifts of segments with satellites. Both ends of the modified chromosomes have satellites because of the interchanges of segments. PT 27 shows the unequal thickness of the $3 \cdot 23$ chromosome,[2] the larger arm, $\cdot 3$, being wider than the smaller $\cdot 23$; such a difference in thickness is also evident in PT's 2 and 41.

**Geographical Distribution of Prime Types.** A survey of the geographical distribution of *D. stramonium* prime types in widely separated regions throughout the world has been made. About two-fifths of all races

[2] The numerical formulas of chromosomes that are modified from those of the standard Line 1A (or PT 1) are shown in boldface type throughout this volume.

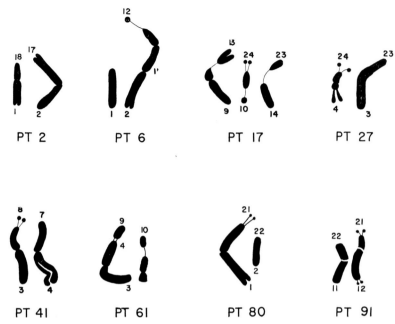

FIG. 22. Modified chromosomes in eight prime types of *D. stramonium*.

studied were collected in the United States. The standard type PT 1 predominates in this country. It is the only type that has been found in Brazil and in Japan and it has been found in Europe, West Africa, Australia, and the West Indies. PT 2 with the modified **1 · 18** and **2 · 17** chromosomes, when crossed to PT 1, forms the so-called B circle in which the four chromosomes are associated in the following order:

$$
\begin{array}{ccc}
1 \cdot 2 & — & 2 \cdot 17 \\
| & & | \\
1 \cdot 18 & — & 18 \cdot 17
\end{array}
$$

PT 2 is the predominant type in Europe, Asia, Africa, Central America, Peru, and Chile. In the United States it is confined to the eastern part of the country. PT 3 has the modified chromosomes **11 · 21** and **12 · 22** and, when crossed with PT 1, forms a circle of four. PT 3 associated with PT 2 is the only type yet found in Peru. This combination is also found in Chile, Central America, and Spain. It is the PT 97 in the *Datura* collection. PT 4, which forms a circle of four when crossed to PT 1, has the modified chromosomes **3 · 21** and **4 · 22**. It is widely scattered in many regions: United States, Barbados, southern Europe, South Africa, Australia, and the Hawaiian Islands. Through the exchange of humps the modified chromosomes in PT 7 become $9 \cdot 10^{20}$ and $19 \cdot 20^{10}$ and form a "necktie" with the standard PT 1 chromosomes. Hybrids between PT 1 and PT 7 show 50 per cent aborted pollen, as do hybrids with other PT's which produce similar necktie configurations. PT 7 is the predominant type in South Africa and has been found in the United States, Barbados, Spain, Italy, Australia, and the Madeira Islands.

Each of the five remaining PT's were found in nature only once. PT 87, with three modified chromosomes, $4 \cdot 22$, $11 \cdot 21$, and $3 \cdot 12$, forming in crosses with PT 1 a circle of six, was collected in Mexico. PT 88, with the modified chromosomes $16 \cdot 24$ and $15 \cdot 23$, forming a circle of four in crosses with PT 1, was found in Argentina. PT 94, from Yucatán, has three modified chromosomes, $1 \cdot 14$, $13 \cdot 18$, and $2 \cdot 17$. The cross with PT 1 forms a circle of six, and about 25 per cent of the pollen of these hybrids is aborted. PT 95, forming a necktie with PT 1, has the modified chromosomes $1 \cdot 2^{20}$ and $19 \cdot 20^2$. It was found in Indiana. PT 96, with the modified chromosomes $7 \cdot 19$ and $8 \cdot 20$, forming a circle of four with PT 1, was found in Ohio. More details on the location of prime types, on the distribution of purple and white races, with maps and tables, can be found in the original papers ($121$, $127$, $152$).

PT 1 was selected as the standard type by chance because of its predominance in the United States. It was found later that PT 2 is more widely distributed in the world and that it has a closer relation to other *Datura* species. It is obvious that if any other chromosomal type had been used as the standard type instead of PT 1, the modified chromosomes in PT's would differ from those discussed here.

Among the 97 prime types that have been analyzed, the same chromosomal ends are involved in interchanges more than once. Some of the evidence accumulated from the breeding work with *Datura* indicates that these breaks of chromosomes probably occur at the same point. This seems to be true in secondaries and in the chromosomal types called tertiaries (Chapter 6). Other observations have shown that the breaks in chromosomes resulting in some PT's have occurred at different loci. As a result of x-ray and radium treatment PT 39 and PT 53 were obtained. Both have the same modified chromosomes $5 \cdot 20$ and $6 \cdot 19$, but the exchanged segments in these PT's differ in size. In PT 39 the $5 \cdot 20$ chromosome is small and the $6 \cdot 19$ chromosome is large. The sizes are reversed in PT 53, the $5 \cdot 20$ being larger and the $6 \cdot 19$ smaller ($113$).

**Synthesized Pure Breeding Types.** *D. stramonium* prime types have been of considerable value in our investigations. Used as testers, they have helped to identify the chromosome ends in other *Datura* species, to locate genes in particular chromosomes, and to furnish material for compensating and pure-breeding types. For example, a pure-breeding type has been synthesized using PT 6. This PT, obtained by radium treatment, has a broken $1 \cdot 2$ chromosome. Its $\cdot 2$ half has been translocated to the $11 \cdot 12$ chromosome, forming a kitelike configuration and leaving the $\cdot 1$ half-chromosome free. By proper breeding, this broken $\cdot 1$ half-chromosome and the normal $11 \cdot 12$ chromosome were eliminated. The normal $1 \cdot 2$ chromosome was returned to the paired condition and the $2 \cdot 11 \cdot 12$ chromosome became doubled. The formula of this synthesized new type is $2n - (11 \cdot 12)_2 + (2 \cdot 11 \cdot 12)_2$. These plants cannot be distinguished in appearance from $2n + 2 \cdot 2$ secondaries, but genetically and cytologically they are different. The new type breeds true and has no extra chromosome because the $\cdot 2$ halves are permanently attached to the $11 \cdot 12$ chromosomes. It was included in the list of prime types as PT 5 (*82, 127*).

Other pure-breeding types with extra chromosomal material have been synthesized in *Datura*. These have been formed by combining appropriate prime types. There are always two prerequisites for the synthesizing of such pure-breeding types. (1) The extra material must be capable of being transmitted through the pollen, as well as through the egg cell, in order to get a double portion in the offspring. (2) The extra material must be attached to a chromosome, or part of a chromosome, which is necessary for the survival of a gamete. When these requirements are fulfilled, it is possible to obtain various synthesized pure-breeding types that are as distinct as the natural species. Two of these have a total of 26 chromosomes. One was obtained by combining the $\cdot 1$ fragment with the $2 \cdot 2$ chromosome. The chromosomal formula for another of these pure-breeding types is:

$$2n - \left\{ \begin{array}{l} (13 \cdot 14)_2 \\ (23 \cdot 24)_2 \end{array} \right\} + \left\{ \begin{array}{ll} (2 \cdot 14)_2 & (\cdot 24)_2 \\ (13 \cdot 23)_2 & \end{array} \right\}$$

In all cases the extra chromosomal material is at the end of a chromosome. As stated by Blakeslee, these types have been called artificial or synthesized "new species." "They differ from the ancestral form not by a single factor but by a whole group of factors. Their greatest difference from species in nature appears to lie chiefly in the fact that we know their method of origin, having made them up to specifications, as it were, from a knowledge of the different parts of chromosomes involved. Whether nature has used such methods we do not yet know" (*86*).

# 5

# *Polyploidy*

## A. G. Avery

A series of polyploid forms has been assembled in *Datura stramonium* which is perhaps more nearly complete than that in any other plant species. In all the other herbaceous species of *Datura* tetraploid races have been established. Plants representing five stages in the polyploid series, in addition to the normal diploid, have been identified in *D. stramonium*. In ascending order of chromosome number the types that have been recognized are: haploid ($1n$), diploid ($2n$), triploid ($3n$), tetraploid ($4n$), hexaploid ($6n$), and octoploid ($8n$). Some of these have occurred spontaneously in the *Datura* cultures or have been obtained from appropriate crosses. Others have appeared only after the treatment of plants low in the polyploid series with the alkaloid colchicine. These types, with varying numbers of chromosomes, are known as balanced types, since any particular one has the same number of chromosomes in all 12 sets. Polyploid series are well known in other genera of plants. Many important papers dealing with polyploidy and its importance in evolution have appeared. References to some of these and further discussion of the subject may be found in the papers of Müntzing (1936), Goodspeed and Bradley (1942), and Stebbins (1947).

These balanced types may be divided into even-balanced, or stable, and odd-balanced, or unstable, types. The former ($2n$, $4n$, $6n$, $8n$) have an even number of chromosomes in each set, form sex cells with half the number of chromosomes, and therefore normally breed true. The odd-balanced types ($1n$, $3n$) have an odd number in each set, are thus unable to form sex cells with an equal distribution of chromosomes, and hence cannot breed true.

**Haploids.** The first haploid ($1n$) plant in *Datura* was observed in the fall of 1921 among a culture grown from seed of a normal *D. stramonium* plant. A. D. Bergner, then an assistant of Belling, made the cytological examination by which this was identified as a true haploid. This plant, 20745–4 (Fig. 23), was the first haploid to be recognized and reported in the adult stage of any flowering plant species (*19, 23*). References to

71

FIG. 23.  Haploid plant of *D. stramonium*.

reports of haploids in other plant genera are given by Kostoff (1942).

Haploids are generally somewhat weaker than normal diploids but under good growing conditions will develop into fairly vigorous plants. Their leaves are always relatively narrower and their foliage paler than that of normals.  The stems and small branches are usually quite slender. The flowers (Fig. 24) are shorter than normal and much more slender, due in part to the shrunken and practically empty anthers.  Haploids always show a very high proportion (85 to 100 per cent) of aborted ("bad") pollen grains (Fig. 25).

Divisions of nuclei in pollen mother cells (p.m.c.) have been studied from the diakinesis stage to the microspore formation.  There is no pairing of homologous chromosomes in the haploid nucleus and 12 monosomes, or univalents, may be seen at diakinesis (Fig. 26a).  They lie over a bipolar spindle at metaphase and pass at anaphase to the poles, forming by random distribution groups of 11:1, 10:2, . . . 6:6 chromo-

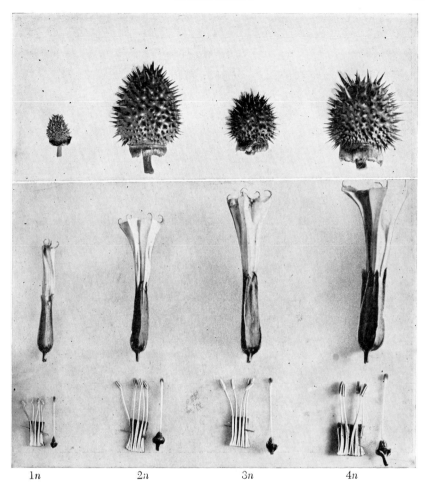

1n          2n          3n          4n

FIG. 24. Capsules and flowers of haploid and polyploid types of *D. stramonium*.

somes. At the second anaphase the split chromosomes divide and four microspores are formed in the pollen mother cells. Each nucleus contains a deficient number of chromosomes. Because of lagging chromosomes, microcytes are also frequently seen. The early death of such microspores and microcytes explains the high percentage of abortive pollen in mature anthers. The presence of 5 to 17 per cent full microspores in p.m.c. and the formation of approximately 12 per cent of good pollen estimated as an average of 8000 pollen counts, is due to the possible but very rare cases of 12:0 chromosome distribution at first anaphase, but they appear predominantly through 5 to 17 per cent of cases of "non-reduction" in p.m.c. (and apparently also in megaspore mother cells). Probably as a result of direct division, the 12 univalents split and form two groups of 12 chromosomes at anaphase I. The second division is suppressed and dyads are formed instead of tetrads (*26, 41, 43*).

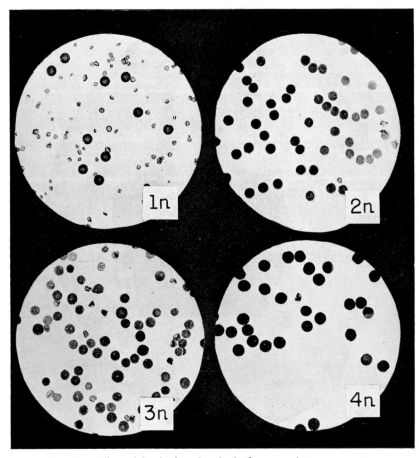

FIG. 25. Pollen of haploid and polyploid types of *D. stramonium.*

The few seeds found in the small capsules occasionally formed by the selfing of haploids would be the result of fertilization between these rare functional sex cells. Such seeds are diploid and give rise to normal diploid plants, which, barring rare new mutations, must be homozygous. Haploidy, therefore, affords a simple and rapid method of developing a pure line from heterogeneous stock. The first haploid recorded in the *Datura* cultures became the origin of Line 1A, which has been used as the standard, or tester, in all later breeding work.

Since 1921, 264 other haploids have been identified. These have occurred in several races of *D. stramonium* as well as in the species *D. pruinosa* and *D. metel.* During the last 25 years (1931–1955) approximately 850,000 *Datura* plants have been grown to adult stage or at least to such size that any haploid would be easily recognized. In this time 137 spontaneous haploids have been recorded—or, on the average, one haploid to each 6,200 normal plants. A study of the origin of the 265

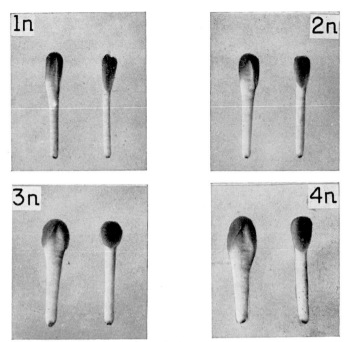

Fig. 25. (Continued.) Stigmas of haploid and polyploid types of *D. stramonium*.

spontaneous haploids gives no valid clue to the cause of their occurrence. The evidence is conclusive that they have all arisen through parthenogenesis of a reduced egg. Haploids that have appeared in crosses between genetically unlike parents in all cases have resembled the female

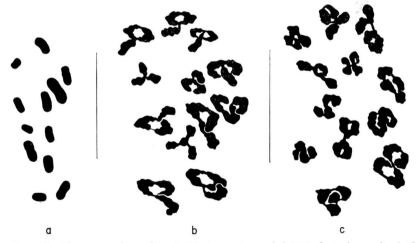

Fig. 26. Three metaphase plates in *D. stramonium*. (a) Univalents from a haploid; (b) trivalents from a triploid; (c) quadrivalents from a tetraploid.

parent. This has been true in species crosses as well as in crosses where the parents were dissimilar in respect to Mendelian characters.

Many unsuccessful attempts have been made to induce parthenogenesis of unfertilized eggs and thus produce haploids. Physical and chemical agents (cold, injury, radiation, chloral hydrate, growth substances, and many other chemicals) have been employed in addition to use in crosses of pollen of distantly related species. Despite our failure to stimulate parthenogenesis, there is good evidence that there are specific causes for the occasional appearance of haploids in considerable numbers.

In the course of our investigations of the differences between the species, many hundreds of crosses of *D. stramonium* with the other nine species have been made or attempted. Eleven haploids have appeared directly from these crosses: two from several crosses of *D. stramonium* × *D. ferox* and nine from nine crosses of *D. stramonium* × *D. meteloides*. The high number of haploids appearing after the latter cross is suggestive that *D. meteloides* pollen, while not effective in fertilization, may, in some way, encourage parthenogenesis. Among some 5,000 $F_1$ plants grown from other species crosses there were no haploids.

A few exceptional cultures have yielded very high proportions of haploids. A plant of *D. stramonium* grown in the greenhouse under apparently ordinary conditions, when crossed with another *D. stramonium*, gave ten offspring, three of which were haploids. Another culture of twelve plants from selfed seed of *D. metel* consisted of eight normal diploids and four haploids. Although these numbers are small, it is obvious that some particular causal agent, or agents, were responsible for these high ratios of haploids to normals. All controlled attempts to obtain similar results have failed.

One or more diploid branches, sectors, have appeared spontaneously on several haploids grown in either the greenhouse or garden. Flowers on these branches have shown a small proportion of aborted pollen grains and the leaves and capsules have been characteristic of normal diploids. Such capsules have produced abundant seed, which have yielded normal diploid seedlings. It has been possible readily to produce such diploid branches, flowers, and capsules on haploids by the treatment of growing tips with colchicine. This technique was discovered in 1937 and is a ready method for quickly doubling the chromosome number of many plants. The formation of diploid capsules on a haploid, when available, is a simple way of quickly obtaining a homozygous diploid race (*118, 119*).

Several haploids have appeared in *D. stramonium* cultures that in appearance have suggested certain $2n + 1$ types. Some of these have been determined cytologically to be actually $1n + 1$ types (see Chap. 6).

The statement was made above that "barring new mutations" the offspring of a haploid should be homozygous and genetically identical. In May, 1927, a paper was published showing that there was some indication that mutations, both chromosomal and genic, did, in fact, occur more frequently in the immediate offspring of haploids than of diploids. Among 393 individuals in the immediate progeny of a haploid, 12, or

3.05 per cent, were $2n + 1$ types. Of 173 offspring of a haploid tested by selfing, four or 2.31 per cent were found to be heterozygous for new genes. These figures (rates of mutation) were considerably higher than were obtained from controls (48).

Since 1927 additional offspring of haploids have been grown and have been tested for the possible increase in mutations. In the immediate progeny of the same haploid previously reported there have been grown 666 additional plants. Six, or 0.99 per cent, of these were $2n + 1$ types. This occurrence of spontaneous chromosomal types is not significantly greater than that commonly obtained from diploid parents. Of these $F_1$ plants, 360 were tested for possible gene mutations by growing offspring from selfed seed. Four, or 1.11 per cent, were found to segregate for new gene characters. Combining the earlier and later records for gene mutations, one finds that 8 plants of the 533 tested, or 1.51 per cent, were heterozygous. These figures seem to indicate that there is a tendency for *Datura* haploids (at least this particular one) to produce new gene mutations. There is only a slight, if any, increase in the production of chromosomal mutations.

**Diploids.** The Diploid ($2n$) stage (Fig. 16) is the normal condition in *Datura,* as in other flowering plants, and needs no discussion here. Haploids may be obtained from diploids by the rare process of parthenogenesis. Tetraploids may arise spontaneously from diploids by a process of doubling of chromosome number or may be produced at will by treatment with the alkaloid colchicine. Triploids may be readily obtained from crosses of tetraploids with diploids. Diploids are thus the standard to which other types are compared and from which they are derived (Figs. 2, 24, 25).

**Triploids.** The first triploid ($3n$) *Datura* was recorded in the summer of 1920. This plant was one of two seedlings obtained from 25 seeds of a cross of a Line 1 tetraploid with a Line 1 diploid. Cytological investigations made by Belling the following year proved that this plant was a true triploid with three chromosomes in each set. The sibling plant was a normal diploid. Since 1920 from over a hundred similar crosses between tetraploids (female) and diploids (male), 103 offspring have been obtained. Of these, 35 were normal diploids, 11 were tetraploids, and 57 were triploids. It is thus not difficult to obtain the triploid member of the series, $2n$, $3n$, $4n$, whenever there is available a tetraploid to use as the female parent in crosses with a normal diploid. Triploids appear spontaneously very rarely, if at all. Only two possible occurrences of such triploids have been recorded in our cultures in 40 years. One of these two plants could not be positively identified as a triploid (*13, 17*).

Triploids, with three chromosomes in all 12 sets, still maintain the same relation or balance between the chromosomes as do diploids (Fig. 26b). For this reason they are not greatly different in appearance from diploids. Because of the considerable proportion (45 to 50 per cent) of aborted pollen (and ovules) found in triploids, they tend to set small capsules with few seeds when either selfed or crossed with diploids (Fig. 25).

For this reason, triploids grown in the field continue to grow and flower after diploids have reached capsule capacity and ceased flowering (*41*).

It was shown many years ago that there is a discrepancy between the number of chromosomes in nuclei formed at meiosis in *Datura* triploid pollen mother cells and the number expected from random chromosomal assortment. The comparisons made since of chromosome behavior between the developing female and male sporophytes and gametophytes showed in both sexes that there were more nuclei with lower and higher numbers of chromosomes formed, resulting in a shift of the bimodal curves toward their ends. It was found that there are 3,000 times more male gametes with a haploid number of chromosomes than would be expected from calculations. This wide increase in the number of haploid nuclei occurs chiefly in the gametophyte. All pollen grains, including those with an excess of chromosomal material, divide, but those with an excess gradually abort after division. Pollen abortion, the failure of many pollen grains to germinate, and the abnormal growth of pollen tubes in the style are the main factors that cause elimination of chromosomally unbalanced male gametophytes. There are 280 times as many haploid female gametes than would be expected from random distribution of chromosomes. This increase of haploid nuclei is due to the high percentages of chromosome eliminations in the sporophyte at both meiotic divisions. No elimination occurs at the mitotic divisions of the gametophyte forming the embryo sac.

This high percentage of elimination in the sporophyte is not alone sufficient to explain the large number of $2n$ offspring from $3n \times 2n$ crosses. The large number of unfertilized eggs, the deterioration of the embryo sac soon after fertilization, the arrest of embryo growth in later stages, the formation of a number of defective embryos, the delayed germination of seeds, and the poor viability of many seedlings should be considered to be the chief factors to explain the increase in the number of diploid offspring from this cross. All these factors bring a further elimination of highly unbalanced zygotes. It is 816 times larger than would be expected from calculation (*17, 122, 123*).

Since triploids have three chromosomes in each set, they give trisomic ratios for all Mendelian characters instead of the usual disomic ratios obtained from diploids or the tetrasomic ratios from tetraploids.

As has been shown cytologically, several chromosomal types of offspring should be expected when a triploid is pollinated by a diploid. In the trisomic disjunction in each set, two of the three chromosomes go to one pole and one to the other, the process taking place at random. Ordinarily, the offspring from such a cross consists of diploids, $2n + 1$ primaries, and an assortment of $2n + 1 + 1$ types, with a few rare $2n + 1 + 1 + 1$ types. Among a total of 1,252 field-grown offspring from crosses of a triploid with 22 different diploids, there were 356 normal diploids, 677 $2n + 1$ plants, with all 12 primaries represented, 217 $2n + 1 + 1$ plants, representing various combinations of primaries, and two $2n + 1 + 1 + 1$ plants.

A study of the size of seeds obtained from $3n \times 2n$ crosses showed the following: the average number of seeds per capsule was 61; the size of seeds ranged from 1.7 to 4.9 mm in length. Among the 1,000 measured seeds, 333 seeds were large (4.0 to 4.9 mm), 523 seeds were of medium size (3.0 to 3.9 mm), and 144 seeds were small (2.9 mm or less). The removal of the seed coat showed that 388 seeds were good; 120 were defective; and the remaining 492 seeds, including all sizes, were empty. All of the 388 good and 48 least defective seeds were sown. Of these 436 seeds, 401 germinated, but 116 weak seedlings died soon after germination. The remaining 285 plants grew to maturity and were recorded. No direct relation was found between the size of the seed and its viability or its speed of germination. There was no relation between the length of dormancy, which in some cases exceeded 100 days, and the viability of the seedlings. But there was a definite relation between the size of the seed and some of the chromosomal types obtained. Seeds smaller than those produced by a normal diploid tended to produce $2n + 1 \cdot 2$ or $2n + 15 \cdot 16$ plants. Seeds larger than normal diploid seed usually produced $2n + 23 \cdot 24$ or $2n + 11 \cdot 12$ plants.

The 285 plants were determined cytologically. Fifty-eight (20.4 per cent) individuals were found to be diploids. The largest number of individuals were $2n + 1$; they formed almost half of the total number, i.e., 138 plants, or 48.4 per cent. The next group, 79 plants, or 27.7 per cent, were $2n + 1 + 1$. Only 10 plants (3.5 per cent) were $2n + 1 + 1 + 1$. The most frequent chromosomes present as extras were the $9 \cdot 10$ and $3 \cdot 4$. The least frequent was the $17 \cdot 18$ chromosome and the $19 \cdot 20$ did not appear at all in this particular experiment. The $13 \cdot 14$ chromosome was the only one that combined with each of the others to form 11 different $2n + 1 + 1$ types. Most of the defective seeds were found to have two extra chromosomes (131).

It is this capacity to produce $2n + 1$ types that makes triploids of great value in genetic work. When a diploid homozygous for a Mendelian character is used as the pollen parent with a triploid, all the $2n + 1$ primary types may be expected if considerable numbers of offspring are grown. Since these $2n + 1$ types are all heterozygous for the character in question, they may be used immediately in selfs or backcrosses to determine which will show trisomic ratios and thereby determine in which particular chromosome the gene in question is located. This method obviates the need of crossing an unlocated gene onto all the 12 $2n + 1$ primaries to obtain each in the heterozygous condition. Most of the *Datura* genes that have been assigned to particular chromosomes have been located by trisomic ratios thrown by heterozygous $2n + 1$ types obtained from crosses of a standard triploid with the homozygous type (Chapter 7).

**Tetraploids.** Among the offspring obtained from selfing a normal *D. stramonium* there appeared, in September 1916, a single unusual plant described as resembling somewhat the Globe ($2n + 21 \cdot 22$) mutant.

This plant was recorded as having broad leaves, large flowers, and globose capsules much like those of Globes. Seedlings from selfing this plant were obtained early in 1917 and on maturity were found to be uniformly of the parent type, while offspring from Globes were always composed of about three-quarters normals. Subsequent breeding work showed that the new type was completely fertile with itself (either crossed or selfed) but was sterile, or nearly so, when used in crosses with any normal *Datura*. This new type was thus provisionally called "New Species" (or N.S.) on account of its sterility with normals and its capacity to breed true. It was so described in several early accounts. In the summer of 1919 there appeared spontaneously several plants resembling the first N.S. These were found to be self-fertile and fertile in crosses with plants of the original N.S. race (*4, 6, 18*).

In 1920 Belling was able to determine cytologically that the plants of the N.S. type had four chromosomes in each set and thus were *Datura* tetraploids ($4n$). Extensive breeding work with these tetraploid forms was carried on. Large numbers of offspring of tetraploids heterozygous for purple ($P$) and white ($p$) flowers showed a close approximation to the ratios expected from a random assortment of four chromosomes in a set. The ratios of all:0, 35:1, and 3:1 from selfing heterozygous tetraploids (*PPPp, PPpp,* or *Pppp*) were obtained. Similar tetrasomic ratios were secured from tetraploids made heterozygous for the recessive type inermis, or smooth capsules (*28, 32*).

Since 1920 tetraploids have occurred spontaneously in the *Datura* cultures many times. They have frequently appeared as bud sports, or sectors, on otherwise normal diploid plants. They also may appear sporadically as complete $4n$ plants in cultures from any *Datura* parent. It has been observed that these new tetraploids usually have, at least in the early stages of growth, a tendency to irregular branching and thick, roughened leaves. It was this characteristic roughening of leaves and malformation that was regarded as an indication of tetraploidy following colchicine treatment. Such plants have been often recorded in the field as "rough tetraploids." It has been determined that this irregular growth is due to different growth rates of the $2n$ and $4n$ tissue involved (Chapter 8).

In some other genera it may be possible that the occasional tetraploids that have been found in experimental cultures, or more rarely in nature, have been formed by the union of an unreduced $2n$ egg with an unreduced $2n$ sperm brought in by the pollen. However, in *Datura* it is well established that this is not the usual method. Buchholz was able to show clearly that $2n$ pollen tubes regularly burst when growing in the style of a diploid plant and hence the $2n$ pollen grains that are occasionally formed by normal plants through nonreduction could not be expected to take part in the production of tetraploid seedlings (*51*).

In several instances it has been possible to prove genetically that new tetraploids have arisen *after* reduction in the diploid parent. Tetraploids in the offspring of $2n$ parents that are heterozygous for a given gene, *a*, should have the constitution $A_2a_2$ if they arise from union of unreduced gametes. Spontaneous tetraploids from such heterozygous diploids often do not have this duplex genic constitution and so must have arisen from the doubling of chromosomes after reduction. The frequent presence of both 2n and 4n tissues (mixochimeras) in newly formed tetraploids is additional evidence that doubling of chromosomes usually occurs in somatic tissue sometime after the division of the zygote. Tetraploids regularly appear in limited numbers among the offspring of triploids. Such tetraploids could be formed by the union of 2n gametes, since in this case 2n pollen tubes could grow in the 3n tissue of the triploid.

Chromosome counts have demonstrated that 4n and 2n cells may be present in the same flower and even in the same anther of these spontaneous "rough tetraploids." Many times single flowers have been found which have pollen grains of two sizes, 1n and 2n. It has been found that such mixochimeras usually sort themselves out into sectors of 2n or 4n tissue as growth is continued.

Tetraploid plants are usually readily distinguished from diploid plants of the same species or race by a series of morphological differences. The shape of mature capsules is perhaps the most distinctive single character by which 4n's can be distinguished from 2n's. Capsules of tetraploid D. stramonium plants are nearly spherical instead of ovate, as are those of diploids (Fig. 24). In certain other species, such as D. leichhardtii and D. pruinosa, diploids of which normally have nearly spherical capsules, this difference is less marked. Capsules of tetraploids are always somewhat smaller than those of diploids of the same race and contain considerably fewer, but larger, seed. The leaves of tetraploids are noticeably thicker and broader than those of comparable diploids but are produced in somewhat lesser numbers. The general aspect of tetraploid plants is more stocky and bushy than that of diploids. In all species of Datura the tetraploids have produced larger flowers than diploids (Fig. 24).

Datura tetraploids are autopolyploids. Their chromosomes at metaphase I are arranged in 12 sets, each containing four joined chromosomes. Such quadrivalents are formed by two connected pairs and all four chromosomes are of the same size (Fig. 26c). At the first meiotic division the two pairs separate, giving to each pole two chromosomes. Such regular distribution does not always occur in all 12 quadrivalents. Because of nonreduction in about one-quarter of the pollen mother cells, the chromosomes assort 23:25 or more rarely 22:26, instead of 24:24. (Presumably the same occurs in megaspore mother cells.) This is a regular phenomenon in D. stramonium and the observations made have agreed closely with calculations. The elimination of chromosomes during meiosis occurs in about 2.3 per cent of p.m.c. (32).

An extensive study of the comparative anatomy of the polyploid series has been made by Sinnott. This study involved the counting and measuring of cells of most of the components of stems and leaves with special emphasis on the flower stalk, which was found to be the least affected by environmental factors. It was found that there are few differences between members of the polyploid series in cell number and general anatomical plan. However, they do show marked difference in size of their structures; this is definitely related to the size of the component cells, which, in turn, are in general proportional to chromosome number (99).

Ample evidence has been accumulated which indicates that all cells of tetraploid plants are larger than corresponding cells of comparable diploids. While actual chromosomal counts may be the only method positively to identify tetraploid plants, other less tedious criteria have commonly been used. In cases where there was any reason to doubt the preliminary determination, chromosome counts have also been made. One of the clearest means of distinction between tetraploids and diploids that we have employed is the difference in the size of pollen grains. Mature pollen may be inspected under a low-power microscope and the size of pollen grains quickly estimated. The method has been extensively checked cytologically over many years and has been found reliable. The volume of a pollen grain is proportional to the number of chromosomes that it contains ($1n$, $2n$, $4n$). Pollen grains of a tetraploid have $2n$ chromosomes and their volume is approximately twice that of the $1n$ grains of a normal diploid plant. The diameter of the former grains is one and one-fourth times that of diploids (Fig. 25).

Among other cells the size of which has been used as an indication of the chromosome number are the guard cells of the stomata. These appear to be less influenced by environmental factors than many other somatic cells. Identification by the determination of guard-cell size has been particularly useful in certain special cases, e.g., weak plants that may not flower. By indicating the constitution of the epidermis, this method has also been of special use in the case of periclinal chimeras, as discussed in Chapter 8.

Tetraploids of the standard L 1A of *D. stramonium* normally have a small percentage of aborted pollen—usually about 5 per cent as compared to about 1 per cent normally found in diploids. This higher proportion of abortion in tetraploids is due to the larger amount of nondisjunction resulting in pollen grains lacking one or more chromosomes. Tetraploids are completely self-fertile and equally fertile in crosses with other tetraploids of the same species. When used as the female parent in crosses with diploids, only a few viable seed result. Offspring from such a cross consist of triploids, a few diploids that apparently are the result of nondisjunction, and an occasional tetraploid. The reason that more triploids are not realized from the $4n \times 2n$ cross was found to be that many of the $3n$ embryos abort when only a few days old. The reciprocal cross, $2n \times 4n$, is ordinarily unsuccessful. This failure of the $2n \times 4n$ cross to form viable seed is primarily due to the inability of $2n$ pollen tubes from pollen of a tetraploid to grow in the $2n$ style of a diploid (51, 155).

The spontaneous appearance of extra chromosomal types $(4n + 1,$
$4n + 2,$ or $4n + 1 + 1,$ etc.) in cultures of tetraploids is much more
frequent than corresponding $2n + 1$ types in diploid cultures. This fact
is due to the more frequent occurrence of nondisjunction in tetraploids
with four chromosomes in each set than in diploids. Tetraploids with a
single extra chromosome show the effect of the extra material less strikingly than diploids because of the lesser degree of unbalance caused by
the extra chromosomal material—48:1 instead of 24:1. Among offspring
of $4n + 1$ types there may be found some $4n + 2$ plants that have the
same relative unbalance as do $2n + 1$ and are equally as distinct. Other
combinations with extra chromosomal material may exist in tetraploids
with less detrimental effect to the plant than would occur with diploids.
Thus $4n + 1 + 1 + 1$ plants as well as $4n + 2$ or $4n + 3$ plants have
been identified. Tetraploids have also been found that have been deficient for one or more chromosomes, e.g., $4n - 1, 4n - 1 - 1, 4n - 1 + 1,$
or $4n - 1 - 1 + 1 + 1.$ The last would represent a plant with a total
of 48 chromosomes with, however, only three in each of two sets and five
in each of two other sets (127, 135).

As stated above, spontaneous tetraploids have appeared frequently in
our *Datura* cultures. In certain seasons we have found a relatively large
number of such new tetraploids but in other seasons few or none at all.
These facts, together with the observation that seed from a given en-
velope may produce many $4n$ plants one season and few in another,
indicated that some environmental factors were involved. As early as
1921 attempts were made to produce an environment favorable for the
production of tetraploids. The first of these experiments involved the
exposure of growing plants to low temperatures. The cold treatment
resulted in the production of considerable aborted pollen and an abundance of large pollen grains of the size formed by tetraploids, but there
was no evidence that the treatment had stimulated the production of
tetraploid seeds. Later, more precise experiments with cold treatments
in a controlled temperature chamber gave results no more encouraging.
Higher than normal temperatures, either continuous or intermittent, at
time of germination were also used extensively but failed completely to
yield tetraploids (23).

In 1926 the first chemical treatments intended to induce the production
of tetraploids were started. These experiments consisted of injecting
solutions of chloral hydrate in varying concentrations into the developing ovary. Gene mutations and chromosomal deficiencies were apparently induced by these treatments, but no doubling of chromosomes
occurred. Chloral hydrate solutions were also later used for the treatment of seeds before planting. This, and most other chemicals tested,
with the exception of colchicine, failed to produce any indication of
tetraploidy (55).

Early in 1937 O. J. Eigsti, then an assistant in the Department of
Genetics, had observed irregular mitotic divisions and some polyploid

cells in onion root tips that he had treated with colchicine. These results suggested that this alkaloid might be effective with *Datura*. Extensive experiments were therefore begun that summer to see if colchicine would produce a consistently high proportion of tetraploids from diploids. Seeds of the standard Line 1A of *D. stramonium* were soaked for different lengths of time in various concentrations of the alkaloid. After treatment the seeds were planted in the usual manner. The colchicine treatment resulted in seedlings with swollen hypocotyls, which in later stages displayed the characteristically roughened leaves that are usually associated with spontaneous tetraploids. These seedlings developed into plants producing flowers with pollen the size of that of tetraploids. Cytological determination gave proof that a method for the induction of tetraploids had been found. The methods of treatment and results with *Datura* and other plants have been reported in detail in the *Journal of Heredity* (*118*) and elsewhere (*117, 119, 126*). Colchicine treatment for the induction of chromosomal doubling is a simple and usually certain method. It has been used successfully by many workers on many species of plants. Of several economically important plants, tetraploid forms produced by the colchicine method are listed in commercial seed catalogues. Extensive references to the use of colchicine and the many polyploid forms obtained are given in Eigsti and Dustin's (1955) valuable review.

**Hexaploids.** Using the colchicine method, it has been possible, in at least one instance, to induce the doubling of chromosomes of a triploid (3n) *D. stramonium*. When the growing tips and young buds of a triploid were treated with colchicine, a few flowers resulted that, from pollen and cytological determinations, were evidently 6n or hexaploid. These flowers failed to set viable seed.

Weak plants with 72 chromosomes have also been identified among the offspring of tetraploids homozygous for the recessive character "dyad," a gene which causes doubling of chromosomes at meiosis. Numerical hexaploids have also been obtained in certain species hybrids and are described in Chapter 13 (*83, 108*).

**Octoploids.** As in the case of hexaploids, it has not been possible to obtain a race of octoploids (8n's). However, by treating seed of *D. stramonium* tetraploids with colchicine, a few weak plants have been positively identified as being of the 8n type. One or two possible octoploids have also been recorded among plants grown from colchicine-treated diploid seed. These have been very small, weak plants and it has not been possible to obtain offspring from them. We have also obtained 8n branches and flowers by treating growing tips of 4n plants with colchicine. These 8n flowers failed to produce seed. As related in Chapter 8, periclinal chimeras with one or two octoploid layers have frequently been obtained. No attempts have been made to obtain the 6n or 8n members of the polyploid series in any other species than *D. stramonium*.

**Summary.** In all of the ten herbaceous species of *Datura* we have available for study and comparison the normal diploid ($2n$) and tetraploid ($4n$) forms. From these forms triploids ($3n$) of all may be obtained at will. Of *D. stramonium, D. metel,* and *D. pruinosa,* haploids ($1n$) have also been identified. It is only in *D. stramonium* that plants representing the complete polyploid series, $1n$, $2n$, $3n$, and $4n$, have been available in considerable numbers and have been adequately studied. Also in *D. stramonium* weak plants or branches identified as hexaploids ($6n$) and octoploids ($8n$) have been induced by colchicine treatment.

# 6

# Extra Chromosomal Types

A. G. Avery

The first $2n + 1$ type, although not then recognized as such, appeared in 1915 among cultures of *Datura stramonium* growing in the botanical garden at Storrs, Connecticut. It may be historically interesting to note the original recording of that plant as it appeared in the garden notebook of that September: "One plant found with globose rather than elongated pods; called Globe. Globe has about 1/2 the No. of seeds usually found in pods. Siblings of this carefully searched but no more like it found."

Preliminary breeding experiments carried on during the succeeding two or three years at the Station for Experimental Evolution at Cold Spring Harbor revealed that the Globe type was also peculiar in the manner in which the Globe characteristics were inherited. The first published account of the Globe mutant is found in the 1916 annual report of the Department of Experimental Evolution as follows: "It is characterized by a globose capsule and broad leaves and is apparently a recessive" (2). Two years later, in the 1918 report of the Department, results of extensive breeding experiments were summarized as follows: "When the Globes are selfed and the Globes as females are crossed with normals about the same results are obtained in the offspring, i.e., approximately 3 normals to 1 Globe; while normals crossed with Globes as male parents throw about 38 normals to 1 Globe. The mutant complex, therefore, seems to be but slightly transmitted through the male parent. It is transmitted through the female parent either when selfed or when crossed with a normal, but appears in only about a quarter of the offspring. The mutant has been selfed for five generations, but as yet it seems impossible to obtain a pure race of Globes." Two other mutants of a similar nature were then known which seemed to be inherited in much the same manner (5).

By 1919 a considerable number of other types, of a similar sort, had been discovered and described. These mutant types were originally referred to by a series of names derived from the more distinct or obvious manner in which the plant, or some part of it, differed from normal,

Thus the type with globose fruit was called Globe (Gl); that with narrow leaves which tended to turn up at the edges was called Rolled (Rl); that with long and large leaves tending to become clustered became Poinsettia (Pn); that with dark leaves with sharply serrated edges, Ilex (Ix); and that with small, narrow, and rather long capsules was named Cocklebur (Ck). In 1930 a system of numbering the ends of the chromosomes was adopted, the types were designated by the chromosome numbers, and the original names were abandoned (63). In 1919 several of these types were described, and pictures of seedlings, mature plants, and capsules were given. Here the peculiar inheritance of these mutant types was referred to as being "chiefly through the female sex" (6).

**Chromosomal Constitution of Types Determined.** In 1920, Belling, a guest at the Station, was doing cytological work with hybrids between the various species of *Canna*. At Blakeslee's invitation, he began a preliminary cytological study of the several mutants of *Datura* that showed such unusual inheritance. Belling's investigations soon established the true character of the mutants in question. In each of the new mutants investigated, chromosomal counts from the first division of pollen mother cells showed that the gametic number was 12 and 13, giving a somatic number of 25, instead of the 24 found in normals. In the 13-chromosome gametes the extra chromosome was thought to occur as a duplication of one of the regular 12. It was then further suggested that each of the mutants was probably determined by the duplication of a different individual chromosome to make up the total of 25 chromosomes characteristic of their somatic cells (8).

At the same time, it was pointed out that if each of these mutants was determined by the presence of an additional chromosome in a definite one of the 12 sets, it should be possible by breeding tests to identify a mutant that has as its extra chromosome one which carries a gene for a particular Mendelian character. This was subsequently demonstrated in the case of Poinsettia, which is the name of the type brought about by the duplication of the chromosome carrying the determiners for purple or white flowers. The terms *monosome, disome, trisome, tetrasome,* and *pentasome* were established to designate sets of one, two, three, four, or five chromosomes. A plant with three chromosomes, two of which carry the factor for purple flowers and one the allele for white flowers, will give trisomic ratios when selfed or backcrossed to the recessive. A tetraploid, or a plant with four chromosomes in any set, will give tetrasomic ratios for characters carried in a chromosome of that particular set (30).

It has since been repeatedly demonstrated that the presence of a specific chromosome as an extra causes a certain recognizable mutant or $2n + 1$ type. It is evident, therefore, that in *Datura* there should be 12 such $2n + 1$ primary types corresponding to the 12 different chromosome pairs which may undergo duplication. All these types have occurred spontaneously many times in our controlled cultures, probably having been brought about by nondisjunction of a particular pair of chromo-

somes in the formation of the egg cell by the seed parent. These primary
$2n + 1$ types may also be obtained from triploids, which have three
chromosomes in each set and which at reduction division will regularly
give many gametes with extra chromosomes. All of the $2n + 1$ primary
types may be expected among the offspring of a triploid, either selfed or
used as female parent, if large enough numbers are grown.

Since there are in *Datura* only 12 chromosomal pairs, we would expect
to find not over 12 mutants of the $2n + 1$ type, each the result of the
presence of a different extra chromosome. Nevertheless, many more than
the expected 12 types have been discovered in our cultures. All these
have been determined to have 25 chromosomes in their somatic cells, or
11 pairs plus one set of three chromosomes. In general, all behave
similarly in breeding in that they reappear in about a quarter of the offspring when the mutant is the female parent and not at all, or only in
small numbers, when it is used as the male parent. It was soon observed
that there existed similarities in the general appearance of these extra
chromosomal types by which they could be arranged into 12 groups. In
all cases the breeding behavior confirmed the tentative grouping by
appearance. When the various $2n + 1$ types were so grouped, the breeding records showed that one member of a group threw the other members in relatively large numbers but only rarely a member of an unrelated
group.

Cytological investigations have verified the groupings made by the
methods just described and have established a clear picture of the relationships of the many $2n + 1$ types in *Datura*. Belling found that in the
$2n + 1$ types the most frequent configuration that the trivalent assumed
was an open **V**. If the odd chromosome was detached, the usual configuration was found to be a bivalent with a detached univalent. The
$2n + 1$ types that seemed, by appearance and breeding, to be related to
the 12 basic types usually showed closed circles as the configuration of
their trivalents. When the odd chromosome was detached, it was often
found to be formed in a small ring or doughnut. Later cytological investigations by Bergner verified the findings of Belling and confirmed
his hypothesis that the extra chromosome of a secondary is composed of a
doubled half-chromosome, while the extra chromosome of a primary is
a whole chromosome like the other two of the set (33).

Thus by visual evidence, by cytology, and by breeding behavior, it is
possible to distinguish primary and secondary $2n + 1$ types. By following the terminology adopted in 1930 whereby the two ends of each chromosome of the standard Line 1A race are numbered like dominoes in
consecutive order, the largest chromosome becomes $1 \cdot 2$, the next smaller
in size $3 \cdot 4$, and so on to the smallest, which is $23 \cdot 24$. The primary,
once called Rolled, thus becomes the $2n + 1 \cdot 2$ type, since it has the
largest chromosome as the extra. Its two secondaries, which were formerly called Polycarpic (Py) and Sugarloaf (Sg), respectively, are now
designated $2n + 1 \cdot 1$ and $2n + 2 \cdot 2$. The type with the smallest chro-

mosome extra, which was originally called Ilex because of the resemblance of its leaves to those of the holly, is $2n + 23 \cdot 24$ (63).

The many chromosomal forms in *Datura* are classified as being either balanced or unbalanced types. Those in which all the chromosome sets have the same number are balanced; and those which have an irregular number in at least one set are unbalanced. Balanced types may be further divided into even-balanced or stable and odd-balanced or unstable types. The different kinds of balanced types are discussed in Chapter 5. The extra chromosomal types discussed in the present chapter are of the unbalanced type. There may be one less, one more, or two more than the normal number in one set; or extra chromosomes in each of two different sets; or other combinations.

**Morphological Characteristics of $2n + 1$ Types.** All the $2n + 1$ mutants, both primaries and secondaries, are slower in growth than normals and in competition are liable to be crowded out by the latter. In this respect, as in all visible characters, they vary widely. There is no consistent difference in vitality of growth between primaries and secondaries. The $2n + 1 \cdot 1$ secondary is the weakest of all and must be carefully tended in the greenhouse, for it is too weak to survive to maturity in the garden or field. The complementary secondary $2n + 2 \cdot 2$ is somewhat more vigorous than the primary $2n + 1 \cdot 2$.

The expected complementary relationship of the two secondaries, when existing, to their primary is evident in most characters. In general the primary is intermediate between its two secondaries in the expression of any particular character. A clear example of this is found in the group of $2n + 1$ types with the $9 \cdot 9$, $9 \cdot 10$, and the $10 \cdot 10$ chromosomes extra (Fig. 27). The $2n + 9 \cdot 9$ (Mutilated) plants have relatively broad, thick, and dark leaves; the flowers are short and dark purple; the capsules are globose with few short spines; and the plants are short and compact in habit. The $2n + 10 \cdot 10$ (Thistle) plants have long, thin leaves; the flowers are very long and slender; the capsules are slender with many long spines (hence the name); the plants are tall and erect in habit. In the primary $2n + 9 \cdot 10$ (Echinus) the expression of these characteristics is intermediate between those shown by the two secondaries. It may thus be assumed that the $\cdot 9$ arm of this chromosome is responsible for the dark, broad leaves, the short flowers, and globose capsules, while the $\cdot 10$ arm is responsible for the opposites. When both are present in the extra chromosome, as in the primary $2n + 9 \cdot 10$, an intermediate condition occurs because of the interaction of opposing factors. This sort of relationship is evident in the other cases where both secondaries are known. The character and amount of divergence in appearance of the primary $2n + 9 \cdot 10$ from the normal diploid is determined by the unbalance that the extra $9 \cdot 10$ chromosome exerts over the rest of the evenly paired chromosomes. Fig. 27 also shows pot-grown plants of the primary $2n + 5 \cdot 6$ and its two secondaries, $2n + 5 \cdot 5$ and $2n + 6 \cdot 6$. It should

$$2n + 11 \cdot 11 \qquad\qquad 2n + 11 \cdot 12$$

$$2n + 5 \cdot 5 \qquad 2n + 5 \cdot 6 \qquad 2n + 6 \cdot 6$$

$$2n + 9 \cdot 9 \qquad 2n + 9 \cdot 10 \qquad 2n + 10 \cdot 10$$

FIG. 27. Pot-grown plants of three primaries and their known secondaries.

Normal $(2n)$

| $2n + 1 \cdot 2$ | $2n + 3 \cdot 4$ | $2n + 5 \cdot 6$ | $2n + 7 \cdot 8$ |

| $2n + 9 \cdot 10$ | $2n + 11 \cdot 12$ | $2n + 13 \cdot 14$ | $2n + 15 \cdot 16$ |

| $2n + 17 \cdot 18$ | $2n + 19 \cdot 20$ | $2n + 21 \cdot 22$ | $2n + 23 \cdot 24$ |

FIG. 28. Capsules of diploid *D. stramonium* and the 12 primary $2n + 1$ types.

be clear that the primary is intermediate between the two secondaries in general habit and in particular characters. Only one secondary, $2n + 11 \cdot 11$ (Wedge), has been identified for the primary $2n + 11 \cdot 12$ (Cocklebur) (Fig. 27).

Table 3 gives the chromosomal formulas of the 12 primaries and the 14 known secondaries and brief notations of their most obvious characteristics. Pictures showing the various primaries and secondaries in

TABLE 3

The Twelve Primary $2n + 1$ Types and Their Known Secondaries
(Names of primaries in capitals)

| Chromosomal Formula | | Name | Abbreviation | Most Obvious Characteristics |
|---|---|---|---|---|
| $2n+$ | | | | |
| | 1·1 | Polycarpic | Py | Small plants; narrow leaves; tiny capsules |
| 1·2 | | ROLLED | Rl | Narrow, in-rolled leaves |
| | 2·2 | Sugar loaf | Sg | Large, pointed capsules |
| | 3·3 | Smooth | Sm | Small, nearly smooth capsules |
| 3·4 | | GLOSSY | Gs | Glossy, dark green leaves |
| | 5·5 | Strawberry | St | Erect habit; compressed capsules |
| 5·6 | | BUCKLING | Bk | Large leaves with surfaces distorted |
| | 6·6 | Areolate | At | Leaves with irregular pale areas |
| | 7·7 | Undulate | Un | Spreading habit; narrow, wavy leaves |
| 7·8 | | ELONGATE | El | Erect habit; elongated leaves |
| | 9·9 | Mutilated | Mt | Broad, dark leaves; capsules malformed |
| 9·10 | | ECHINUS | Ec | Large capsules; very long spines |
| | 10·10 | Thistle | Th | Capsules narrow; spines many, slender |
| | 11·11 | Wedge | Wd | Spreading habit; capsules tapered |
| 11·12 | | COCKLEBUR | Ck | Spreading habit; small, narrow capsules |
| | 13·13 | Marbled | Mb | Leaves mottled |
| 13·14 | | MICROCARPIC | Mc | Small, depressed capsules |
| | 14·14 | Mealy | Ml | Capsules and young leaves glaucous |
| | 15·15 | Scalloped | Sc | Spreading habit; narrow, irregular leaves |
| 15·16 | | REDUCED | Rd | Spines short, blunt |
| | 17·17 | Dwarf | Df | Small plants |
| 17·18 | | POINSETTIA | Pn | Leaves long, clustered |
| | 19·19 | Divergent | Dv | Very spreading habit |
| 19·20 | | SPINACH | Sp | Leaves dark, puckered |
| 21·22 | | GLOBE | Gl | Capsules globose |
| 23·24 | | ILEX | Ix | Small capsules, leaves sharply toothed |

seedling and adult stages, as well as their capsules, have been published elsewhere (*70, 86, 128*). When grown under favorable and comparable conditions, the differences are striking and present little difficulty to those familiar with the material in recording segregating cultures. Under poor conditions certain types (notably the $2n + 13 \cdot 14$ and its secondaries) may be very difficult to record and may require extra checking. Mature capsules (before dehiscence) are the best single part of the plant whereby the different $2n + 1$ types can be recognized. Fig. 28 shows mature capsules of the 12 primaries and one from a normal $2n$ plant for comparison. However, the general over-all appearance of these types is distinct and is the criterion by which the records are usually made. Fig. 29 shows three-week-old seedlings of three primaries, $2n + 1 \cdot 2$, $2n + 5 \cdot 6$, and $2n + 9 \cdot 10$, and their respective secondaries. At this

FIG. 29. Seedlings of $2n$ D. *stramonium* and of three primaries and their secondaries.

stage all the primaries and secondaries may be identified with a fair degree of certainty.

The differences between the $2n + 1$ types apparently extend to all parts of the plant both internal and external. Sinnott has shown that the primary and secondary types show consistent differences in their internal anatomy by which they can be identified (99). These $2n + 1$ types may also be recognized by differences in form of such parts as leaves, flowers, and stigmas. Fig. 30 shows the stigmas of 11 primaries and a normal

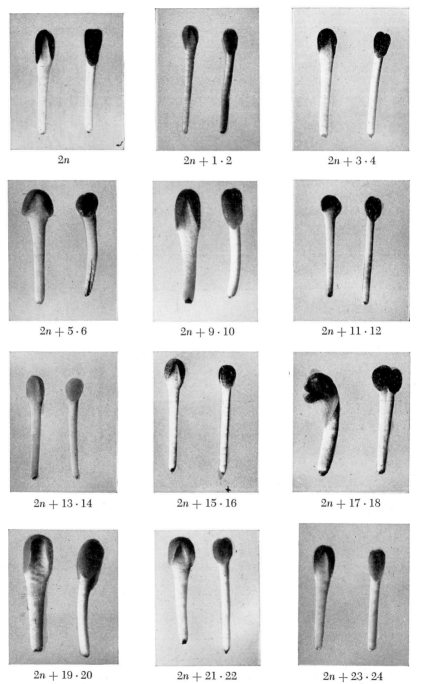

FIG. 30. Stigmas of *D. stramonium*. Normal diploid and 11 primary $2n + 1$ types.

($2n$). Unfortunately the reproduction does not show well the differences in color intensity. The shape, size, and color of the stigma is often used to determine the identity of a plant of which there is doubt.

Since 1921 all the 12 primary $2n + 1$ types have been recognized and extensively investigated by cytology and breeding. For four of the primaries both secondaries are known; for six others only one secondary of the two possible has been discovered. In the case of the two primaries with the smallest chromosomes extra, $2n + 21 \cdot 22$ and $2n + 23 \cdot 24$, no secondary has been recorded. All of these $2n + 1$ types have appeared in the highly uniform Line 1A, which had been inbred for ten generations, when it was further purified in 1922 by being passed through a haploid. Most of these types had been inbred for more than 20 generations at the time of the last planting in 1954.

**Breeding Behavior of Primaries and Secondaries.** In Table 4 are shown figures representing the offspring of the $2n + 1$ primaries and secondaries recorded in summer plantings since 1923. The accumulated offspring from 570 diploid ($2n$) parents of Line 1A for the same years are given for comparison. All the cultures used in this tabulation were derived from selfings, except 684 offspring of the $2n + 1 \cdot 1$ secondary, which were from female backcrosses to a Line 1A diploid. It has repeatedly been shown that female backcrossing gives as many parental types as selfing.

The offspring from $2n$ and $2n + 1$ parents, tabulated here, are all from cultures grown in the summer and recorded under nearly ideal conditions. Lack of sufficient greenhouse space prevented keeping all individuals of segregating cultures in pots until complete records could be taken and, moreover, some of the chromosomal types are often difficult to identify under greenhouse conditions. Types have a much better opportunity to express their distinguishing characteristics when grown to maturity in the field. This is especially true when more than a single extra chromosome is present. For these reasons the records used in these tabulations are from cultures that, with the exception of a few small or weak individuals purposely kept in the greenhouse, have all been grown in the field or garden plots.

In March or April of each year selfed seed from the $2n + 1$ types and diploids have been sown in sterilized soil. Sterilized soil is always used to prevent the germination of any stray *Datura* seeds that might be present in the composted soil. Germination is usually very good and seedlings begin to appear from seven to ten days after planting; they are put into 3-inch clay pots from one to two weeks later. If more seedlings have germinated in a particular culture than is desired, care is always taken to save from one side of the seed pan so that a fair random sample will be retained. If an inadequate number of seedlings have germinated by this time, the pan may be kept for two or three weeks longer and a second potting made. There is evidence that these later pottings give a higher proportion of $2n + 1$ types than do the earlier pottings (*128*). This fact seems to indicate that the $2n + 1$ types are somewhat slower

TABLE 4

Offspring of Primary (I) and Secondary (II) $2n + 1$ Types *
(Records taken from summer plantings of 1924–1952)

| Parents ** | Number of Parents | Plants Recordable | $2n$ | Parent Type | Related | | Unrelated | | $ln$ | $4n$ | Other Types |
|---|---|---|---|---|---|---|---|---|---|---|---|
| | | | | | I | II | I | II | | | |
| **$2n+$** | | | | | | | | | | | |
| 1·1 | 15 | 1969 | 1870 | 48 | 47 | | 4 | | | | |
| 1·2 | 24 | 3425 | 2947 | 421 | | 6 | 27 | | | 24 | |
| 2·2 | 22 | 2150 | 1661 | 364 | 99 | | 6 | 1 | 1 | 18 | |
| 3·3 | 32 | 2965 | 2681 | 154 | 97 | | 19 | 1 | 1 | 11 | 1 |
| 3·4 | 24 | 2618 | 2085 | 530 | | | 1 | | 1 | 1 | |
| 5·5 | 25 | 2750 | 1767 | 796 | 152 | | 18 | 1 | | 12 | 4 |
| 5·6 | 25 | 2887 | 1975 | 860 | | 2 | 25 | 2 | | 18 | 5 |
| 6·6 | 20 | 2893 | 2192 | 482 | 185 | | 2 | 2 | 1 | 29 | |
| 7·7 | 28 | 3182 | 2269 | 839 | 56 | | 6 | | 1 | 9 | 2 |
| 7·8 | 21 | 2434 | 2165 | 254 | | | 13 | | 1 | 1 | |
| 9·9 | 26 | 2972 | 2247 | 396 | 295 | | 26 | 1 | 2 | 2 | 3 |
| 9·10 | 22 | 2440 | 1689 | 731 | | 1 | 13 | | | 3 | 3 |
| 10·10 | 25 | 2440 | 1721 | 631 | 58 | | 24 | | | 1 | 5 |
| 11·11 | 25 | 2722 | 2225 | 447 | 30 | | 9 | | | 8 | 3 |
| 11·12 | 24 | 2799 | 2234 | 544 | | 2 | 15 | 1 | | 1 | 2 |
| 13·13 | 17 | 2314 | 1920 | 255 | 128 | | 7 | | 1 | 2 | 1 |
| 13·14 | 24 | 3679 | 2884 | 741 | | | 41 | 1 | 1 | 7 | 4 |
| 14·14 | 20 | 2780 | 2141 | 537 | 81 | | 17 | | 1 | | 3 |
| 15·15 | 25 | 2750 | 2071 | 541 | 89 | | 13 | | | 33 | 3 |
| 15·16 | 23 | 2765 | 2193 | 546 | | 1 | 21 | | 1 | 2 | 1 |
| 17·17 | 22 | 3238 | 2711 | 321 | 186 | | 10 | | 3 | 7 | |
| 17·18 | 26 | 2645 | 2013 | 615 | | 1 | 11 | | 2 | 2 | 1 |
| 19·19 | 27 | 3350 | 2347 | 980 | 2 | | 20 | | | | 1 |
| 19·20 | 48 | 5565 | 5294 | 151 | | 7 | 102 | 4 | 1 | 3 | 3 |
| 21·22 | 24 | 2905 | 2070 | 806 | | | 4 | | | 11 | 14 |
| 23·24 | 22 | 2385 | 1635 | 742 | | | 1 | | | 6 | 1 |
| **$2n$** | 570 | 23251 | 23162 | | | | 33 | 1 | 6 | 49 | |

* All the offspring were from selfings except 684 from $2n + 1·1$, which were from female backcrosses to L 1A.

** All plants used as parents were in the highly homozygous Line 1 of D. *stramonium*; and all but 11 ($2n + 1·1$) were in Line 1A, which originated from a haploid within Line 1.

to germinate than diploids. It has been specifically shown from the offspring of triploids that one (and possibly others) of the 12 chromosomes, when it is present as an extra, delays germination (*131*). It has not been practical, however, to keep the seed pans much more than a month. Occasionally seed have germinated as late as six months after planting. The error from discarding the pans before all viable seeds have germinated results in a reduction in the apparent viability of the $2n + 1$ types. Since, in most cases, very good germination (90 to 95 per cent) has been obtained, this is not a serious error.

Three to four weeks after potting the plants are transplanted to the field. Field rows are $3\frac{1}{2}$ feet apart and the plants are set 18 inches apart in the row unless special use is to be made of the plants, which requires wider spacing. From the time the seedlings are transplanted to pots in the greenhouse until they are finally recorded in the field a small proportion of the plants (usually less than 10 per cent) may become unrecordable from a number of causes, such as death by damping off, cutworms, disease, or accidents. The records used are all based on recordable adult plants. If every plant could have been given individual care, the proportion of $2n + 1$ types would have been slightly higher, since they are more susceptible to unfavorable conditions than diploids. In view of the very large number of offspring recorded over so many seasons, it is believed that the uniform treatment of the cultures has resulted in reliable data and that the differences evident between the effects of different chromosomes are valid.

These field cultures grown during more than 30 years total nearly a hundred thousand plants—98,273. The final recording of the plantings has usually been done by two persons working together. Over the years three individuals have been principally responsible for these records: A. F. Blakeslee, G. Morrison, and A. G. Avery. Since some types, especially $2n + 1 + 1$ forms, are not always readily distinguishable before maturity and fruiting, the records of all cultures have been checked two or more times during the growing season. Plants, the identity of which the recorders were in doubt, have often had their chromosomal constitution determined cytologically. Many such plants not immediately identified have been further tested by determining the character of their offspring. The number of seed parents as given in the second column of Table 4 range from 15 in the case of the secondary $2n + 1 \cdot 1$, which is of weak growth, to 48 in the case of the primary $2n + 19 \cdot 20$, which, since it reappears among its offspring infrequently, requires extensive plantings. The balanced $1n$ and $4n$ types, which appeared spontaneously, are represented in this table but are not included in later summary tables, which are concerned only with diploids and modified diploids. The last column (other types) is composed largely of $2n + 1 + 1$ types, which in later tables are counted twice. Thus a $2n + 5 \cdot 6 + 13 \cdot 14$ plant that appeared in the offspring of a $2n + 5 \cdot 5$ is, in later tables, included among both the related and unrelated primaries. Also, in this column are included certain $2n - 1$ types and a fragment type $2n + \cdot 11$; these are omitted in later tables.

Table 5, which is derived from the data of Table 4, gives in percentages the different types of offspring thrown by the primaries and secondaries. From this table it is clear that there are great differences in the degree to which the different extra chromosomes are transmitted. The primary with the smallest chromosome extra ranks first in viability, reappearing

TABLE 5

| Parents | Viability Rank | | Per Cent $2n + 1$ Offspring | | | | | Per Cent $2n$ Off-spring | Plants Recorded |
| | | | Parent Type | | Related Types | | Un-related Types | | |
| | I | II | I | II | I | II | | | |
|---|---|---|---|---|---|---|---|---|---|
| **$2n+$** | | | | | | | | | |
| 1·1 | | 14 | | 2.43 | 2.39 | | .20 | 94.97 | 1969 |
| 1·2 | 10 | | 12.37 | | | .18 | .79 | 86.65 | 3401 |
| 2·2 | | 7 | | 17.08 | 4.64 | | .33 | 77.94 | 2131 |
| 3·3 | | 13 | | 5.22 | 3.29 | | .68 | 90.82 | 2952 |
| 3·4 | 6 | | 20.26 | | | 0.0 | .04 | 79.70 | 2616 |
| 5·5 | | 2 | | 29.17 | 5.59 | | .87 | 64.53 | 2738 |
| 5·6 | 2 | | 30.15 | | | .07 | 1.12 | 68.87 | 2869 |
| 6·6 | | 8 | | 16.84 | 6.46 | | .14 | 76.56 | 2863 |
| 7·7 | | 3 | | 26.51 | 1.77 | | .25 | 71.53 | 3172 |
| 7·8 | 11 | | 10.44 | | | 0.0 | .54 | 88.96 | 2432 |
| 9·9 | | 10 | | 13.34 | 10.01 | | 1.04 | 75.78 | 2968 |
| 9·10 | 3 | | 30.12 | | | .04 | .66 | 69.31 | 2437 |
| 10·10 | | 4 | | 26.01 | 2.38 | | 1.23 | 70.56 | 2439 |
| 11·11 | | 9 | | 16.55 | 1.11 | | .41 | 82.01 | 2713 |
| 11·12 | 9 | | 19.51 | | | .07 | .64 | 79.81 | 2798 |
| 13·13 | | 11 | | 11.03 | 5.82 | | .39 | 83.09 | 2311 |
| 13·14 | 7 | | 20.21 | | | .01 | 1.25 | 78.56 | 3671 |
| 14·14 | | 6 | | 19.43 | 2.96 | | .68 | 77.04 | 2779 |
| 15·15 | | 5 | | 20.02 | 3.24 | | .59 | 76.22 | 2717 |
| 15·16 | 8 | | 19.20 | | | .01 | .80 | 79.39 | 2762 |
| 17·17 | | 12 | | 9.95 | 5.76 | | .31 | 83.98 | 3228 |
| 17·18 | 5 | | 23.32 | | | .04 | .45 | 76.22 | 2641 |
| 19·19 | | 1 | | 29.25 | .06 | | .63 | 70.05 | 3350 |
| 19·20 | 12 | | 2.73 | | | .13 | 1.97 | 95.19 | 5561 |
| 21·22 | 4 | | 28.29 | | | | .21 | 71.52 | 2894 |
| 23·24 | 1 | | 31.23 | | | | .08 | 68.72 | 2379 |
| Averages | | | 20.70 | 17.35 | 3.96 | .06 | .63 | 78.35 | |
| $2n$ | | | | | | | .15 | 99.85 | 23,196 |

in 31.23 per cent of its offspring, while the one with the third smallest chromosome extra ranks twelfth, reappearing in only 2.73 per cent of its offspring. The primary with the largest chromosome (1·2) extra ranks tenth in viability. Of the 14 known secondaries, the $2n + 19 \cdot 19$ is first in viability, with a transmission of 29.25 per cent, while the $2n + 1 \cdot 1$ is last, reappearing in only 2.43 per cent of its offspring.

From this table it is clearly evident that the viability, or transmission rate, is not correlated with the size of the chromosome that is carried as an extra. There seems to be no consistent difference between the viability of primaries and secondaries. The average of the viabilities of the primaries is 20.70 per cent, as compared to 17.35 per cent for the secondaries. In some cases the primary may have better viability than a secondary, as the $2n + 3 \cdot 4$ and $2n + 17 \cdot 18$, while in other cases the primary is less viable, as the $2n + 19 \cdot 20$. In the four cases where both secondaries of a primary are known, the $2n + 1 \cdot 2$ is intermediate between its secondaries, the $2n + 5 \cdot 6$ has practically the same viability as one of its secondaries, and two others, the $2n + 9 \cdot 10$ and $2n + 13 \cdot 14$, have greater viability than either secondary.

Most of the $2n + 1$ primaries and secondaries are not transmitted through the pollen. However, certain ones may occasionally reappear following crosses in which the $2n + 1$ type was the male parent. Buchholz has shown that pollen tubes from $1n + 1$ pollen grains grow more slowly than do those from $1n$ grains. By the cutting of styles at the proper times after pollination and discarding the portion containing the faster growing tubes and retaining, by splicing, that part with the slower $1n + 1$ tubes, it has been possible to obtain a high proportion of $2n + 1$ plants in crosses with certain $2n + 1$ types as male parents. This technique is described more fully in Chapter 14 and in the original papers (64, 66, 79).

A glance at Table 4 shows that among the offspring of all the primaries and secondaries there occasionally appear unrelated $2n + 1$ types, both primary and secondary. This is also true among the offspring of diploids. Table 5 shows in percentages the spontaneous appearance of unrelated extra chromosomal types from such parents. The appearance of these unrelated types may be classed as chromosomal mutations. There is a great variability between the various $2n + 1$ types in their capacity to produce these mutations. Of the primaries, the $2n + 19 \cdot 20$ is apparently outstanding in producing new mutations, 1.97 per cent, while the $2n + 3 \cdot 4$ is the poorest in stimulating chromosomal mutations, giving only .04 per cent unrelated types. There seems to be no relation between the size of the chromosome that is extra and the proportion of new types in the offspring. The primaries, however, seem to rank slightly higher than secondaries in their ability to produce such new forms. Primaries throw an average of .71 per cent unrelated types, while secondaries yield only .55 per cent. In only two cases ($2n + 3 \cdot 4$ and $2n + 9 \cdot 10$) does the primary fall below one or both secondaries in this respect. In viability and in their ability to stimulate new chromosomal mutations the primaries are thus not always intermediate between their two secondaries as they are in respect to morphological characters. Both primaries and secondaries rank higher in throwing new $2n + 1$ types than diploids, which gave only 34 $2n + 1$ types among 23,196 offspring (.15 per cent).

Diploids can produce unrelated chromosomal mutations in all 12 sets; primaries and secondaries, however, only in 11. Why the presence of an extra chromosome increases the mutation rate is not entirely clear. The increase is probably brought about by some interference in the regular mechanics of meiotic division that is caused by the extra chromosome. It cannot, however, be directly related to the size of the extra chromosome that is present, as Table 5 clearly shows. Of all the primaries and secondaries, the $2n + 3 \cdot 4$ has the lowest rate of new mutations, .04 per cent, which is approximately a quarter of that obtained from diploids. This particular chromosome may even have an inhibiting effect on the mutation rate.

Since the presence of an extra chromosome in the parent increases the occurrence of unrelated $2n + 1$ types in the offspring, it would be reasonable to expect that two extra chromosomes would still further increase the rate of chromosomal mutation. However, there is some evidence that the opposite is the case. The number of offspring obtained from $2n + 1 + 1$ types is usually small because plants of this type are weak and produce seed only scantily. Among 1,176 offspring from ten different $2n + 1 + 1$ types there appeared only two unrelated types, or .17 per cent. Simple tetrasomic plants ($2n + 1_2$) produce even less seed than do $2n + 1 + 1$ plants. However, the available records do not indicate any increase of mutation rate due to a second extra chromosome in the same set. Among 130 offspring of the tetrasomic $2n + (15 \cdot 16)_2$ there was no new unrelated $2n + 1$ type. The reason why extra chromosomes in two sets or two extra in one set seem to decrease the mutation rate is not apparent.

It has been shown above that the $2n + 1$ types vary greatly in their capacity to produce new chromosomal mutations (unrelated types). Similar data will be used to show which chromosomes are more likely to occur as extras in the formation of spontaneous $2n + 1$ types. The origin of a new $1n + 1$ gamete, which is necessary for the occurrence of a $2n + 1$ zygote, presumably is in the nondisjunction of a single disome, leaving $1n - 1$ daughter cell that will not survive. Since the 12 primary chromosomes differ widely in viability, it is not possible to use without correction the percentage of an unrelated primary in the offspring as an index of the rate at which nondisjunction of the primary chromosome takes place. It has been shown that in the reduction division of a $2n + 1$ plant the chromosomes of pollen mother cells segregate so as to give equal numbers of $1n$ and $1n + 1$ daughter cells. Presumably a similar situation exists in the megaspore mother cells. Equal numbers of $2n$ and $2n + 1$ plants might then be expected in the offspring from a primary $2n + 1$ parent.

That so high a proportion of the parental type is never realized must be due to the elimination of the extra chromosome or of cells containing this chromosome during some stage or stages in the development of the gametophyte or zygote. A viability correction (V.C.) is thus necessary for each primary. This may be derived by dividing the number of non-primaries in the offspring of a primary by the number of parental types. Thus the V.C. for $2n + 1 \cdot 2$ is from Table 4: $2980 \div 421$, or 7.08. The V.C. for the $2n + 19 \cdot 20$ primary is 35.81. By the use of this viability correction factor on the observed occurrences of spontaneous new mutants a calculated nondisjunction (N.D.) rate can be arrived at as follows:

$$\text{N.D.} = \frac{2M \times V.C.}{N + 2M \times V.C.}.$$ Here M represents the observed spontaneous

occurrence of a new primary mutant and the N represents the normals or all individuals except the primary mutant in question. By the use of this formula it is possible to compare the observed mutation rate with the calculated rate of nondisjunction. When this is done, it is found that the rank in frequency of nondisjunction for a particular chromosome may be very different from its rank in percentage of observed spontaneous mutants. Thus on account of the very low viability of the $2n + 19 \cdot 20$ type, the calculated percentage of nondisjunction responsible for the few spontaneous $2n + 19 \cdot 20$ plants is many times the percentage observed.

There seems to be no relation between the size of a chromosome and its chance of taking part in nondisjunction. The largest chromosome is the one most frequently involved in nondisjunction; however, the next three in order of size are those least frequently taking part. The rate of nondisjunction from trisomics, either primaries or secondaries, is apparently significantly higher than from diploids. This would seem to indicate that the presence of an extra chromosome encourages in some way nondisjunction in other sets. In all but one instance the calculated rate of nondisjunction was found to be greater from primaries than from secondaries. Cytological studies have shown that the secondary chromosome may frequently form a "doughnut" at metaphase, which is detached from its related primary chromosomes that pair normally. This fact may be responsible for the lower rate of nondisjunction from secondaries (128).

Most of the secondaries have appeared spontaneously more than once in the Line 1A cultures. They have also appeared spontaneously in other lines. In all the cultures of *Datura* the $2n + 2 \cdot 2$ has occurred 15 times. The $2n + 10 \cdot 10$ is the only secondary that has appeared only once. No *new* secondary has been discovered since 1929. Rarity of secondaries may be due to poor viability after the zygote is formed or to the infrequency of the unusual behavior of the primary chromosomes necessary for their origin.

Secondaries arise spontaneously from unrelated primary parents occasionally but from unrelated secondaries or diploid parents only rarely. They most frequently appear spontaneously in the offspring of related primaries. Positive information is lacking as to the mechanism involved in the origin of secondary chromosomes. Belling suggested that secondary chromosomes might originate from crossing-over between sister strands that lay side by side but with the ends of one reversed. Unequal crossing-over between sister strands so as to retain spindle attachment points for the new secondary chromosomes formed by the joining together of the broken ends of the two similar arms affected may also be a possibility. The secondary chromosome, however formed, could be incorporated into a viable gamete by a process of nondisjunction. There is no known method whereby the occurrence of new secondaries can be increased. It has been impossible to recognize any differences in the appearance of any particular secondary regardless of its spontaneous origin. It is therefore probable that the chromosomal breaks responsible for the origin of secondaries always occur at or near the same points (33).

**Tertiaries.** In addition to the primary and secondary $2n + 1$ forms discussed above, a third class of $2n + 1$ types has been identified in *Datura*. In these *tertiaries* (III's) the extra chromosome is made up of attached parts of two nonhomologous chromosomes, instead of the whole or the doubled half of one chromosome. They appear regularly only in generations following radiation treatment or from hybrids between two races of different prime types (Chapter 4).

The first tertiary recognized in the *Datura* cultures was called Wiry (Wy) on account of its slender erect habit. That it was related to the $2n + 17 \cdot 18$ primary was evident by similarities in appearance, by the fact that $2n + 17 \cdot 18$ plants regularly appeared in its offspring, and by the trisomic ratios it gave for genes known to be located in the $17 \cdot 18$ chromosomes. These Wiry plants were observed only in cultures that came from plants heterozygous for certain races from nature, which, because of unusual breeding behavior, were known as "B" races in distinction from the "A" races to which the standard Line 1A belongs. It was from the cytological study of Wiry that Belling found the clue to the nature of the "B" races and was thus enabled to establish his hypothesis of segmental interchange (40). Prime types with different chromosomes modified by segmental interchange have been found in nature and have been quite readily induced by various treatments. PT 2 has the chromosomes $1 \cdot 18$ and $2 \cdot 17$ instead of $1 \cdot 2$ and $17 \cdot 18$ of the standard Line 1A. Wiry is now designated as the $2n + 1 \cdot 18$ tertiary; the other tertiary derived from the "B" race (PT 2) is $2n + 2 \cdot 17$. These tertiaries might then be considered as primaries if PT 2, instead of Line 1, is taken as the standard.

Tertiaries have appeared spontaneously in the *Datura* cultures only very rarely. In fact, among the approximately two million *Datura* plants grown to adult stage at which a new tertiary could have been recognized, only six instances of such spontaneous occurrences from untreated or homozygous parents have been observed. The rarity of the occurrence of secondaries and tertiaries in these extensive cultures indicates that the individual chromosomes of *Datura* are relatively stable in their natural structure.

Tertiary types have been identified which have as part of the extra tertiary chromosome a half-chromosome (or approximately half) from each of the 12 pairs. In several instances in which the secondary $2n + 1$ type is not known it is possible to obtain an accurate concept of the character of the missing secondary from the appearance of the tertiary having that arm of the chromosome as part of its extra chromosome. In the case of the $2n + 21 \cdot 22$ primary no secondary has ever appeared. From the tertiary types $2n + 3 \cdot 21$ and $2n + 11 \cdot 21$ a good idea of the characters carried by the $\cdot 21$ arm of the $21 \cdot 22$ chromosome may be obtained. There exist also the tertiary types $2n + 4 \cdot 22$ and $2n + 12 \cdot 22$; and with the knowledge obtained from these, from related tertiaries, and from the primary $2n + 21 \cdot 22$, the appearance of the unknown secondaries $2n + 21 \cdot 21$ and $2n + 22 \cdot 22$ can be accurately visualized.

Tertiaries may be used to locate a gene in a particular half of a chromosome and are especially useful in those cases in which one or both secondaries are missing. The various possible combinations of the 24 half-chromosomes make it theoretically possible for 264 different tertiaries, or $2n + $ III types, to occur. By proper breeding procedures about 30 of the most useful of these have been obtained.

Table 6 summarizes the data on the inheritance of eight different

TABLE 6

OFFSPRING OF TERTIARY (III) $2n + 1$ TYPES
(Percentages in parentheses)

| Parents | Total Recordable Plants | 2n Offspring | Parent Type | Primaries a | Primaries b | Secondaries a | Secondaries b | Unrelated Types |
|---|---|---|---|---|---|---|---|---|
| **2n+** | | | | | | | | |
| 1·9 | 2731 | 2289 (83.81) | 393 (14.39) | 14 (0.51) | 27 (0.99) | 1 (0.04) | 2 (0.07) | 5 (0.18) |
| 1·18 | 2094 | 1773 (84.67) | 295 (14.14) | 5 (0.23) | 10 (0.48) | | | 3 (0.14) |
| 2·5 | 2075 | 1360 (65.54) | 665 (32.05) | 16 (0.77) | 21 (1.01) | | 1 (0.05) | 17 (0.81) |
| 2·17 | 2781 | 2210 (79.46) | 553 (19.88) | 12 (0.43) | 2 (0.07) | 1 (0.04) | | 1 (0.04) |
| 4·6 | 2806 | 1966 (70.64) | 821 (29.26) | 1 (0.04) | 3 (0.10) | | 1 (0.04) | |
| 4·22 | 979 | 715 (73.03) | 262 (26.55) | | | | | 1 (0.10) |
| 6·19 | 598 | 433 (72.41) | 159 (26.58) | 5 (0.84) | | | | 2 (0.34) |
| 9·20 | 1428 | 1075 (75.28) | 331 (23.17) | 17 (1.19) | | | | 6 (0.42) |

The header spans: "2n + 1 Offspring" covers Parent Type, Related Types (Primaries a, b; Secondaries a, b), and Unrelated Types. "Related Types" covers Primaries (a, b) and Secondaries (a, b).

tertiaries. These are the ones which have been most extensively used in breeding work. As in the case of the data from primaries and secondaries, these figures are obtained from field-grown cultures only. The records summarized in this table cover the years from 1924 to 1947. Since tertiary chromosomes are composed of parts of chromosomes from two unlike (in terms of L 1A) sets, each tertiary $2n + 1$ type is related to two primary types; these are called $a$ and $b$ in the table, the $a$ being the one having the extra chromosome with the lower end-numbers.

From this table it will be seen that as a result of segregation of chromosomes connected at metaphase these tertiary $2n + 1$ types usually throw, in addition to the parent type, small proportions of both related primaries. The proportion of related primaries in the offspring is much higher than that of other $2n + 1$ types. The tertiaries also occasionally throw plants of the related secondaries. No unrelated secondary has been recorded among the offspring of these tertiaries. As is true in the case of the $2n + 1$ primaries and secondaries, the different tertiaries vary greatly in their viability (reappearance of the parental type) and in their capacity to throw other related or unrelated $2n + 1$ types. Linkage with various genes as well as cytological studies have demonstrated that the chromosomes of these tertiary $2n + 1$ types are constituted as the formulas indicate.

**Compensating Types.** Another group of 25 chromosome types that has proved of special usefulness in gene location work we have called *compensating types.* The first one of these recognized was called Nubbin (Nb). This appeared in 1921 among the offspring of a plant that had been exposed to radium emanation and has not appeared spontaneously since. Its parent was a normal $(2n)$ plant of the standard Line 1 which had been inbred by selfing for nine generations. Its appearance and especially its breeding behavior soon indicated that it belonged to a category of chromosomal types distinct from anything then known in *Datura.*

Among the offspring of Nubbin when selfed or used as a female parent, there regularly appeared a small percentage of two other new types called Pinched and Hedge, both of which were also found to be $2n + 1$ types. A complete analysis of the chromosomal constitution of this new type was published in 1927. By use of the numerical system of labeling chromosome ends, Nubbin can be designated by the following formula: $2n - 1 \cdot 2 + 1 \cdot 9 + 2 \cdot 5$. The missing $1 \cdot 2$ chromosome is thus compensated for by the $\cdot 1$ and $\cdot 2$ arms permanently attached to the $\cdot 9$ and the $\cdot 5$ arms of the $9 \cdot 10$ and $5 \cdot 6$ chromosomes, respectively. The extra chromosomal material is, therefore, the $\cdot 9$ and the $\cdot 5$ arms of these sets. The resulting plant should then demonstrate characters carried by the $\cdot 9$ and $\cdot 5$ halves. This is indeed the case (*44, 45*).

The missing chromosome may be compensated for by two tertiary chromosomes or by a secondary chromosome and a tertiary chromosome. Thus the $1 \cdot 2$ chromosome of the $2n - 1 \cdot 2 + 1 \cdot 1 + 2 \cdot 17$ compensating type is compensated for by a $\cdot 1$ arm of the $1 \cdot 1$ secondary chromosome and by the $\cdot 2$ arm of the $2 \cdot 17$ tertiary chromosome. Compensating types can be formed also when there is a free fragment that can take part in the compensation with a tertiary chromosome, e.g., $2n - 15 \cdot 16 + 15 \cdot 5 + \cdot 16$, or $2n - 21 \cdot 22 + \cdot 21 + 22 \cdot 4$. Of the large number of combinations by which compensating types can be formed, about 50 have appeared or have been purposely synthesized. Two or more have been identified for each of the 12 primary chromosomes. As will be more fully developed in the section on genes and gene location, the compensating types have proved to be particularly useful as a means of locating a new gene in a particular chromosome (Chapter 7). For this reason a special effort has been made to develop a series of compensating types involving all 12 chromosomes.

Compensating types may be obtained in various ways, such as by crossing a prime type to the appropriate secondary $(2n + 1)$ form and obtaining the compensating type in the $F_2$ generation. Thus, when the Line 1A $2n + 3 \cdot 3$ secondary was used as the female in a cross with PT 4, which has the chromosome formula $3 \cdot 21$ and $4 \cdot 22$ instead of $3 \cdot 4$ and $21 \cdot 22$, a $2n + 3 \cdot 3$ plant was obtained that was heterozygous for PT 4. Cytological examination of such an $F_1$ plant would show a circle of five as follows:

$$3 \cdot 3 - 3 \cdot 21 - 21 \cdot 22$$
$$3 \cdot 4 - 4 \cdot 22$$

In the $F_2$ generation, among 76 offspring there were 68 normal diploids, two $2n + 3 \cdot 3$, four plants not completely identified, and two of the desired compensating type $2n - 3 \cdot 4 + 3 \cdot 3 + 4 \cdot 22$

Among the offspring of a diploid plant with a circle of six or more attached chromosomes, one may expect one or more compensating types according to the manner in which the abnormal chromosomes have been modified. Thus, radiation treatment induced a circle of six with the following composition:

$$11 \cdot 12 - 12 \cdot 17 - 17 \cdot 18$$
$$11 \cdot 13 - 13 \cdot 14 - 14 \cdot 18$$

In the next generation a compensating type was obtained in which the $11 \cdot 13$ and the $12 \cdot 17$ tertiary chromosomes compensated for the $11 \cdot 12$ normal chromosome thus: $2n - 11 \cdot 12 + 11 \cdot 13 + 12 \cdot 17$. Circles of six and more chromosomes may be obtained as sources of compensating types by crossing two appropriate prime types. By this method, circles composed of as many as ten chromosomes have been obtained. The larger the number of chromosomes in a circle, the greater the opportunity for the occurrence of compensating types among the offspring.

The breeding behavior of seven representative compensating types is tabulated in Table 7. The records summarized here are taken from field plantings only and are therefore comparable to the figures given for other $2n + 1$ types. These figures are accumulated from cultures grown from 1923 to 1941. Cultures obtained from selfing and from female backcrosses to Line 1A diploids are included. Since a compensating type does not regularly throw the $2n + 1$ primary, the extra chromosome of which is compensated for, the column headed "Related Primaries" includes only those "related" in terms of the tertiary ($a$ and $b$) chromosomes.

**Combination Types.** In addition to the various $2n + 1$, or 25 chromosome types discussed above, there have appeared in the *Datura* cultures a considerable number of forms which are combinations or modifications of the above four types. Besides the primary $2n + 1$ types with a single chromosome extra, combinations of these as double ($2n + 1 + 1$) forms with 26 chromosomes are known. The simplest double type is a combination of any two primaries, thus: $2n + 21 \cdot 22 + 23 \cdot 24$, or, as it was originally known, "Globe-Ilex." Fig. 31 shows capsules of the simple $2n + 21 \cdot 22$ and $2n + 23 \cdot 24$ types and a capsule of the double

TABLE 7

OFFSPRING OF SEVEN REPRESENTATIVE COMPENSATING $2n + 1$ TYPES

(Percentages in parentheses)

| Chromosomal Formula of Parents | Recordable Offspring | 2n | Parent Type | Tertiaries (a and b) | Related Primaries | Unrelated Types |
|---|---|---|---|---|---|---|
| $a \qquad b$ <br> $2n - 1 \cdot 2 + 1 \cdot 9 + 2 \cdot 5$ | 2956 | 1645 (55.64) | 1127 (38.12) | 148 (5.01) | 24 (0.81) | 7 (0.21) |
| $2n - 1 \cdot 2 + 1 \cdot 9 + 2 \cdot 17$ | 2370 | 1534 (64.72) | 722 (30.46) | 79 (3.33) | 27 (1.13) | 3 (0.13) |
| $2n - 5 \cdot 6 + 5 \cdot 15 + 6 \cdot 19$ | 652 | 448 (68.71) | 188 (28.83) | 15 (2.30) | | |
| $2n - 7 \cdot 8 + 7 \cdot 16 + 8 \cdot 22$ | 787 | 501 (63.66) | 239 (30.37) | 42 (5.32) | 1 (0.13) | 3 (0.38) |
| $2n - 9 \cdot 10 + 9 \cdot 13 + 10 \cdot 2$ | 743 | 564 (75.91) | 153 (20.59) | 19 (2.56) | 4 (0.54) | 2 (0.27) |
| $2n - 11 \cdot 12 + 11 \cdot 13 + 12 \cdot 17$ | 1059 | 717 (67.75) | 302 (28.52) | 30 (2.83) | 8 (0.76) | 2 (0.19) |
| $2n - 19 \cdot 20 + 19 \cdot 1 + 20 \cdot 15$ | 472 | 350 (74.15) | 100 (21.19) | 7 (1.48) | 9 (1.91) | 7 (1.48) |

$2n + 21 \cdot 22 + 23 \cdot 24$ type, with a capsule from a normal diploid for comparison. The $21 \cdot 22$ chromosome, among other effects on the mature plant, causes a depressed or globose capsule. The $23 \cdot 24$ chromosome is responsible for small capsules with slender spines. The capsule of the $2n + 21 \cdot 22 + 23 \cdot 24$ type in which both the $21 \cdot 22$ and the $23 \cdot 24$ chromosomes are extra has the globose shape due to the extra $21 \cdot 22$ chromosome and the fine spines and small size brought about by the extra $23 \cdot 24$ chromosome. The characters of the capsule and all other parts of the plant in such double mutant types $(2n + 1 + 1)$ result from the interaction of factors in the two extra chromosomes (86).

These double $2n + 1 + 1$ types have occasionally occurred spontaneously. They are found frequently in the offspring of triploids. Of the 66 different $2n + 1 + 1$ forms involving primaries theoretically possible, 52 have been identified. In these the two extra chromosomes are dissimilar inasmuch as they belong to different pairs. A very few plants have been recorded that have been determined to have an extra chromosome in three different sets. The following are examples: $2n + 13 \cdot 14 + 21 \cdot 22 + 23 \cdot 24$, $2n + 5 \cdot 6 + 11 \cdot 12 + 13 \cdot 14$, and $2n + 9 \cdot 10 + 13 \cdot 14 + 23 \cdot 24$. All these plants have been very small and weak.

Plants with 26 chromosomes, but with the two extra chromosomes of the same pair, have occasionally been found in *Datura*. Thus the

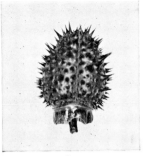

2n

$2n + 21 \cdot 22$       $2n + 21 \cdot 22 + 23 \cdot 24$       $2n + 23 \cdot 24$

FIG. 31. Capsules of a diploid, two primaries, and of the double $2n + 1 + 1$ type.

$2n + (21 \cdot 22)_2$, or "Double Globe" as it was originally called, has two $21 \cdot 22$ or "Globe" chromosomes and shows all the Globe characters to an extreme degree. Such a plant is also very weak because of the extreme unbalance resulting from the two extra chromosomes of the one set. The $2n + (11 \cdot 12)_2$ and $2n + (15 \cdot 16)_2$ types have also been recorded (127).

Secondary and tertiary chromosomes may also take part with related or unrelated primary chromosomes or with related or unrelated secondary chromosomes to produce other $2n + 2$ types. The variety of such combinations is almost limitless. The few examples of these types identified have occurred spontaneously. No effort has been made to accumulate a stock of such types, since they have little use in a breeding program. Examples of some of those that have been identified are: $2n + 15 \cdot 16 + 14 \cdot 14$, $2n + 5 \cdot 5 + 19 \cdot 20$, $2n + 1 \cdot 1 + 11 \cdot 11$, $2n + 21 \cdot 22 + 2 \cdot 5$, and $2n + 5 \cdot 6 + 9 \cdot 20$.

**Sectorial Chimeras.** Plants have occurred with one or more abnormal branches that have been identified as chromosomal deficiencies ($2n - 1$). Such deficiencies may occur on $2n + 1$ plants as well as on diploids. Thus a $2n + 11 \cdot 12$ plant was found with an abnormal branch which was identified by appearance and cytological determinations as $2n + 11 \cdot 12 - 1 \cdot 2$. The deficient branch thus had 24 chromosomes but had only one in the $1 \cdot 2$ set and three in the $11 \cdot 12$ set. Such sectorial chimeras are more fully discussed in Chapter 8. It has been established that nearly all of the deficiencies thus far examined have been caused by the dropping out of the whole, or parts, of one of two specific chromosomes, either the 1 · 2 or the 17 · 18.

**Modified Haploids.** Haploids have occasionally been found with an extra chromosome, or 13 chromosomes in all. Among the 265 haploids that have occurred spontaneously in the *Datura* cultures, five have been recorded as apparently being of this type. Both $1n + I$ (primary) and $1n + II$ (secondary) plants have been identified. In three instances the identifications made by observation of morphological characters have been verified cytologically. The unbalance caused by an extra chromosome in a haploid plant is so severe that the resulting plant is always very small and weak. This, together with the natural weakness of haploids, has made it impossible to get cytological determinations of all.

One of these five modified haploids was recorded as a $1n + 1$ from the appearance of the plant. The plant was small and so poorly developed that the identity of the extra chromosome could not be established from its appearance. One other was recorded as probably a $1n + 5 \cdot 5$. No cytological determinations of either somatic or germ cells were made of these two plants. Another haploid was recorded as a $1n + 13 \cdot 14$ plant and chromosome counts and configurations verified this classification. Another was described as a $1n + 7 \cdot 7$. This plant was small and weak and only somatic cells could be studied cytologically. The number of chromosomes in somatic tissue of buds and root-tips was found to be 13.

The fifth modified haploid was recorded as being probably a $1n + 15 \cdot 15$ plant. This plant was more vigorous than the other four, and it was possible to obtain chromosome counts in somatic tissue and at the first and second division in the megaspore mother cells and pollen cells. Counts in the pollen mother cells and in the megaspore mother cells invariably showed the presence of 13 chromosomes, as in the somatic tissue of the buds. However, all preparations made from root-tips showed 26 chromosomes. All cells examined in the cortex and in the central cylinder were $2n + 2$. This plant was, therefore, a chromosomal chimera; it had haploid buds, both in somatic and sporogenous tissue, but diploid root-tips. Since the plant was small and looked like a modified haploid rather than a modified diploid, it may be assumed that it started as a modified haploid and a portion of it became, by doubling, $2n + 2$ (*124*).

**Modified Triploids and Tetraploids.** The modified diploids discussed above are the most distinct of the extra chromosomal types with the exception of the rare modified haploids. Triploids or tetraploids may occur with one or more extra chromosomes. The addition of a single extra chromosome to a $3n$, or to a $4n$ type, brings about relatively little change in the appearance of the plant. However, $3n$ or $4n$ types may be strongly modified by the addition of a larger number of chromosomes than is possible in the diploid ($2n$) series. Thus, a $4n + (21 \cdot 22)_2$

(Globe) is as distinct as the $2n + 21 \cdot 22$ and a $4n + (21 \cdot 22)_3$ plant has been obtained that shows the Globe characters to nearly the extreme degree that the $2n + (21 \cdot 22)_2$ does.

Likewise, deficiencies may occur in $3n$'s and $4n$'s with less detriment to the plant. Furthermore, deficiencies may be transmitted by the sex cells of $4n$ parents, since the normal sex cells of $4n$ plants are $2n$. A $2n - 1$ sex cell would be a deficiency but might be viable, since it would have at least one chromosome of each kind. A $4n$ plant has been cytologically determined as $4n + 1 + 1 - 1 - 1$. This plant thus had a total of 48 chromosomes, but in each of two sets there were five instead of four and in two other sets there were three. Among plants obtained following colchicine treatment a "$4n$" plant was found which had only three chromosomes in six different sets, or 42 chromosomes in all (135).

**Summary.** By means of extra chromosomes and parts of chromosomes, it has been possible to secure a wide range of variations in *Datura*. These variations affect the structure of all parts of the plants that have been studied. Some of these extra chromosomal types (e.g., the $2n + 1$ secondaries) have occurred only spontaneously and efforts to induce their appearance have failed. Others, such as the 12 $2n + 1$ primaries, may be readily obtained from triploids; and others, such as the compensating types and tertiaries, may be synthesized by crossing appropriate prime types or by crossing prime types to the proper secondaries.

While some of these extra chromosomal types are neither of much value in further breeding work nor of much theoretical interest, others, such as the primaries, secondaries, tertiaries, and compensating types, have been of the greatest value in the study of *Datura* genetics. *Datura* is probably not an exception among plants in being capable of producing large numbers of visible variations as a result of major changes in the amount of specific chromosomal material. Probably other plants sufficiently adapted to breeding experiments would show similar results when adequately investigated. There is evidence that certain select horticultural varieties of some plants, which have been continued in their original form by vegetative propagation, may be the result of the presence of extra chromosomal material. As has been demonstrated in *Datura*, extra chromosomal types will not breed true. Such types, however, may be maintained by grafts, cuttings, or other methods of vegetative propagation. By such means, horticulturists of the past have unwittingly propagated desirable chromosomal types, which were only later recognized as such when studied cytologically. In the future, types with extra chromosomes may be deliberately sought as a source of desirable variations in other plants of economic importance.

# 7

# Gene Mutations

## A. G. Avery

In the wild condition the various species of *Datura* rarely show any characters that segregate in a Mendelian manner. Despite the large amount of breeding work with *D. stramonium*, only two allelomorphic pairs of characters, purple *vs.* white flowers and spiny *vs.* smooth capsules, had been described in the literature previous to 1919, when the first of the many new mutations observed by our group was reported (*6*). Early in the work it was considered important to have a large collection of suitable genes by which the various chromosomes and parts of chromosomes could be tagged. Toward that end there has been gradually accumulated a large number of new types that carry mutant genes derived from natural or experimental sources. These types have become available as a result of more careful study of variants or rare spontaneous mutations in material already available. They have also been obtained from extensive new collections from many parts of the world or from hybridization with other species. A large number have been obtained from germ cells or seeds exposed to radiation or other physical and chemical treatments, or from aged seed or pollen. Naudin, Godron, de Vries, and Bateson had only the two pairs of alternative characters with which to work, whereas we have had several hundred usable mutants available to use as tools or testers. *Datura* now probably displays a larger number of distinguishable types due to gene mutations than any other species of plants except corn (*Zea*).

Blakeslee found that the two pairs of contrasting characters, purple *vs.* white flowers and spiny *vs.* smooth capsules, made excellent material with which to demonstrate the simple Mendelian laws of inheritance to his classes in genetics at the Connecticut Agricultural College (now the University of Connecticut) at Storrs. In 1917 figures were published giving the results of breeding work involving hybrids between these forms. The figures confirmed the results of the earlier workers and in different crossing experiments the actual numbers closely approached expectations for the 1:1, 3:1, 1:1:1:1, and 9:3:3:1 ratios (*3*). Since that time large numbers of offspring of hybrids involving these characters have been grown. Both pairs of characters have since been located in particular chromosomes (17·18 and 11·12) and linkage data with other genes have been accumulated (30).

In 1919 a third pair of contrasting factors, tall *vs.* short habit, was reported. The short (few-noded) type had been extracted from plants grown from seed obtained from a commercial seed source in Germany. This was the first of the many new gene types that appeared in the *Datura* cultures. The total number of gene pairs that have been found to show the dominant-recessive relation or have been tentatively so classified, is nearly 550. In *Datura*, as in other organisms, nearly all the new mutations that have appeared spontaneously or as a result of various treatments, have been found to be recessive. In fact, only four gene mutations that are dominant to the usual wild condition have been recognized (6).

**Description and Classification.** Specific genes affecting all parts of the plant have been identified in *Datura*. Among the genes that have the most marked effects on the plant are those which determine the color, shape, and size of the cotyledons; color of the stems; growth habits; flower shape, size, and color; leaf shape and texture; capsule form; length of time to maturity; and seed color (Figs. 32 to 35). In addition there are a considerable number of others that produce no gross or visible change in the plant and for the identification of which special techniques are needed. The latter group is largely composed of genes affecting pollen abortion and pollen-tube growth, as also certain male or female sterility genes, or genes for other pollen types. In Table 8 the 541 genes that have been identified in *Datura* are grouped according to the most obvious characters displayed. The source or treatment from which these mutations originally appeared is also shown. It is clear that no particular treatment can be expected to produce any definite kind of mutation.

The genes differ greatly in their value as labels by which chromosome behavior can be followed. Those which are especially valuable are the genes for green stems and certain of the "pales," since they do not adversely affect the growth of the plant and yet are recognizable in early seedling stages. A character such as red seed, while not detrimental to the plant, cannot be recorded until seed capsules have matured, a period of about four months. Others, like the albinos and extreme pales, while recordable early, produce weak plants or are not viable beyond the seedling stage. If breeding work is to be done with such weak or nonviable types, it is usually necessary to use as parents plants that are heterozygous for the character. This greatly adds to the time and material involved in any breeding project. Certain of the homozygous albinos have been made available for breeding work by the laborious method of grafting the albino seedlings onto normal green stock. By this method a few of the different races of albinos will produce healthy but pale leaves, flowers, capsules, and viable seed if the stock is allowed to bear normal leaves to carry on photosynthesis for the parasitic scion (Fig. 32d).

## TABLE 8

### Classification and Source of Gene Mutations

| Characters by Classes | Total Recognized | Genes Located in Specific Chromosomes | Source or Treatment | | | | | | | | |
|---|---|---|---|---|---|---|---|---|---|---|---|
| | | | Nature | Spontaneous in Cultures | Aging or Heating | Wounding | X-rays | Gamma Rays | Thermal Neutrons | Cyclotron | Nuclear Detonation |
| Albino | 69 | 4 | 2 | 3 | 3 | | 38 | 10 | 4 | 3 | 8 |
| Pale | 91 | 10 | 2 | 5 | 5 | | 55 | 9 | 5 | 6 | 4 |
| Leaf forms | 127 | 15 | 2 | 3 | 7 | 1 | 89 | 8 | 9 | 4 | 4 |
| White flowers | 8 | 3 | 1 | | 1 | | 3 | | | | 2 |
| Wilted | 15 | 3 | | | 1 | | 12 | 1 | | | |
| Capsule forms | 15 | 4 | 2 | 1 | 1 | | 7 | 3 | | | 1 |
| Cotyledon forms | 14 | 2 | | 2 | 3 | 2 | 5 | 1 | | | |
| Habit types | 144 | 8 | 3 | 1 | 9 | 3 | 106 | 14 | 1 | 2 | 1 |
| Male steriles | 7 | 1 | | 1 | | | 5 | 1 | 5 | | |
| Pollen abortion * | 30 | 16 | 1 | 1 | 4 | | 17 | 7 | | | |
| Other pollen types | 4 | 4 | 2 | | | | | 2 | | | |
| Pollen-tube types | 11 | 7 | | | | | 3 | 8 | | | |
| Miscellaneous | 6 | 4 | | | | | 4 | 1 | | | 1 |
| Totals | 541 | 81 | 15 | 17 | 34 | 6 | 344 | 65 | 24 | 15 | 21 |

* Many "pollen-abortion" types observed directly following various treatments are not included in this table. These figures include only those that have been tested by further breeding work.

112

FIG. 32. Recessive gene mutations in *D. stramonium*. (a) Bunchy; (b) pale; (c) rough-5; (d) albino, grafted on normal stock.

Among the commonest visible mutant types are those with some degree of chlorophyll deficiency. There is no sharp distinction between those characters grouped as albinos and those which we have called pales. In general those classed as albinos do not survive the seedling stage without special care, as just mentioned. The pales range from extremely weak plants practically devoid of chlorophyll and which may never produce flowers to healthy plants recordable as pales only under the most ideal conditions (Fig. 34c, g). In one case a weak pale type (pale-24, Fig. 33d), which is barely able to survive on its own roots, grows vigorously and produces normal green leaves when grafted on normal stock. The inhibition to growth and formation of normal chlorophyll in this case seems to be located in the root system of the pale mutant.

One of the pale mutants is of special interest on account of its apparently unusual chlorophyll. In 1938 O. L. Inman of the Charles F. Kettering Foundation made preliminary spectroscopic determinations of the chlorophylls of a considerable number of the chromosomal mutant types of *Datura* and especially of the gene mutants that showed visible color differences, such as the pales and the albinos. The chlorophyll of all the mutants so examined, with one exception, gave a spectrum in agreement with that of normal chlorophyll-*a* and chlorophyll-*b*, which are the only chlorophylls that have been found in other higher plants. The single exception was a rather weak pale (pale-7) mutant, which first appeared in 1930 among the offspring of a plant grown from seed that had been exposed to x-rays (Fig. 33c). Pale-7 is a very distinct type with yellow- or olive-colored leaves. In the field the homozygous recessives are very weak and seldom reach flowering stage. When grown in the greenhouse, pale-7 plants are fairly vigorous and abundant seed may be obtained. By trisomic ratios it has been found that pale-7 is located in the ·1 arm of the 1·2 chromosome. Plants heterozygous for the gene are not visibly different in leaf color from other normal plants, nor does a spectroscopic test show any unusual chlorophyll condition.

Inman found the absorption spectrum of extracts of pale-7 leaves to be different from that of all other known leaves. Purified extracts showed the same differences as the crude material. From spectroscopic and chemical tests it was concluded that the chlorophylls of pale-7 were isomeric forms of the normal chlorophylls *a* and *b*. Microchemical analyses of the composition of the molecule were not undertaken. This would be needed for a final determination of the nature of this chlorophyll. In the period 1946 to 1948, A. F. Johnson (1948) continued the researches on the chlorophyll of pale-7 at the Charles F. Kettering Foundation. His findings, largely confirming those of Inman, indicated that the green pigments of pale-7 are more complex than of other higher plants. The spectroscopic properties of several of these pigments were investigated and none of them were found to be identical to chlorophyll-*a* or *b* or their derivatives. The principal pigment of pale-7 was analyzed and found to be related to chlorophyll-*a* (*130*).

A few other mutant types of particular interest may be noted. Some, such as the gene that changes the normally dicarpel ovary to a tricarpel,

(a)

(b)

(c)

(d)

Fig. 33. Recessive gene mutations in *D. stramonium*. (a) zigzag; (b) quercina; (c) pale-7; (d) pale-24.

and that which changes the black seed to red, as well as the classic ones for white flowers and inermis capsules, alter characters that have been used to distinguish species and even genera taxonomically. The gene for the tricarpel character (tc) has been located in the 15·16 (Reduced) chromosome. When a heterozygous plant is used as the male parent in backcrosses, a deficiency of tricarpel plants always occurs. Buchholz found that bursting of tc pollen tubes in the stylar tissue was the reason for this unusual breeding behavior (*48, 49*).

At least four mutations resulting in white flowers have appeared in addition to the original wild white. Two of these white-flowered forms have normal purple stems as does the original purple-flowered type. That these are different genes producing somewhat similar effects has been proved by inter-se crosses and by the fact that they have been located in different chromosomes. These have all occurred spontaneously or after treatment within our highly inbred Line 1A of *D. stramonium* (139).

Several independent genes are responsible for the "wilt" condition. Plants in the field homozygous for any one of these genes become very wilted in sunlight despite an abundance of moisture in the soil. Potted plants in the greenhouse show the condition to a much lesser degree. Sinnott found that these "wilts" have a poorly developed vascular system, which appears to be inadequate to meet the demands of rapid transpiration in sunlight (99).

A large number of mutations has occurred that result in various habit variations. Some of them, if not too extreme, are very useful as genetic tools, such as "zigzag" (Fig. 33a). Others, of which the prostrate type called "lazy" is an example, are so weak in growth that they do not produce flowers and so are of little genetic use (Figs. 32a, 34d, e, g). One small type is so modified that it can hardly be recognized as a *Datura*. This type rarely attains a height of more than 6 inches, has linear leaves resembling pine needles, and was named "equisetum" (Figs. 34f, 35a). Flowers with viable pollen are occasionally produced. There are compact, dwarf, spreading, early and late maturing forms that have proved to be excellent genetic testers.

There are several mutations that seem to affect the form or color of the cotyledons only; the mature plants of these are indistinguishable from normals. While they have little adverse effect on the plant, these are somewhat difficult to handle in large segregating cultures, for the young seedlings must be individually marked if it is necessary to grow them to maturity to record their adult characters.

A recessive gene that appeared following the exposure of seed to x-rays is recordable only by observation of insect injury. Normal *D. stramonium* plants are only moderately susceptible to injury by flea-beetles, of which *Epitrix cucumeris* is a common example. Plants homozygous for this character appear to be especially attractive to the beetles and segregating cultures are easily recorded in any season that the beetles are numerous. The normal resistant condition appears to be completely dominant, and 3:1 or 1:1 ratios are closely approached. It is not known what change has taken place to make the recessive plants more attractive to the beetles. Change in sap composition, texture of the leaf or its epidermis, or odor, are possibilities. The gene responsible for this character has not been located in a specific chromosome.

One of the recessive mutant types closely resembles the effects of a particular virus disease. Many years ago a type was found that was first thought to be a gene mutation, but which later proved to be due to

Fig. 34. Normal (a) *D. stramonium* and seven recessive gene mutations; (b) slender capsules; (c) pale-20; (d) lazy; (e) blind; (f) equisetum; (g) pale-29; (h) short.

the effect of a virus disease that may be propagated from one *Datura* plant to another by grafting. This was called "quercina" on account of its eroded leaves, which resemble the leaves of certain oaks. From seed exposed to x-rays a recessive mutant type appeared, which is almost indistinguishable from plants severely infected with the quercina disease. When the quercina gene type is grafted on normal stock, no visible effect on the stock is produced. Both quercina forms have deeply eroded leaves, smooth instead of spiny capsules, and petals that are separated from each other instead of united as in the normal form (Figs. 33b, 35b). It has been found that in the young buds the developing petals take the form of a horseshoe by the more rapid growth of the outer side and hence the petals are never able to meet and unite at their edges as they do in normals. In neither the virus infection nor the gene mutation is there a separation of the lobes of the calyx. The similarity of the end results

Fig. 35. (a) Equisetum, a recessive mutation in *D. stramonium*.

suggests that both the virus particle and the gene bring about their like effects by a similar change at some point in the development of the bud (*11, 152*).

There is a large number of gene mutants that affect male or female sterility to a greater or lesser degree. There are types that are male sterile and female fertile as well as types that are both male and female sterile. Of particular interest and of considerable use as genetic testers are the genes that cause abortion of the pollen grains without affecting the viability of the egg cells. These pollen-abortion (pa) genes have been extremely useful in locating new genes in particular chromosomes or at particular loci. They can be used in determining the position of other genes within a given chromosome through linkages without the difficulties encountered in working with double recessives.

In addition to the pollen-abortion genes there are a number of mutations involving pollen formation or pollen form. Two such genes have been found in cultures obtained from seed collected in the wild. One of these prevents the pairing of the homologous chromosomes at meiosis. Since it was obtained from Baltimore, Maryland, it is called "Baltimore-bad" (bd). Plants homozygous for this recessive gene are characterized by large pollen grains and a high proportion of aborted pollen (92 to 98 per cent). These homozygous plants are easily recognized in the

FIG. 35. (Continued.) (b) Quercina.

field because of their sterility—both male and female. Such plants produce only small capsules with only abortive ovules; and they will continue flowering until killed by frost. Aside from the peculiarities directly connected with the inability to set capsules, there is no obvious difference in appearance between these plants and normals. Pollen from such plants has induced the formation of a few viable seeds when applied to stigmas of tetraploids. This fact, as well as chromosomal studies, is evidence that there are produced some $2n$ pollen grains with twice the normal number of chromosomes. Meiotic divisions and pollen in plants heterozygous for this gene are normal (85, 88).

A recessive that has been located by trisomic and linkage ratios in the $\cdot 12$ arm of the $11 \cdot 12$ chromosome was found in a culture grown from seed sent from Kompolt, Hungary. This gene, when homozygous, causes doubling and twinning of the chromosomes at meiosis. When the doubling occurs early in microsporogenesis, twin nuclei are formed. In both single and twin nuclei further doubling may take place, producing nuclei that may contain as many as 96 chromosomes. A further peculiarity is that the normal bivalent arrangement may be retained instead of the usual formation of tetravalents in $4n$ cells. Cells have been found that contain at metaphase 12 or 24 tetravalents or 12, 24, or 48 bivalents. Formation of four, six, or eight pollen grains from one pollen mother cell has been observed. These contain 12, 24, or 48 chromosomes each. The meiotic reduction must be regular because very few aborted pollen grains are found. Plants heterozygous for the gene show no irregularity in the division processes (68).

Another recessive mutation that affects cell division was obtained after radium treatment of pollen. This gene causes a doubling of chromosomes at meiosis, through the formation of dyads instead of tetrads of pollen grains because of the failure of the second meiotic division. This gene, called "dyad," is located in the $9 \cdot 10$ chromosome. A dyad plant when selfed gives rise to some dyad tetraploids in which the somatic tissue is $4n$ and the pollen grains have 48 chromosomes. Among the offspring of such a plant there have occurred weak plants presumably of the hexaploid type, since chromosome counts of approximately 72 have been obtained (83, 108).

There are several genes that in the recessive condition affect the apparent shape or condition of the pollen grains at the time of the dehiscence of the anthers. Few of these have been of much genetic usefulness, since most of them are rather difficult to record. One, which is characterized by pollen that begins to germinate and show pollen tubes while still in the anther, has been located in the $13 \cdot 14$ chromosome. Other genes of this sort affect the starch content of the pollen grains or their shape. In one case there is such a pronounced effect on the shape of the pollen grains that the character has been called "bean-shaped pollen." In another type the pollen consists of 50 to 75 per cent aborted grains, while the rest appear either as large grains or as more or less nondivided tetrads. This has been called "compound pollen." In this case some pollen grains are functional and it has therefore been possible to obtain homozygous individuals.

Genes that affect the growth or behavior of the pollen tubes are numerous. The genetic result of some of these is similar to that of the pollen-abortion genes, since pollen grains carrying the gene are ineffective in fertilization, and, like the pollen-abortion genes, are transmitted through half the egg cells only. Several of these have been located in particular chromosomes and later were used as testers. While about 40 different pollen-tube genes were identified by Buchholz, only a few have been extensively investigated. Seven of these have been located in six different chromosomes. Genes of this class are lethal only to the male gametophytes that carry them. Therefore only half of the pollen tubes from a heterozygous plant show the character. The most distinct of these types are characterized by pollen tubes that grow very slowly or by tubes that grow slowly and burst early in the tissue of the style. Included with these pollen-tube types is a type called "lobed-pollen" (lp) in which the pollen grains carrying the gene ordinarily fail to germinate on the stigma. These ungerminated grains become swollen at the germ pores of each pollen grain, causing the "lobed" appearance. The special techniques needed to identify plants heterozygous for these pollen-tube genes are so tedious that they are not usually used as genetic testers (65, 114).

REVERSE OR BACK MUTATIONS. Only one of the many recessive genes of *Datura* has ever been observed to undergo reversion to its dominant allelomorph. This has occurred in plants heterozygous for the mutant "swollen," which was obtained in 1922 following the first radiation exposures. The recessive is easily recognized by its small size and by its short, thick, and brittle stems. The gene responsible for the character is located in the smallest $(23 \cdot 24)$ chromosome.

Several cases of the failure of recessives to appear among offspring of plants heterozygous for "swollen" have occurred. Such parents have been tested when possible by planting seed from other capsules from the same plant. Numerous cases have been studied in which the seeds from one capsule of a heterozygous plant threw offspring segregating for swollen, but the seeds from another capsule of the same plant failed to produce any. In one case pollen failed to transmit the gene, while it was transmitted by the egg cells of the same flower. In two cases the parent was a heterozygous $2n + 23 \cdot 24$ and threw the $2n + 1$ type in the usual proportion even from the capsule from which no recessives were recovered. This, and the fact that no visible chromosomal deficiency was observed in any of the parents, indicates that the peculiar behavior was not due to chromosomal elimination but was a true reversion. Swollen has never been known to revert in the homozygous condition.

**The Origin and Induction of Mutations.** The collection of genes in *Datura,* some of which have been described above, has been assembled from many sources. The first *Datura* plants investigated genetically at

Storrs came from seed, the original source of which is unknown, supplied by the United States Department of Agriculture. This seed gave cultures that segregated for purple- and white-flowered plants. The recessive "inermis" was first grown from seed obtained in 1914 from a commercial seed company in Germany. It should be noted here that inermis races have been obtained only from botanical gardens or commercial seed dealers. Somewhat similar inermis forms have appeared in our own cultures following radiation treatments. The dominant character Bronze first appeared in plants grown from seed from the Stockholm (Sweden) Botanical Garden. Two other races of Bronze were obtained from two botanical gardens in Germany and both were found to be genetically identical to that from Sweden. An early maturing and low-growing race has also been obtained from European botanical gardens. It is now impossible to ascertain where these distinct races, which have been in cultivation for so many years, originally arose. It may be assumed that some of them, at least, arose as spontaneous mutations and have since been disseminated by the exchange of seed between botanical gardens. Some of these forms in cultivation have been long continued under specific names, as: D. "inermis" (smooth capsules), D. "laevis" or D. "bertolonii" (white flowers and smooth capsules).

Over the years a great many collections of plants, or seed, of wild Daturas from many parts of the world have been made by members of our group. In addition, many collections have been made for us from still other localities. In spite of the usual uniformity in appearance of races of D. stramonium, these collections from the wild have yielded a few characters that are the result of gene mutations. A race that is ordinarily tri-forked instead of di-forked was collected in Cuba; a genetically equivalent type was found in Australia. A distinct race with very deeply serrated leaves was collected near Naples, Italy. The gene responsible for this "ragged" condition, as it was called, is located in the $23 \cdot 24$ chromosome. The character "slender capsules" was discovered in a single plant near Petersburg, Virginia (Fig. 34b). The recessive gene causing this character is located in the $21 \cdot 22$ chromosome. Also located in the $21 \cdot 22$ chromosome is the gene for "pale-1," the designation given to a pale-leaved type collected near Angol, Chile (88). Nearly 1,400 collections of D. stramonium from widely scattered locations, representing all continents and nearly all major countries of the temperate zones, have been investigated. Only 15 (including the types from botanical gardens) of these have yielded distinguishable types that have proved to be mutations from the normal type. This is evidence of the stability of the species under natural conditions.

Mutations yielding many distinct new forms of a wide variety have been readily induced in our material by various treatments in the laboratory. A few new types have occurred as segregates in cultures which have not followed any treatment likely to cause mutations. In 1933 among the offspring of a secondary $2n + 6 \cdot 6$ of the highly inbred Line 1A there appeared a new pale (pl-16). Such spontaneous mutations have occurred only very rarely. There have been recorded only five or six such occurrences of new types from untreated material among the many thousand cultures grown from selfings.

Some efforts have been made to extract distinct characters due to single genes from species hybrids. The only useful gene obtained from this source is one for white flowers derived from a cross of *D. stramonium × D. ferox*. This form is characterized by having purple stems below the cotyledons and green stems above and by producing white flowers. The gene responsible for this mutation is located in the 3·4 chromosome and the seedlings differ in appearance from the white of *D. stramonium* in that they have purple stems when emerging from the soil.

Intentional and controlled treatments of growing plants, dry seed and pollen by various agents have yielded an abundance of new types, many of which have been found to be the result of gene mutations. Cartledge found that aging may be responsible for an increase in the mutation rate. Among the offspring of plants grown from seed "aged" in the laboratory, the appearance of new pollen abortion types was found to increase from about 1 per cent among offspring from seed less than 2 years old to 7 or 8 per cent among plants from seed 8 to 10 years old. Under ordinary conditions of laboratory storage *Datura* seed is not viable for more than 10 to 11 years (*94*).

A limited series of experiments by Cartledge with pollen that had been aged from 4 to 13 days before its use in pollination showed that there was also a higher mutation rate, as shown by the pollen-abortion index, among plants from pollinations made with the oldest pollen (*107*). It was found in the case of seed that temperature and moisture were factors directly influencing the mutation rate. Mutation rates were increased by the increased moisture content of the seed, by increased temperature, as well as by increased duration of the treatments. Within the limits of the experiments, heat treatment of the seeds did not yield as high mutation rates as aging under ordinary laboratory conditions. In addition to mutations identified only by pollen abortion a few distinct morphological types that have been determined to be gene mutations have resulted from the aged seed, aged pollen, or heated seed experiments. A "wilt" (wt-3) type appeared in the $F_2$ from pollen aged 10 days; a dwarf, "bunchy," type from pollen aged 25 days. A similar "bunchy" mutant appeared in the offspring of a plant that was grown from seed "aged" for nine and a half years in ordinary laboratory storage. A type with curled cotyledons (c-4) appeared in offspring of a plant grown from seed held at 5 per cent moisture and 75° C for 24 hours (*115, 116*).

In 1941, 367 seeds of *D. stramonium* were received from the U. S. Department of Agriculture. These had been buried in the ground in 1902 as part of an experiment to test the viable life of a considerable number of crop and weed seeds. Excellent germination was obtained from these 39-year-old seed; 358 seedlings (97.5 per cent) were recorded. The following year offspring from 78 of these plants were grown and examined for possible new types. Four (5.1 per cent) were found to segregate for new characters that were later shown to be due to gene mutations. These results, as well as others obtained from seed buried in the ground for 22 years, would seem to indicate that the high mutation rate obtained from seeds aged in the laboratory may be the result of factors other than age alone. It is fairly clear that high temperature is one of these factors inducing mutation in aged seed (*106, 157, 211,* Chapter 9).

A few unsuccessful experiments have been undertaken to test the effects of various chemicals in inducing gene mutations. Among the first chemicals so tested was chloral hydrate. Solutions of the chemical were injected into young buds, flowers, and small capsules. Controls at the same stages were pricked with a needle without injection of the chemical. Following these treatments, several mutations, both chromosomal and gene, appeared. Since similar results were obtained following the pricking without injection of the chemical, it was assumed that the effects were induced mechanically (*55*).

Extensive tests have been conducted to determine whether colchicine, which is so effective in bringing about doubling of chromosomes, has any influence on gene mutation. These tests have given no evidence that colchicine has any effect on mutation rate as measured by pollen abortion or the appearance of new morphological types.

As related in Chapter 5, there is a tendency for *Datura* haploids to produce new mutations at a slightly higher rate than diploid controls. From 533 plants that were the direct offspring of haploids, eight mutations—seven recessive and one dominant—have been recovered. Six of the most useful of these have been located in specific chromosomes.

In *Datura*, as in other species of plants and animals in which extensive attempts have been made intentionally to increase the natural mutation rate, either chromosomal or genic, the exposure to some form of radiation has proved to be the most productive method. The radiation experiments with *Datura* are discussed in detail in Chapter 9. Only the results of these experiments carried on from 1921 to 1954 in yielding an extensive collection of new gene mutations will be reviewed here.

The first treatments involving radiant energy were begun in 1921. In these experiments flower buds, flowers, and young capsules were exposed to the radiation. While a marked increase in the proportion of $2n + 1$ types was observed among the offspring, only a few of these were tested by selfing to determine if gene mutations had occurred. Offspring were obtained from 18 of these and 2 were found to be heterozygous for two new types. These two new forms, an albino and a short swollen-stemmed type (both later shown to be the result of gene mutations), were the first of many that have since appeared following various radiation treatments.

In 1927 Buchholz began an extensive series of radium experiments. The experimental procedure was planned in such a way that there would be less likelihood of $2n + 1$ types appearing than in the 1921 experiments. Mature pollen and pollen tubes were selected as the stages in the life cycle to be treated with radium. This technique of treating male haploid stages gave very few $2n + 1$ forms. However, over half of the plants that resulted from the fertilization of untreated eggs of normal females by treated pollen were abnormal in appearance. Most of these abnormalities were found to be due to chromosomal deficiencies. Many plants, both normal and abnormal in appearance, also showed abnormal chromosomal configurations when examined cytologically. From the experiments in which pollen was exposed to radium before pollination some 20 new recessive types were obtained. These included such morphological types as bunchy, albinos, pales, and rough-leaved forms, as well as pollen-abortion and other pollen types. New types were also obtained from plants following radium treatment of the styles or young ovaries after pollination. It was not possible to carry out sufficiently extensive experiments involving radium treatment of dry mature seed to find the optimum dosage. Most of the exposures given completely inhibited germination. Of 14 plants obtained from seed given a short exposure, 2 were found to be heterozygous for new morphological types.

As related in Chapter 9, the exposure of mature seed to x-ray radiation has produced many mutations of the gene type. Dosages of 6,000 to 20,000 roentgens have been used without materially lowering the germination rate of the seed. Since the radiation of seed may affect any of the many cells of the embryo, the resulting plants are often found to have sectors affected differently. Individual capsules from a single plant may show segregation for none, one, or more new types. In general a corresponding increase in gene mutation rate has been observed as the dosages have been increased. From the highest dosages (17,500 to 20,000 roentgens) to which seed has been exposed a mutation rate of nearly 80 per cent has been obtained.

Seed exposed to thermal neutrons, nuclear detonations, or to neutrons in a cyclotron produced plants yielding mutations in about the same frequency as those exposed to x-rays. A classification of all the new genic types that have appeared following the various radiation treatments indicates that there is no specific effect of the different forms of energy in the production of mutations. Albinos, pales, and other seedling types are the most common forms observed following any mutation-inducing treatment.

**Location of Genes in Specific Chromosomes.** From the early years of the *Datura* work it has been considered important to have available a number of genes located in all the 12 chromosomes. Such located genes are essential as testers, or labels, for chromosomes and parts of chromosomes. The use of these labels has helped in establishing many important facts of *Datura* genetics. No attempts have been made to locate many of the genes responsible for the more than 500 recessive mutations that have been recognized. Only those mutations that possess distinct characteristics and are also reasonably vigorous and of such a sort as to be most usable in crosses, have been intensively worked with. Genes responsible for 81 distinct mutations have been located in specific chromosomes. These include representatives from all the 13 artificial classes into which the mutations have been grouped (Table 8). The location of genes in particular chromosomes for the purpose of mapping has never been of major importance in the *Datura* investigations.

Genes responsible for recognized characters have been located in all the 12 chromosome pairs. The chromosome with the fewest known genes is the $7 \cdot 8$, which has only three, while the $3 \cdot 4$ chromosome, with the most, has eleven. Forty-two of the genes located in specific chromosomes have been definitely placed in particular half-chromosomes. All except 6 of the 24 arms are now labeled by having one or more genes for recognizable characters.

**METHODS.** For the location of genes in particular chromosomes, or in particular parts of chromosomes, several independent methods have been utilized. Some of these methods have been developed in the work with *Datura* and have been found to be especially economical in respect to the breeding material and time needed to complete the necessary tests. The following five methods have been used: (1) linkage with other genes of known position; (2) trisomic ratios from various $2n + 1$, primary, secondary, or tertiary types; (3) linkage with compensating types; (4) linkage with pollen-abortion (pa) genes; (5) linkage with certain prime types (PT's) that show a definite proportion of aborted pollen in the heterozygous condition. Each of these various methods is of special value in particular circumstances. These methods will be described briefly in the following paragraphs.

Genes may be located in particular chromosomes by determining their linkage in disomic inheritance with other previously located genes. This is the oldest and best known of the methods usually followed. It has been in general use for many years, having been given considerable impetus by the investigations of gene location in *Drosophila* initiated by Morgan and his colleagues. Partly because of the large amount of material and time needed, and since other more effective ones have been available, this method has not been generally used to locate *Datura* genes in their proper chromosomes. In cases in which it has been established that a certain gene is located in a given chromosome, its exact position within the chromosome may be determined by linkage figures with two or more other genes. For this purpose it is necessary to obtain plants homozygous for both recessive characters. In *Datura* many of the gene mutations are of such a nature that the homozygous recessive plants are weak. When two or more recessive characters are combined, the resulting plants are often too weak to use effectively in breeding work. Two genes may be located in the same chromosome but, if they are not rather closely linked, the linkage figures obtained by this method may not positively prove that linkage exists, even when very large numbers of offspring are grown. Since many characters are recordable only when the plants are mature, this is often impractical. These are some of the reasons why other, more effective, methods have been used to determine the location of genes in *Datura*.

For locating genes in a particular chromosome the preferred method in *Datura* has been that of trisomic ratios from heterozygous primary $2n + 1$ types (Chapter 6). Thirty-eight of the 81 genes that have been definitely located in specific chromosomes were located by this method. This method is suitable for testing all gene mutations except those that do not produce viable pollen or that for other reasons cannot be transmitted through the pollen. The method is simple, usually reliable, and is independent of the effects on ratios of viability, vitality, or crossing-over due to the simultaneous presence of a second gene.

The heterozygous primary $2n + 1$ types may be readily obtained by crossing the recessive to be located onto a L 1A triploid ($3n$). Among the offspring of such a cross there will be plants of all the $2n + 1$ primaries if sufficient numbers are grown (Chapter 5). These will all be heterozygous for the gene in question and may be used directly in backcrosses or selfed.

These heterozygous $2n + 1$ plants are usually both male and female backcrossed to the recessive. Male backcrosses avoid the necessity of recording the $2n + 1$ types in the backcross generation and are preferred unless the mutation being tested is so weak that capsules with sufficient seed cannot be obtained. All the primary types will give in backcrosses $1 \cdot 1$ ratios of normal to recessive plants among both diploids and $2n + 1$ types, except the particular $2n + 1$ type the extra chromosome of which is the one carrying the gene being tested. The latter will give $2 \cdot 1$ ratios in male backcrosses and among the $2n$ offspring of female backcrosses. None of the $2n + 1$ offspring in a female backcross will show the recessive character. Formulas of all possible combinations of $2n + 17 \cdot 18$ plants heterozygous for white flowers (P = purple, p = white flowers; located in the $17 \cdot 18$ chromosome) and their offspring from backcrosses and selfs, and the expected ratios of dominant (P) to recessive (p) have been published. This method has been found to be by far the most satisfactory for the location of the genes responsible for most mutations. It has been the usual method followed when a new mutation appeared which seemed to be of such a nature that it might be valuable as a tester after its location in a specific chromosome was determined (30).

Secondary and tertiary $2n + 1$ types may be used to locate genes in particular half-chromosomes in much the same way as the primary types. Thus, when it had been determined from backcrosses of heterozygous $2n + 1 \cdot 2$ plants that the gene for pale-7 was located in the $1 \cdot 2$ chromosome, the tertiary $2n + 1 \cdot 18$ was rendered heterozygous and used in female backcrosses to pale-7. Among the 282 diploid offspring of this backcross there were 147 normal green to 135 pale plants, and all (51) of the $2n + 1 \cdot 18$ offspring were normal green. This was interpreted as a 1:1::all:0 ratio and accepted as evidence that the gene for pale-7 is in the $\cdot 1$ arm of the $1 \cdot 2$ chromosome.

Compensating types are $2n + 1$ forms that have the equivalent of an individual chromosome compensated for by parts of two compound chromosomes (Chapter 6). Such a type, when heterozygous for a gene with its locus in the compensated chromosome, will breed true for the gene among its $2n$ offspring, except for crossing-over. Types are available with extra chromosomes that compensate for all the 12 chromosomes. Such types have been very successfully used in the location of genes. To test adequately an unknown gene mutation, crosses must be made to at least 12 different compensating types—one with chromosomes compensating for each of the 12 chromosome pairs. These twelve $F_1$ compensating types may then be male backcrossed to the homozygous recessive. The backcross cultures will all segregate in a normal 1:1 ratio except the one from the type which has chromosomes that compensate for the chromosome containing the locus for the gene. The latter will give an excess of plants of the recessive type.

This method has been particularly useful in locating the factors for certain mutations which are of such a character that they can be recorded in the seed pan, e.g., certain pales, albinos, and green-stemmed types. When the $2n - 1 \cdot 2 + 1 \cdot 9 + 2 \cdot 5$ compensating type heterozygous for albino-11 was male backcrossed to the homozygous recessive (albino-11 grafted on green stock produces flowers and capsules), 36 normal and 199 albino seedlings were obtained. This indicated that the gene for albino-11 is in the $1 \cdot 2$ chromosome.

There are in *Datura* a number of pollen-abortion types. These have come, as Table 8 indicates, from a number of sources or have appeared following various treatments. It has been well established that many of these are the result of gene mutations causing the abortion of the pollen grains in which the gene is present, but which do not affect the viability of the egg cells. These pollen-abortion (pa) genes are of value in determining the location of genes in specific chromosomes and are especially valuable in determining the position of genes within a chromosome after their presence in that chromosome has been indicated by other methods.

If a plant heterozygous for both a pollen-abortion gene and a recessive gene causing a visible character mutation is male backcrossed to the recessive mutation, all the offspring will be homozygous for the recessive except for crossing-over. The use of pollen-abortion testers in locating genes at specific points within chromosomes avoids the loss of time in making up double recessives, necessary for the usual linkage method, and also the difficulties inherent in working with double recessives, which in *Datura* are often very weak. Sixteen pollen-abortion genes have been located in ten different chromosomes. An effort has been made to obtain at least one pa gene in each half-chromosome. *Datura* is one of the few, if not the only form, in which such pollen-abortion genes have been utilized in determining linkages between genes.

Since pollen-abortion genes cannot be transmitted by pollen, certain methods only can be employed for their location. The determination of linkage with previously located genes causing "visible" mutations is the usual method used.

For three recessive genes located in the $17 \cdot 18$ chromosome the crossover percentages with a pollen-abortion (pa-5) type also in the $17 \cdot 18$

chromosome have been determined. Since these were characters that could be easily determined in the seed pan, it was possible to record large numbers of backcross individuals. It was found that the locus for white-1 is 4 units from that of pa-5; curled-1 is 24 units distant; wilt-1 is 26 units, and pale-6 is 29 units. Other pollen-abortion genes have been used to determine linkages in other chromosomes.

In Chapter 4 are discussed the numerous prime types (PT's) that have occurred as a result of the interchange of ends of nonhomologous chromosomes. Many of these induce a definite proportion of aborted pollen in the heterozygous condition. These PT's may be used as testers to locate genes. An $F_1$ is obtained between the gene to be located and the PT chosen as a tester. These $F_1$ plants are backcrossed to the recessive. It is then necessary to record the ratios of individuals in the offspring with good pollen to those with the characteristic percentage of aborted pollen for both normal and recessive plants. If linkages are found among the four groups of individuals, it is assumed that the gene is located in one of two chromosomes if the prime type has two chromosomes modified. It is then necessary to use another PT with one of the two, but not both, chromosomes modified for additional testing or to test which of the two possible chromosomes carries the gene by other means. Since many pollen determinations are required by this method, it has not been used so often as the other methods described above, which give more precise results with less effort.

**Location of Genes at Particular Points.** The methods described above have been used to locate 81 of the known genes responsible for the many mutations that have been recognized in *Datura*. Table 9 summarizes the results of this work. The table shows the number of genes that have been located in particular chromosomes and half-chromosomes. Genes have been located in specific halves (arms) by ratios thrown by hetero-

TABLE 9

PROBABLE LOCATION OF 81 GENES IN DATURA STRAMONIUM

| Chromosome | Number Genes Located in Chromosome | Located in Odd-numbered Arm | Located in Even-numbered Arm | Position in Chromosome Not Known |
|---|---|---|---|---|
| 1·2 | 6 | 4 | | 2 |
| 3·4 | 11 | | 4 | 7 |
| 5·6 | 8 | 2 | | 6 |
| 7·8 | 3 | | | 3 |
| 9·10 | 5 | 1 | 2 | 2 |
| 11·12 | 9 | 2 | 6 | 1 |
| 13·14 | 9 | 1 | 1 | 7 |
| 15·16 | 8 | 2 | 4 | 2 |
| 17·18 | 6 | 2 | 3 | 1 |
| 19·20 | 5 | 3 | 1 | 1 |
| 21·22 | 6 | 2 | | 4 |
| 23·24 | 5 | 1 | 1 | 3 |
| Totals | 81 | 20 | 22 | 39 |

zygous $2n + 1$ secondaries and tertiaries or by linkage with previously
located genes and pollen-abortion types.

In a preceding paragraph some figures were given of the linkages
found between some of the genes located in the 17·18 chromosome.
Fig. 36c shows the probable linear arrangement of the six known genes in
this chromosome. For some of the other chromosomes it has been possible to construct similar "maps." The necessity of growing large cultures

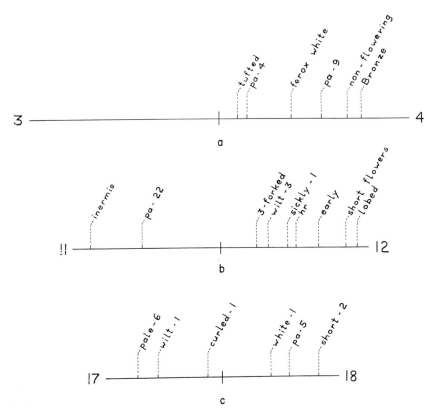

Fig. 36. Probable linear arrangement of some genes in three chromosomes.

in order to obtain reliable data and the lack of a sufficient number of
suitable testers has made it impractical to devote much time to this work.
The data from which these figures are constructed are the result of attempts to locate suitable testers to be used for labeling specific chromosomes or half-chromosomes. Distances as given in the figures are approximate only. Many more determinations of linkage relationships need
to be made and much larger numbers of individuals grown before the
exact linear arrangement of genes in the *Datura* chromosomes can be
definitely established.

In Fig. 36a is given the probable linear arrangement of six genes in the ·4 arm of the 3·4 chromosome. This is the next to the largest chromosome and in it are located the largest number (11) of known genes. It is not known in which arm the other five genes are located. None have, as yet, been found in the ·3 arm.

The 11·12 chromosome is known to contain nine genes for as many strikingly distinct mutant types. One type, inermis (in), has smooth instead of spiny fruit and was formerly considered a distinct species (*D. "inermis"*). A type with very short flowers is known as short flowers (sh. fl.); one, called sickly (sk), has an appearance resembling the mottled effect caused by a virus disease. Three types are recognized by their pollen characteristics: one has lobed pollen (lp); in another (hr) the pollen is twice its normal size as a result of chromosome doubling; the third is a pollen-abortion type (pa-22). A type called early (e) is of low stature and matures much earlier than normal. A wilt (wt-3) type and a type that is usually 3-forked (3-fk) instead of 2-forked have been located in the ·12 arm. These nine types have been sufficiently investigated to enable us to establish their probable linear arrangement within the 11·12 chromosome (Fig. 36b).

**Summary.** From extensive collections from nature, from various experimental treatments, and as a result of spontaneous mutations, an extensive collection of types presumably determined by gene mutations has been assembled in *Datura*. These mutations have become apparent from their various effects on seedlings or mature plants. Many variations in the normal green color of the cotyledons and leaves have resulted from these mutations. These have ranged from those only slightly paler than normal to complete albinos. Variations in leaf form and growth habit (stature) of the mature plant are also frequent. Any part of the plant may be affected by mutations, although changes in flower and capsule forms are less common. There are also mutations that have an affect on mitosis and chromosome reduction but that cause no change in external appearance of the plant.

Eighty-one of the 541 genes recognized have been located in specific chromosomes. Some of the methods used for the location of genes have been developed particularly for *Datura*. Genes have been located in all the 12 chromosomes and in most of the individual half-chromosomes. From the results of various experiments involving combinations of genes it has been possible to construct "maps" showing the probable linear arrangement of some of the genes in most of the 12 chromosomes. When located, genes may be used as labels for specific chromosomes or parts of chromosomes, and so become useful genetic tools.

# 8

# *Chimeras*

SOPHIE SATINA

The term *chimera* was introduced by Winkler (1907) for the five different types of "graft hybrids" that he had obtained by grafting two species of solanaceous plants, *Solanum lycopersicum* and *S. nigrum*, on each other. Some of these chimeras looked more like the scion, others like the stock. The origin of these "graft hybrids" was erroneously explained by Winkler as due to fusion of two vegetative cells. The correct interpretation of the nature of these chimeras, as of the well-known grafts *Cytisus Adami* and *Crataegomespilus,* was offered by Baur (1909, 1930), who based his conclusions both on his experiments with variegated *Pelargonium* and on Winkler's grafts. Baur called some of these chimeras *sectorial chimeras,* others *periclinal chimeras.*

The induction of polyploid races of *Datura* from colchicine-treated seeds or branches mentioned in Chapter 5 was not limited to the formation of plants with total polyploidy. The cytological effects following colchicine treatment resulted also in the appearance of a wide range of chimera types. Chimeras are plants formed by dissimilar components arranged in various patterns. Polyploidy in such plants, for example, might be confined only to inner tissue, leaving the epidermis diploid, or the same might happen in the reverse combination of tissues. In other types of chimeras a branch may be aberrant due to polyploidy or to a deficiency of a chromosome or chromosome fragment while the rest of the plant remains normal diploid.

The term chimera is applied to grafts, the tissues of which are formed by components belonging to two or three different species (Winkler, 1907, 1935; Jørgensen and Crane, 1927; Krenke, 1933), as well as to plants in which the dissimilar components originate in an individual spontaneously in nature or as a result of some chemical or physical treatment. Most of these are cytochimeras, which appear due to chromosome or possibly to gene mutations.

At present, four types of chimeras are recognized:

132

1. **Sectorial chimeras,** in which a whole branch or a well-defined sector of tissues differs in color, or in chromosomal constitution, or in some other way from the rest of the plant.
2. **Periclinal chimeras,** in which one layer, or more, of internal tissue is covered by or envelopes a different type of tissue.
3. **Mericlinal chimeras,** in which the sector is incomplete, forming a portion of modified tissue only one or a few tiers thick. Such a chimera is often regarded as sectorial, but it should be considered to be an incomplete periclinal chimera.
4. **Mixochimeras,** in which the normal and polyploid or otherwise modified patches of tissues or group of cells are growing without a well-defined order. Such a chimera is in a transitional state of development. The segregation and rearrangement of tissues is still going on.

Reports on the spontaneous formation of chimeras in other species are numerous. They are frequently found as bud sports, showing leaf variegation (Baur, 1930; Renner, 1936), or forming sectors with variously colored stripes on plant organs (Blaydes, 1944), sectors with chlorophyll deficiencies (MacArthur, 1928), or with evident chromosome mutations. They are usually considered to be sectorial chimeras, but only a few have been studied in detail and the true nature of many is unknown. According to Jørgensen and Crane (1927) and Neilson-Jones (1937), most of them are probably mericlinal chimeras. The diversity of bud sports is discussed in reviews by Chittenden (1927) and Cramer (1954).

As early as 1914 Blakeslee had made observations of sectorial chimeras in *Portulaca* and in 1920 he published results of extensive experiments on the inheritance of the mutant "dwarf" and flower colors in that genus. The occurrence of sectorial and periclinal chimeras in *Portulaca* and their effect on genetic ratios were recognized (Blakeslee, 1920). Conspicuous sectorial chimeras, or bud sports, are rather common in *Datura*. The morphological differences observed in the aberrant branches of *D. stramonium* have been caused by chromosomal mutation in all cases investigated. Sectorial chimeras due to simple gene mutations, or reversions, are exceedingly rare in untreated material. The only instance of such a possible gene mutation, the reversion of a recessive gene in the heterozygous condition, is described in Chapter 7.

**Sectorial Chimeras.** The most frequent sectorial chimeras found in *D. stramonium* are those involving a doubling of the whole chromosome complement to produce a diploid branch on a haploid or a tetraploid branch on a diploid. Elimination of a single chromosome or a chromosome fragment is also a common cause of the appearance of morphologically different branches. The first sectorial chimeras in *Datura* were observed in 1922 and were of this sort (23). Records of 51 such chimeras on diploid plants show that these deficiencies are confined almost entirely to those involving the $1 \cdot 2$ or $17 \cdot 18$ chromosome, with the former more commonly eliminated. Forty-three of the 51 cases were found to have lost the $1 \cdot 2$ chromosome, four the $17 \cdot 18$, and one the $11 \cdot 12$, with three cases in which the missing chromosome was not identified. The $1 \cdot 2$ and $17 \cdot 18$ chromosomes have also been frequently eliminated when they have occurred as the extra chromosome in $2n + 1$ plants. We have recorded more than 20 cases of the primary $2n + 17 \cdot 18$ showing aberrant branches resembling diploids in appearance. Cytological and genetical evidence has proved that each of these diploid branches was the result of the elimination of the $17 \cdot 18$ chromosome. The $1 \cdot 1$ chromosome of the secondary $2n + 1 \cdot 1$ is so frequently lost with $2n$ branches remaining that it is difficult to keep this type growing without reversion to diploid. The $21 \cdot 22$ chromosome of the $2n + 21 \cdot 22$ primary has been once known to have been eliminated to form a normal diploid branch. Fragments, or half-chromosomes, especially the $\cdot 1$ half (arm) of the $1 \cdot 2$ chromosome and the $\cdot 18$ half of the $17 \cdot 18$, are particularly likely to be eliminated when present as excess chromosomal material. In *Datura* a sex cell ($1n$) apparently cannot survive unless all the 12 different chromosomes are present. Hence, deficiencies would not be expected directly from sexual reproduction but would appear only as abnormal branches. In no case has it been possible to carry a deficiency (whole or major part of a chromosome) over to a second generation.

The fact that few certain cases of bud sports due to the mutation of single genes have been observed in *Datura*, while sectorial chimeras resulting from chromosomal changes are common, is evidence that chromosome and not gene mutations may be responsible for many of the sectorial variations reported in other forms in which the bud sports have not been adequately analyzed (*120, 135*).

The spontaneous doubling of the chromosomes in the roots of haploid *Datura* plants has been recorded quite frequently. An unbalanced haploid plant ($1n + 15 \cdot 15$) having $2n + 2$ chromosomes in its roots was also found (Chapter 6).

**Periclinal Chimeras.** Spontaneous periclinal chimeras have been reported in *Citrus* (Frost and Krug, 1942), in apples (Einset *et al.*, 1946; Blaser and Einset, 1948), in *Nicotiana* (Clausen and Goodspeed, 1923), and potatoes (Asseyeva, 1928), but they have not been observed in *Datura*.

The majority of the chimeras that have been studied in detail was obtained experimentally by: (1) grafting (Winkler, 1907, 1935; Jørgensen and Crane, 1927); (2) some physical treatment (Kachidze, 1932; Asseyeva, 1928, 1931) or radiation of *Datura* (*221*); (3) chemical treatments of seeds or other parts of plants—*Datura* (*118*), cranberry (Dermen and Bain, 1944), peach, apple (Dermen, 1947b, 1951), pineapple (Kerns and Collins, 1947), and potato (Baker, 1943).

None of the methods thus far applied to *Datura* have been so effective as the use of colchicine. Seeds soaked for two to five days in a 0.2 to 0.5 per cent water solution of this alkaloid have yielded large numbers of various types of cytochimeras. The effectiveness of the treatment depends on a number of factors, such as the concentration of the solution, the length of time that the seeds are kept in colchicine, the temperature during treatment and during the germination of the seed, and the vitality of the latter.

PRIMORDIUM OF THE SHOOT APEX. Periclinal chimeras in *Datura* from colchicine-treated seeds offer excellent material for studying a number of problems. Studies on the structure of primordia in shoot apices have given new evidence of the presence of several initial cells in the primordium. They also proved that the initial cells in *Datura* are located in three superimposed uniseriate germ layers, that each germ layer is independent from the other two, and that each layer gives rise to specific tissues contributing to the growth of the shoot and leaves. Each layer acts like a histogene (*137*).

Nebel and Ruttle (1938), Levan (1938), and others have shown that colchicine affects the cell during division by inhibiting the spindle formation. The duplication of chromosome number, the deficiency of a chromosome, or other effects caused by the failure of normal mitotic function thus occur in individual initial cells in the primordium of the shoot apex. More than one initial cell might be affected by treatment and the effect might be different in each cell. This has been demonstrated in earlier studies of *Datura* plants grown from seeds treated with various agents. One plant from such an experiment produced at least five different types of branches due to different gene mutations in the initial cells of the subepidermal layer. Studies made on a large number of chimeras offer new data that support these earlier observations (*94, 152*).

The affected initial cells perpetuate indefinitely and form patches of modified tissues in the developing shoot. The activity of each modified individual initial cell is correlated with the activity of adjacent initial cells. Some of these may be affected the same way, others differently, and some remain normal, forming patches of $2n$ tissue. These alternating diploid and polyploid patches of tissues in the growing shoot apex lead most frequently to the formation of mixochimeras in which both diploid and polyploid cells will form the tissue contributed by the layer in which the initial cells were located. Such mixoploidy has been also reported by Dermen (1945) in cranberry.

The width of the developing patches depends primarily on the number and location of the affected initial cells in the primordium and on the growth vigor of the cells forming the patches. The diploid tissue developing from the unaffected initials may dominate a narrow patch with modified cells and in some cases entirely suppress its growth. If two or three similarly affected initial cells are adjacent, the patch of the modified tissue is wide and has a better chance for survival and further development.

Due, apparently, to differences in their rate of growth, patches of modified and of normal $2n$ tissue in the mixochimera may gradually segregate and ultimately branches grow out in the developing shoot. Some may develop as types of periclinal chimeras with diploid and polyploid components, other branches may become sectorial chimeras wholly composed of polyploid tissue, some form normal $2n$ tissues throughout, and some branches may develop as mericlinal chimeras. Branches in which segregation is completed appear usually only in late stages and rarely before maturity of the affected plant. This has also been observed in the formation of entirely polyploid plants resulting from colchicine treatment (144).

A survey was made of a random sample consisting of the first 100 of 1,400 plants grown from seeds treated with colchicine. Of these 100 plants, 41 were 2n throughout. A section through the shoot and floral apices of such a diploid plant is shown in Fig. 37c. Such a large number

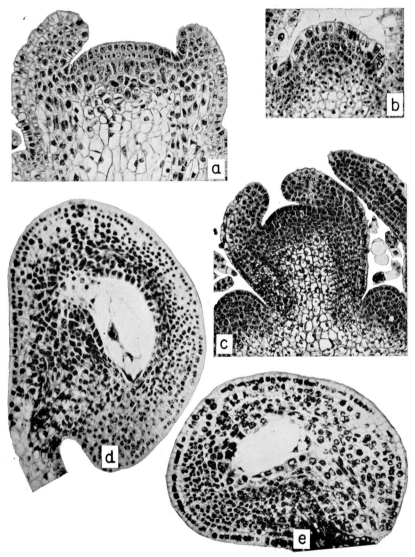

Fig. 37. Periclinal chimeras. Longitudinal sections. (a) Floral apex, 4n,2n,8n; (b) shoot apex, 8n,2n,2n; (c) normal control of two shoot apices and a floral apex; (d) ovule, 2n,4n,4n. The larger portion of the coat is formed by the 2n integument, the smaller chalazal end by 4n nucellar cells; (e) ovule, 8n,2n,2n. The larger portion of the coat is formed by the 8n integument, the smaller portion by the 2n nucellar cells.

of unaffected plants was rather expected because it was already known that more heavily treated seeds germinate considerably later and that the seedlings produced grow slower than normal diploid plants. The remaining 59 plants were all affected by the treatment. Two of these plants had five chromosomally different types of branches; however, the combinations of components were not the same in each. One plant had four types of chromosomally different branches, 15 plants had three types, 36 plants had two types of branches, and only 5 plants showed the same individual modification in all branches. One of these plants was an octoploid throughout, 2 were periclinal chimeras, and 2 were mixochimeras. This survey indicates that a similar effect in all the branches of an individual plant occurred only in a few cases. The data obtained also indicate that more than one initial cell contributes to the growth of the shoot apex in *Datura*.

Of the 59 affected plants, one, as has been just mentioned, was an octoploid; in all the other 58 plants the modified tissue was 4n. Only 7 plants were periclinal chimeras throughout without any mixoploidy as seen in mixochimeras. Two of these "pure" chimeras differed in the combination of the 2n and 4n components, but in each plant all the branches were alike. Each of the remaining 5 chimeras had branches with different combinations of their 2n and 4n components. In 23 plants the segregation of tissues in the shoot resulted in forming normal 2n branches, branches of periclinal and mericlinal chimeras, as well as 4n sectorial chimeras. In 16 plants, in addition to the types of branches already listed, other branches were also formed in which separation of 2n and 4n tissues had not been completed. In 12 plants some branches were sectorial chimeras, others still mixochimeras throughout (Table 10). Thus, of the 59 plants affected, 46 were found to have periclinal chimeras in some or all of their branches, and in 28 plants the segregation of tissue was not yet completed (*173*).

The fact that the formation of sectorial or periclinal chimeras is usually preceded by the formation of mixochimeras and that some branches have the constitution of mericlinal chimeras is of great importance. This indicates that any chimeras selected for study should be carefully checked and that the selection should be deferred until the plant reaches maturity. The use of material in which separation of tissues of different ploidy might not be completed leads to incorrect interpretations and conclusions.

TABLE 10

TYPES OF BRANCHES FOUND IN 100 PLANTS FROM COLCHICINE-TREATED SEED *

| Types of Branches | Number of Plants |
| --- | --- |
| Each branch octoploid | 1 |
| Each branch periclinal chimera | 7 |
| Periclinal, sectorial, and mericlinal chimeras | 23 |
| Periclinal, sectorial, mericlinal, and mixochimeras | 16 |
| Sectorial and mixochimeras | 12 |

* 41 unaffected 2n plants; 59 plants with variously modified branches.

To avoid the use of possibly misleading material, it was found desirable to graft and regraft the particular chimeras selected for investigation successively three or four times before using them for further histogenic studies. A large number of grafted periclinal chimeras was kept over four years in the greenhouses. They proved to be quite stable and, with only two exceptions, none of them reverted into a 2n, or a polyploid plant, or into a periclinal chimera with other combinations of components. The stability of periclinal chimeras has also been reported by Chittenden (1927) and by Krenke (1933). Such stability is proof that the chimera no longer contains mixoploid tissue.

As has already been indicated, the three germ layers with initial cells in the primordium of the *Datura* shoot apex are independent. The response of any one layer to treatment is independent of the response of the other two. For convenience they were labeled as follows: the outermost layer L I, the second layer L II, and the innermost layer L III. Thus a chimera with a 2n outermost layer, L I, a 4n second layer, L II, and an innermost 8n layer, L III, will be written 2n, 4n, 8n.

The independence of each germ layer and the presence in each of a number of initial cells explain the variability in the combination of 2n, 4n, and 8n components in *Datura* periclinal chimeras (Fig. 38). Altogether, 15 different types were obtained and studied in detail. These included chimeras with all the six possible combinations of 2n and 4n components in the three layers and chimeras in which at least one of the layers was 8n (Fig. 37a, b). These 15 selected types offered all the material needed for further work on ontogeny and other problems. Additional types of chimeras found later were not kept for further studies.

A survey made of 192 periclinal cytochimeras with 4n and 2n components has shown that the induction of polyploidy occurred most frequently in the innermost layer, L III: 92 cases against 43 and 57 cases in L I and L II, respectively. The doubling of chromosome number was less frequent in two layers than in a single layer: 52 cases with tetraploidy in two layers against 140 cases with tetraploidy in one layer (Table 11). The conclusion that the *Datura* shoot apex has only three germ layers is based on the survey made of the 192 chimeras just mentioned as well as on a large number of periclinal chimeras obtained from other experiments with colchicine treatment and checked by counting the chromosome numbers in dividing cells of the primordium (152).

TABLE 11

LOCATION OF 4n LAYERS IN PERICLINAL CHIMERAS

|  | L I | L II | L III | Total |
|---|---|---|---|---|
| A single layer | 35 | 36 | 69 | 140 |
| L I and L II | 3 | 3 | — | 6 |
| L I and L III | 5 | — | 5 | 10 |
| L II and L III | — | 18 | 18 | 36 |
| Total branches | 43 | 57 | 92 | 192 |

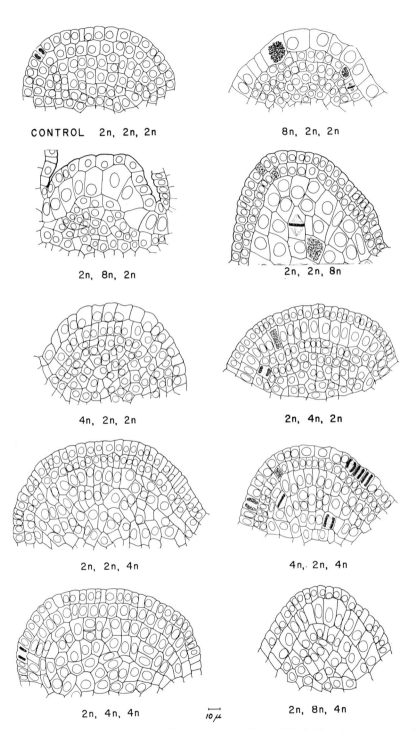

CONTROL  2n, 2n, 2n

8n, 2n, 2n

2n, 8n, 2n

2n, 2n, 8n

4n, 2n, 2n

2n, 4n, 2n

2n, 2n, 4n

4n, 2n, 4n

2n, 4n, 4n  $\overline{10\,\mu}$

2n, 8n, 4n

Fig. 38. Longitudinal sections of shoot apices. Normal diploid and nine types of periclinal chimeras. Polyploidy in different germ layers.

139

The cells in the outermost layer of the primordium divide anticlinally, adding to its surface growth. The cells in L II divide anticlinally during plastochron [1] and periclinally at leaf initiation in the primordium cells located in the region of initiation. The cells of L III divide both anticlinally and periclinally, but the latter predominate over the anticlinal plane and add considerably to the volume of the primordium. This innermost germ layer contributes to the formation of the central core of the primordium. After division the upper daughter cell retains the meristematic nature of the layer and the lower daughter cell becomes a member of the core. The young outermost layers of the core are filled with cytoplasm, stain dark, and divide in various planes, contributing to the bulk of the core. Occasionally they form one or two orderly arranged tiers of cells, but, in most cases, due to frequent divisions in different planes, their arrangement is irregular. Later, when they become covered by newly formed cells of the central core and are pushed farther down, the cells stain light, have large vacuoles, and divide only occasionally. Regardless of their location, all the cells of the central core invariably have the same chromosomal constitution as the cells of L III and must be considered as descendants of this germ layer.

The following method was developed and used in the work with chimeras. Off-type branches that appeared on plants developing from seeds treated with colchicine were recorded and labeled at least three times until they reached maturity: in early summer about a month after being transferred from pots into the field, later in the summer, and once more in the early fall. The later records showed that some of the previously labeled off-type branches had lost, or were losing, their aberrant appearance, apparently as a result of suppressed growth of the modified tissue by the more vigorous diploid tissue. In other plants new off-type branches emerged from the shoot, apparently due to segregation of tissues in the plant as it approached maturity. Preliminary analysis of the stomata and of dividing pollen mother cells immediately followed each recording and labeling of the branches. The stomata in a $4n$ epidermis are larger and they are more widely scattered than in a $2n$ epidermis. Their size is still larger and the number smaller in an $8n$ epidermis. The ploidy of the subepidermal L II was determined either by counting the chromosome number of dividing pollen mother cells or by comparing the size of pollen grains with those of control plants. No quick method was possible in analyzing the ploidy of tissues originating from L III. Reliable information about the latter as well as confirmation of the preliminary data on tissues of L I and L II were obtained from studies made on fixed and sectioned material collected from field plants or from grafted chimeras.

The morphological appearance of the several types of periclinal chimeras was found to be quite distinctive. Observations and records taken late in the season agreed surprisingly well with the composition of the chimeras as determined from sectioned material. Plants or branches

---

[1] The period of time between the initiation of two successive leaf primordia.

having only the outer layer modified were consistently recorded as having roughened leaves, usually larger than those of normal diploids. A modified second layer, L II, was the most difficult to distinguish from unaffected plants, but plants so modified were usually recorded as "off-type" diploids. Plants with a modified third layer, L III, were not distinct from normals in leaf form or habit, but mature capsules were very characteristic. Capsules on such 2n, 2n, 4n plants were somewhat intermediate between those of diploids and tetraploids and distinct from either. Periclinal chimeras of this sort bore large capsules that were broader at their base and less flattened than 4n capsules. The combination of nearly normal leaves and general habit with the large and distinctively shaped capsules enabled us to record all these as being a specific type before their true composition had been determined cytologically.

PRIMORDIUM OF THE FLORAL APEX. The various types of periclinal cytochimeras with each layer properly checked and labeled according to their ploidy in shoot apices proved to be very useful in ontogenetic *Datura* studies. As has been mentioned, each germ layer in the primordium of the shoot apex contributes to the growth of the shoot by giving rise to specific tissues. It has been found that in the shoot L I contributes to the formation of epidermis and of its derivatives, L II to the formation of tissues in the cortex, and L III to the stele and pith.

A study of floral primordia followed that made on the structure of shoot primordia. For this comparison we used the same plants with 15 different types of periclinal cytochimeras that had been selected for studies on shoot apices. A comparison of the floral apex of a 4n, 2n, 8n chimera with an 8n, 2n, 2n shoot apex showed no essential difference in the structure of their primordia (Fig. 37a, b). The floral primordium has three independent germ layers and, as in shoot apices, the cells beneath the L III layer of the floral apex have the same ploidy as the innermost layer. The surface growth in the floral primordium also depends primarily on the activity of L I and L II, and their cells divide anticlinally. Periclinal divisions in L II occur only at the initiation of the sepals and petals. Cells in L III divide in various planes. The similarity in structure of both apices supports the classic view that they are homologous and that the floral apex is a modified axis with restricted growth in length. It differs somewhat from the shoot apex in size and shape. Its primordium is broader and its shape and size change during development. At early stages it is small and flat. It becomes slightly dome-shaped at the initiation of sepals and it broadens and flattens again after the initiation of petals and stamens.

INITIATION OF THE LEAF, SEPAL, AND PETAL. The use of cytochimeras proved to be particularly helpful in tracing the participation of the three germ layers in the formation of the leaf and floral appendages. The most convincing results were obtained by using the 2n, 8n, 2n chimeras. The presence of an 8n subepidermal layer with very large cells and nuclei containing over 90 chromosomes in contrast to the outermost and innermost diploid layers is quite striking and very helpful in following the contribution of each layer to the developing organ. Chimeras of the reverse combination, with a $2n$ L II and $8n$ or $4n$ L I and L III, were used to check the observations and to make sure that the results obtained were not due to a possible overgrowth of the polyploid tissues against the diploid tissue.

The comparison of slides obtained from such reverse types of chimeras proved that such possible hypertrophy did not occur in the organs analyzed. The leaf primordium develops from the shoot apex, the primordia of the sepal and petal from the floral apex. Each of the three primordia are initiated by periclinally dividing cells of L II (Fig. 39a, e, i). The small projection of these primordia are covered by one layer of cells contributed by L I. Further upward growth of the leaf, sepal, and petal depends primarily on the activity of cells originating from L II and located in the apical and subapical regions of the leaf, sepal, and petal (Fig. 39b, f, j). Their lateral expansion and the increase in thickness depends on the activity of the L II cells located near the base of these young organs. The participation of the innermost germ layer begins later, after the inner parenchymal tissue in the leaf, sepal, and petal has been formed by the rapidly perpetuating cells of L II. The cells derived from L III differentiate into a strand of procambial cells which ultimately give rise to a vascular bundle. The latter never extends to the tip of the leaf, sepal, or petal, being confined to the lower regions of these organs (Fig. 39c, g, k).

All three layers participate in the formation of the leaf, sepal, and petal and the contrast in size between the polyploid and diploid cells helps to define quite clearly the contributions made by each germ layer in these organs. The mesophyll in each is formed only by cells derived from L II. It was either $8n$, or $4n$, or $2n$ when the L II layer in the chimeras used was $8n$, or $4n$, or $2n$, respectively. The cytological difference seen in the mesophyll cells in each case depended entirely on the ploidy of the L II. The initiation and early structure of the leaf, sepal, and petal is seen best in longitudinal sections. Their structure in more advanced stages is most evident in cross sections (Fig. 39d, h, l). Their close resemblance supports the classic theory that sepals and petals are modified leaves (149).

Additional observations were made on the activity of epidermal cells in petals and sepals in later stages. They indicated that cells derived from the epidermis are not confined exclusively to functioning as protective tissue. Patches of inner connective tissue appear at the edges of the free adjacent petals when they are ready to join and to form the sympetalous corolla of Datura. This is also observed in sepals forming the calyx (Fig. 40c). It had been found that such connective tissue is formed exclusively by cells derived from the epidermis. Dividing epidermal cells located near the margins of petals and sepals deviate from the ordinary anticlinal mode of division and form patches of inner tissue (165). This change in the mode of division is a regular process in the normal developing floral organs and is not a result of the restorative activity of adjacent cells in regeneration after injuries. A deviation in the mode of division has also been observed in bud scales (Cross, 1938) and in leaves (Renner, 1936; Foster, 1937).

INITIATION OF THE STAMEN. The initiation of stamens begins at the same time as that of petals, and five stamen primordia alternating with petal primordia appear on the floral apex. Externally the former look similar to those of the leaf, sepal, and petal, but their initiation and inner structure are different. In contrast to these organs, the initial cells of the stamen are derived from periclinally dividing cells of the innermost germ layer, L III, and not from L II (Fig. 39m). Again, in contrast to the leaf, sepal, and petal, cells derived from L III and not from L II contribute to the formation of the inner tissue of the growing stamen, as shown in Fig. 39n, o, p. The difference in structure of the petal and stamen is best seen in the longitudinal section made through these adjacent organs in a 2n, 8n, 4n chimera. The bulk of the petal is formed by the octoploid cells of L II. The bulk of the stamen is formed by the tetraploid cells of L III. At this stage of division the contribution of L II is limited to the formation of a single-cell layer covering the rest of the inner tissue in the stamen (Fig. 40a). Cells derived from L I and L II add only to the surface growth. Cells from L III continue to dominate over the cells contributed by L II until the stamen begins to assume the four-lobed shape of the adult organ. It is at this stage that the first periclinal divisions appear in the cells of the uniseriated subepidermal layer and that the cells contributed by L III stop perpetuating, become cramped, and remain as an inactive connective tissue between the four lobes of the anther (*149*). In the adult stage the sporogenous tissue is derived from L II; its formation is discussed in Chapter 10.

The comparison of the initiation and development of the stamen with those of the leaf, sepal, and petal and the difference between the stamen and these three organs contradict the classic viewpoint that stamens are modified leaves. The similarity in initiation and in early growth of primordia in stamen and in shoot apices, both depending primarily on the activity of L III, suggest rather the cauline mode of stamen origin. Recent reports on stamen initiation and early primordia growth in *Agropyrum* (Sharman, 1947), *Triticum* (Barnard, 1955), and *D. metel* (Nozeran, 1955) are in agreement with this conclusion. The stamen primordia differ from leaf primordia and look like bud primordia. It is in agreement with Wilson's (1942) concept that stamens are derived from a branch system with terminal sporangia.

INITIATION OF THE CARPEL. Intensive studies made in the past on the nature of the carpel have resulted in a number of diverse and contradictory hypotheses: the carpel is foliar in nature, it is a sporogenous axis, it is *sui generis*, it is derived from a branch system, etc. Factual material supporting the various concepts has been offered. Detailed discussions on this subject are found in accounts of the original researches and in

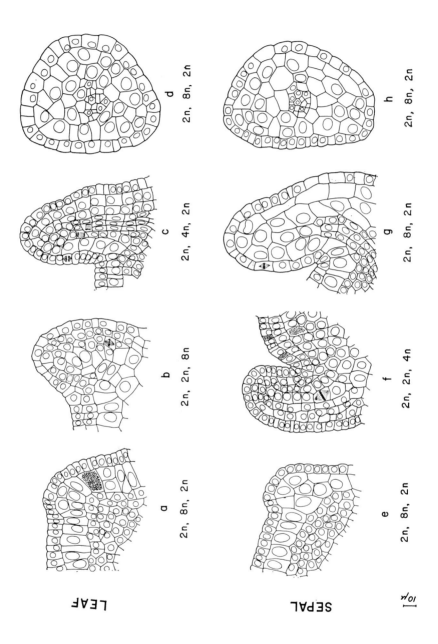

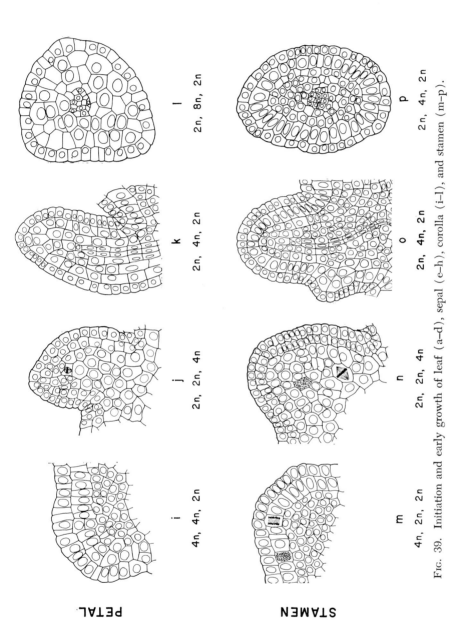

Fig. 39. Initiation and early growth of leaf (a–d), sepal (e–h), corolla (i–l), and stamen (m–p).

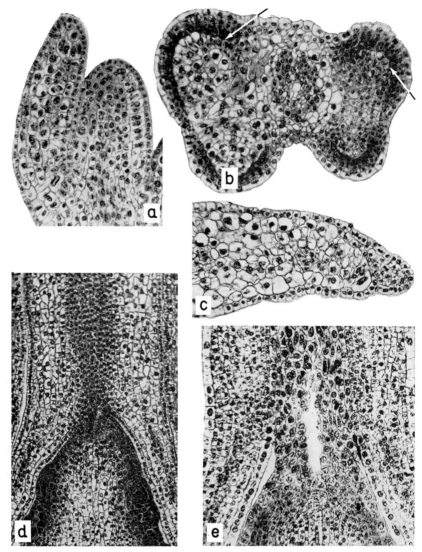

Fig. 40. (a)(c)(d)(e) Longitudinal sections of periclinal chimeras; (b) transverse section of sectorial mixochimera. (a) Adjacent petal and stamen, 2n,8n,4n; (b) stamen, the left sector 4n,2n,8n, the right sector 4n,2n,2n; (c) petal, 2n,8n,4n; portion of 2n inner tissue derived from epidermis; (d) style, 2n,4n,2n; diploid transmitting tissue; (e) style, 8n,2n,2n; octoploid transmitting tissue.

reviews and need not be repeated here (Thomas, 1932; Arber, 1937; Grégoire, 1938; Wilson, 1942). It is obvious that the nature of the carpel is far from being settled and that additional information from different branches of botanical science is necessary for a radical revaluation of its true origin.

Observations on the development of the *Datura* carpel from the earliest stages up to the formation of the pistil with stigma, style, and ovary offer some information that should be taken into consideration in future studies on the nature of the carpel. After the formation of the petal and stamen primordia, groups of active meristematic cells in the floral apex are located within the circle of the stamen in two opposite outer zones of the apex and in its residual central zone. The latter is separated from the lateral ones by regions that remain inactive and later become the base of the locules of the ovary. The two lateral carpel primordia are initiated by periclinally dividing cells in L III. Both primordia grow up, soon become crescent in shape, and form the carpel walls. L III cells located in the central zone of the residual floral apex give rise to the septum and false septum with the placenta. Their growth at early stages depends primarily on the activity of the cells derived from L III. The anticlinally dividing cells of the uniseriated layers L I and L II add only to the surface growth of the carpel. In later stages a few L II cells located at the tops of both crescent-shaped carpel walls and of the septum divide periclinally and form in each a small group of meristematic cells. These cells begin soon to perpetuate intensively and from then on further growth in the lower and upper portions of the carpel proceeds quite differently. The development in the lower portion, which eventually becomes the major part of the ovary, depends on cells derived from L III, while the upper portions of the carpel walls and septa grow in length and width due to the division of cells derived from L II (*161*).

DEVELOPMENT OF STYLE AND STIGMA. The continuous upward growth of the two carpel walls leads to the formation of an elongated stalk—the style with its two expanded stigmatic lobes and the stylar canal. Following Hanf's (1935) classification, *Datura* has a half-closed type of style, i.e., its canal is filled with cells forming a loosely arranged transmitting tissue. The use of periclinal chimeras with an 8$n$ epidermis and 2$n$ L II and L III and, as control, a 2$n$,4$n$,2$n$ cytochimera, proved without any doubt that the stylar transmitting tissue is formed entirely by cells derived from L I (Fig. 40d, e). Its development starts near the base of the stigma and proceeds downward toward the base of the style. This epidermal transmitting tissue forms a continuous track that connects the secretory stigmatic epidermis with the epidermis at the top of the ovary and locules. The formation of the stylar walls depends primarily on the activity of cells derived from L II. Cells derived from L III contribute to the formation of two vascular bundles, which grow upward from the dorsal bundles of the ovary on each side of the stylar wall (*165*).

These observations show that the initiation and early development of the carpel primordia, septa, and placenta depend primarily on the activity of cells derived from L III and suggest that they are not foliar but rather axial in nature. Such evidence favors the concept that the carpel has evolved from fertile branch systems (Thomas, 1932; Hunt, 1937; Wilson and Just, 1939).

INITIATION OF THE OVULE. Studies on the initiation and structure of the ovule showed again that each of the three germ layers takes part in its growth. There is a clearly expressed alternation in the activity of the layers, one succeeding the other. The growth of the ovule is initiated by periclinal divisions in the cells of L III. They form small projections that appear first in the upper portion of the placenta, the previously smooth surface of which becomes irregular. Soon after the ovule's initiation, the activity of cells derived from L III decreases, but intensive divisions and rapid multiplication begin in cells contributed by L II. They form the nucellus tissue and continue to perpetuate until the differentiation of the archesporial cell. It is then that intensive divisions appear in the cells contributed by L I. They initiate the formation of the integument and alone participate in its development. The first epidermal cells, located at the level of the archesporial cell, divide periclinally to start its growth. Illustrations of some of these young stages of ovule initiation are given in Chapter 10, as is a description of the further development of the ovule. Contrary to reports by Souèges, the cells of epidermal origin alone participate in the formation of the integument of *D. stramonium* (*169*). The same has been found in *Myosurus* by Buvat (1952).

**Discussion.** The utilization of various types of periclinal chimeras offers an easy and efficient method for obtaining precise information on the initiation and development of leaves and floral appendages as compared to the histological method generally used in studying the contribution of the tunica and corpus layers to the formation of plant tissues. It is difficult to trace the origin of cells derived from these layers and to determine merely by appearance of cells the proper demarcation between cells contributed by the tunica and by the corpus. The illustrations offered as evidence for interpretation do not always appear to be convincing. The heavy lines frequently used in illustrations to avoid misinterpretation seem to be somewhat arbitrary. According to Boke (1949) in his work on *Vinca*, "a definite statement concerning the respective contributions of T 2 and of corpus cannot be made since there was no method of definitely distinguishing the derivatives of the several layers of the floral apex."

Periclinal cytochimeras offer a great advantage in this respect. The line of demarcation between tissues derived from layers with different ploidy is clear and any possible doubt can be easily overcome by counting the chromosome numbers in dividing cells and by using as controls cytochimeras with reverse combinations of components. This is a simple method. Chimeras of many species, in addition to *Datura*, may be readily obtained by proper colchicine treatment. The only tedious, but a most important, part is the isolation of *pure* periclinal chimeras. As has been seen from our work with *Datura*, one should hardly expect pure periclinal chimeras to appear directly in shoots developing from colchicine-treated seeds. This has been indicated also by Jørgensen and Crane (1927) and by Neilson-Jones (1937) in grafts. The first two authors state that the five chimeras obtained from grafts of two solanaceous species "were from the start mericlinal and that . . . a complete periclinal shoot was never observed to arise directly from cross grafted plants." Sufficient and convincing information on the histogenesis of tissues can be obtained only by using chimeras in which the separation of mixed $2n$ and polyploid tissues has been completed and thoroughly checked. A transverse section through a stamen with mixed $2n$ and $8n$ cells is shown in Fig. 40b. A few $2n$ cells are located among the $8n$ cells in the left sector and a few $8n$ cells are among the $2n$ cells in the right sector. The use of such a mixochimera or of periclinal and sectorial chimeras in tracing the origin of tissues from histogen layers must be avoided. This important factor has not always been taken into consideration. No adequate or correct information with constant results can be expected using chimeras in a transitional state of development, chimeras which revert at various times "*in toto* or in part" to $2n$ branches or to other types of chimeras, as has been done in one of the recent papers on histogenesis in cranberry (Dermen, 1947a).

Observations made upon hundreds of pure periclinal chimeras of *Datura* have proved without a single exception that each of the germ layers, regardless of their ploidy, contribute specific tissues to the developing organs and that they do not vary in this respect. This is the reason why chimeras cannot be kept by selfing. The sporogenous tissue is formed by cells derived from L II and the embryos in seeds from selfs carry only the ploidy of L II. Periclinal chimeras can be continued only by vegetative means.

The constant character and function of the germ layers in *Datura* permit us to draw the conclusion that the three germ layers in the primordia of *Datura* shoot and floral apices are *histogens.* The possibility of tracing the origin of tissues from the labeled layers offers evidence in favor of Hanstein's (1868) theory. However, the terms *periblem* and *pleurome* cannot be applied to the layers L II and L III of *Datura* (*137*).

The histogen theory, though still accepted by some workers, is at present doubted and abandoned by a large group of botanists. Their studies on apices are based on zonation as seen in primordia according to the tunica-corpus concept offered by A. Schmidt (1924). This theory emphasizes the dynamic aspect of growth in shoot apices and the presence of two zones of growth with contrasted planes of cell division. The layers forming the tunica divide anticlinally, adding to the surface growth; the cells of the corpus divide in various planes and add to the growth in volume. In a limited sense the L I and L II in *Datura* which divide anticlinally correspond to the tunica and L III to the corpus. There is, however, an essential difference between the germ layers and the layers considered as tunica and corpus. According to observations made with periclinal chimeras, the function of the three germ layers implies predestination for their derivatives. This contradicts the tunica-corpus concept. The presence of such specifically determined cell layers in shoot apices is emphatically denied in studies based on this concept.

According to the latter, the tunica and corpus layers should not be treated as independent morphological entities.

The interest raised by the tunica-corpus concept resulted in the appearance of a vast number of reports. Literature on this subject is given in a number of papers. Additional information concerning the interrelation between layers forming the tunica and the corpus, some justified criticism on this concept, and a number of new concepts are offered (Sifton, 1944; Philipson, 1949; Popham and Chan, 1950; Buvat, 1952; Bersillon, 1955; Nozeran, 1955). An excellent analysis of recent concepts is given in the review on the shoot apex by Gifford (1954).

Several reports on fluctuations in the inner tunica layers support Foster's (1941) statements that the cell arrangements in these layers are flexible, that the tunica varies widely between species, and that the tunica and corpus are interdependent zones. Most of the recent studies reflect the growing interest and the importance attached to various zonal patterns found in shoot apices. Zonal patterns were found to be present in the tunica and corpus zones themselves. Cells in these zones differ in size, in contents, and in staining capacity (Foster, 1949; Gifford, 1950). According to a number of authors a concept on the structure of shoot apices based only on morphological studies and on planes of cell division is not entirely satisfactory. Attention has been called to the lack of data on the physiology and cytology of cells forming the zones in the apices (Buvat, 1952). His observations on the cytoplasm in the cells located in different zones give important information about the changes found in the cytoplasmic content at various stages of development. A complementary zonation based on metabolic processes in primordia in addition to the tunica-corpus zonations is suggested by Philipson (1949). The importance of studying metabolic processes is stressed by Wardlaw (1952, 1955) in a number of papers. The constitution and activity of shoot apices as determined by genetical factors, as a dynamic geometrical system, and as a system of interrelated zones, etc., were analyzed and discussed by Wardlaw (1957).

The shoot apex can no longer be regarded as a homogeneous body. Its cells are already differentiated at the earliest stages and the apex is composed of portions that differ in structure, in manner of growth, and in metabolic processes, and so form well-defined zones. There apparently is a coordination between the vital activities in these zones. Additional information from all possible sources is still necessary for a complete understanding of the growth and structure of the apex. Studies on the genetical factors that control the growth of the plant, and that thus far have been almost completely neglected in the work on shoot apices, should be included in the investigations.

The work with chimeras should be continued and applied to other species. This will show whether *Datura*, *Solanum* (Winkler, 1935), and cranberry (Dermen, 1945) should be considered only to be individual cases or whether histogen layers are also present in other species. Questions concerning their presence or absence, their number in other species, and their function would be easily answered if the modern technique with properly analyzed and pure periclinal cytochimeras were used in such studies.

Beside the utilization of chimeras in histogenesis, chimeras have proved to be of help in various other studies, such as in the analysis of the relation between phylotaxis and polyploid sectors (Bain and Dermen, 1944). As has been shown, chimeras offer evidence of the diverse functions of the epidermis, which fully supports Linsbauer's (1930) view that one of the main properties of the epidermis is its ability to carry on a variety of functions. Chimeras have demonstrated the advantages of obtaining exact information about the origin of tissues in plant-breeding experiments. By using a $4n,2n,2n$ chimera instead of a $2n$ female plant, it is possible to overcome the barrier to crossability in $2n \times 4n$ crosses (Chapter 14). Studies on development of axillary buds and the initiation and growth of the epicotyl primordia in seeds treated with colchicine were interrupted and unfortunately discontinued because of a virus disease that spread to the greenhouses. Periclinal chimeras could undoubtedly be used in a number of other investigations. Experimental work on embryology, on plant immunity, and plant physiology seem to be particularly promising.

# 9

# Radiation Experiments

A. G. Avery and Jean M. Cummings

Spontaneous mutations, either chromosomal or genic, have been relatively rare in *Datura*. No extra chromosomal types have been observed in the wild, nor have any appeared in cultures grown from seed collected from wild plants. True breeding types due to spontaneous gene mutations have been almost equally rare. Aside from the 12 primary $2n + 1$ types, some secondaries, the $1n$ and $4n$ types, and three or four recessive genes, no other forms were available in the *Datura* stock for genetic work before 1920. As late as 1924 Blakeslee wrote: "The search for gene mutants goes on in *Datura* since they are essential as labels for chromosomes and parts of chromosomes" (38).

**Preliminary Radiation Experiments.** In 1921 the first experiments were begun to discover the possible effects of radium emanations upon gene and chromosomal mutations. These preliminary experiments were conducted in collaboration with C. S. Gager of the Brooklyn Botanic Garden. Flowers, buds, and young capsules of the inbred Line 1 of *D. stramonium* were exposed to gamma rays by inserting into them small sealed capillary glass tubes containing radium emanation for varying lengths of time. The buds or flowers used varied in degree of maturity from unopened flowers to young capsules formed after fertilization. Anthers, at about the time of reduction in their pollen mother cells, were also exposed to the radiations, but the pollen produced was ineffective in pollination.

These early experiments resulted in the production of many chromosomal types. Among 113 offspring from a single treated capsule, 20, or 17.7 per cent, were types with one or more than one extra chromosome. Among these there was a new type, Nubbin, a compensating type (Chapter 6) that appeared for the first time. Unfortunately the interest at this time was in the possible appearance of chromosomal mutations and only a few of the offspring procured were selfed to ascertain if they were heterozygous for new genes. However, of 18 plants tested, 2 (11.11 per cent) were found to be heterozygous (52).

While the total number of plants in this experiment and the number tested by selfing were not large, the number of mutations, chromosomal and gene, was much larger than had ever before been obtained and it was concluded that the radium treatments were responsible for their occurrence. These induced types, new appearances of known mutations, and new chromosomal and gene types were among the first mutations to be produced experimentally in flowering plants by irradiation.

The results of these preliminary radiation experiments carried on by Gager indicated the advisability of continuing radium treatments to obtain additional genes. In 1927 Buchholz began a series of radiation experiments with radon (radium emanation), which yielded a considerable number of both chromosomal and gene mutations.

Since it was particularly desired to increase the stock of usable mutant genes, the new experiments were planned so that there was less likelihood of $2n + 1$ types appearing. Pollen and pollen tubes were selected as the stages to be exposed to radiation, since by treating these haploid stages there was less possibility of causing nondisjunction than if the treatments were given during meiosis. Mature pollen grains were treated in the laboratory away from any plants to be used as females. Pollen tubes growing naturally in the style were also treated but with a weaker source of radiation and for a longer time than the mature pollen. Details of the 1927 experiments and some of the results obtained were published in 1930. The treatment of approximately 1.6 millicurie (mc) hours given the mature pollen was found to be too severe, as only one viable seed was obtained when this treated pollen was used to pollinate untreated normal females. The treatment of pollen tubes in styles with a radon tube of 1.14 mc per hour strength resulted in a considerable number of offspring. Very few new gene mutations resulted from these treatments. A recessive pale type, an albino, and several mutations affecting pollen abortion and pollen-tube growth were recovered in $F_2$ generations. One plant showed a chromosomal translocation that resulted in a pure breeding type with extra chromosomal material. Other translocations also occurred from which several new types were derived (59, 65, 82).

In 1928 experiments similar to those of 1927 were carried on more extensively. Mature pollen was again exposed to radon, as were small buds and flowers at the time of pollination and at various intervals after pollination. The results of these experiments agreed with those of the previous year. Again, the exposures used for treating mature pollen were too severe—only three seedlings resulted. Treatment of flowers or young capsules yielded a total of 110 plants. Three chromosomal translocations were recovered in the offspring from this seed. Four weak types that may have been the result of gene mutations appeared in $F_2$'s but could not be tested further.

The final work with treatments of mature pollen with radon was commenced in the summer of 1930 with $F_2$'s grown in 1931. The treatments in this series of experiments were made with very much weaker dosages continued over a longer time (1 to 4½ hours). Of the 447 plants obtained from the fertilization of the eggs of a normal female by treated pollen, over half were abnormal in appearance. Of these abnormal plants nearly all showed chromosomal modifications, as indicated by high proportions of aborted pollen grains and verified in many cases by cytology. Of the plants recorded as normal in appearance, about one-third showed modified chromosomes or more than a normal proportion of aborted pollen. Of 329 normal-appearing plants examined cytologically, 127 showed a total of 137 unusual configurations. From these we were able to extract and purify 39 new prime types with different chromosomal constitutions (Chapter 4). However, in spite of the high proportion of chromosomal abnormalities that appeared in this material, only nine (or possibly ten) new gene mutations affecting visible characters were recovered. In addition to the considerable number of types with translocations, and the few visible genes, there were recovered several new types, apparently of a genic nature, which affect pollen abortion or pollen-tube growth. These pollen-abortion and pollen-tube genes are similar in their genetic effect. Either one is lethal to the male gametophyte that carries it and thus can be transmitted only by the heterozygous female parent (74, 114).

In 1929 a preliminary series of experiments was set up to test the effect of radon on mature dry seed. Lots of ten seeds, all from a single selfed capsule of Line 1A, were exposed for varying lengths of time from 3 to 132 hours. Only those seeds exposed for 12 hours or less germinated. Of the 30 seedlings obtained, nearly all were seriously malformed, weakened, and the leaves of many were spotted with light-colored patches. It was possible to obtain offspring from only 14 plants grown from the treated seed. Three of these were found to segregate for new visible characters—one albino and two habit types. Unfortunately no cytological investigations were made to determine whether chromosomal breaks or translocations had also occurred. Experiments involving exposure of seed to such radiations were not continued, for at about this time it was found that the exposure of seeds to x-rays was more easily controlled and was highly successful in producing all types of mutations.

The first treatments of mature seed with x-rays were given early in 1929. As in the experiments with radium, lots of ten seeds each, all from a single selfed Line 1A capsule, were used. These were exposed to dosages estimated as 6,000 to 8,000 roentgens. Only 16 plants from these treatments were adequately tested. A wide range of new types, both chromosomal and genic, were observed in their offspring. At least 16 cases of chromosomal interchanges or aberrations were observed; 12 of these were later established as prime types. There were many plants that showed different percentages of aborted pollen grains. Some of those with 50 per cent aborted pollen were found to have normal chromosomes with no unusual configurations. These were considered to be due to recessive genes which are lethal in the pollen grains that contain them. Several genes affecting pollen-tube growth were determined by Buchholz. In addition, 20 types were recovered with distinctly changed visible characters. These were assumed to be due to recessive mutations. These last included albinos, pales, glaucous types, wilts, nonflowering, and several habit types (*80, 83*).

As is evident from these figures, some plants were found in which more than one mutation had occurred. This was to be expected, since the radiation could affect any of the many cells of the embryo in the seed. From one plant grown from the treated seed, seven capsules were harvested and the seed planted separately. The offspring from one capsule segregated for four different new types. Another capsule gave two other types and offspring of the other five capsules segregated for only one type, which was the same as one of those from the first capsule tested. From this one plant six new types were recovered. If more capsules had been tested, it is possible that other mutations would have been discovered.

The following year (1930) a more extensive and better controlled series of experiments with x-rays was started. The seeds were exposed as before, but the dosages ranged from 5,000 to 20,000 roentgens. None of these treatments had any ill effects on germination or any visible effects on the mature plants grown from the treated seed. No $2n + 1$ types were observed, as had been after the exposures of seed to radium emanations. However, an abundance of other mutations appeared in the $F_2$ cultures grown from these plants. Altogether over 100 different and distinct visible types were observed in the segregating cultures. Over 20 types with segments of chromosomes interchanged were identified and later established as prime types. About 15 types due to different genes for pollen abortion were discovered. It was not possible to examine the pollen of plants in all the $F_2$ pedigrees. Had this been done, the number of pollen-abortion types discovered as well as chromosomal aberrations causing pollen abortion undoubtedly would have been greater.

Among the radiation-induced mutations those affecting the pollen and the appearance or amount of abortion are the most frequent. They include both the results of single genes and of chromosomal abnormalities. Pollen abortion can be used to advantage, therefore, as an index of the mutation rate. Since the majority of pollen genes show in the individual grains affected, it is possible by this method to gain a generation in estimating the mutation rate over waiting for the tabulation of recessive genes that cause changes in somatic tissue and that first appear only in the $F_2$ generations.

Although more attention was given to those plants obtained from the higher dosages—14,500 to 20,000 roentgens—a fairly regular increase in mutation rate was observed as the dosage was increased. Table 12 gives the percentage of mutations (of all types) recovered from 277 plants from seed given four different exposures to x-rays.

The primary objective of these x-ray experiments—new visible characters—having been so well attained, no further exposures were given until 1939, at which time another series of exposures was made using dosages of 15,000 to 19,500 roentgens. Again germination was excellent and the plants grown from the treated seed showed no visible abnormalities. Offspring from 200 of these plants were grown in 1940 and 1941 and 162 "visible gene" types were recorded. Breeding work with about 20 of the best of these has been continued. No attempt was made to identify chromosomal translocations or pollen-abortion types in this series.

Of the 541 types that have been identified and classified as gene mutations, more than half (344) have been observed first among offspring of plants grown from seed that had been exposed to x-rays (Chapter 7, Table 8). While our attention has been concerned mainly with mutations producing new visible morphological differences, chromosomal mutations causing interchanges or translocations of parts of chromosomes are also commonly produced by such radiations, as are mutations indicated only by a high proportion of aborted pollen.

TABLE 12

MUTATIONS FOUND IN PLANTS FROM SEED EXPOSED TO X-RAYS

| Dosage (Roentgens) | Number of Plants Tested | Mutations (%) |
|---|---|---|
| 5,000–8,000 | 67 | 17.9 |
| 8,500–11,000 | 30 | 40.0 |
| 11,500–17,000 | 93 | 55.9 |
| 17,500–20,000 | 87 | 79.3 |
| Total | 277 | |

**Miscellaneous Experiments with Other Agents.** In addition to the experiments to discover the effects of radium and x-rays on the chromosomes of *Datura*, experiments with other agents have also been conducted. These will be mentioned only briefly, for none were found to be as effective as x-rays in producing mutations.

In 1928 anthers of *D. stramonium* ready to dehisce were exposed to an intense source of ultraviolet rays. After being exposed the pollen was used to pollinate normal Line 1A flowers. The treatment had no apparent ill effect on the pollen, since capsules with viable seed were obtained. Plants grown from this seed were normal in all respects. Twenty-seven of these plants were tested by selfing to determine if any concealed mutations had occurred. No new types were observed. It is quite possible that the walls of the anthers prevented the ultraviolet rays from reaching the pollen grains.

Exposure of mature seed to supersonic vibrations (varying intensities for varying times) resulted in greatly reducing their ability to germinate. The plants that were obtained showed no indication of any genetic change.

An experiment with extremely high pressure may be mentioned here. Mature seed of Line 1A was subjected in 1936 to 500 to 9,000 times normal atmospheric pressures for varying lengths of time from 5 to 90 minutes. Germination of the treated seed was greatly reduced. However, 50 plants were obtained, and all appeared normal in every respect. Pollen determinations of these plants showed that no mutations causing pollen abortion had occurred. Since it had been established that pollen abortion is a reliable measure of mutation frequency, it was not considered necessary to grow $F_2$'s.

Several series of experiments having to do with aging, or conditions under which seed have been stored, have been carried on. The results of some of these are so similar to results obtained from radiation experiments that they may be properly reviewed here. These experiments were conducted over a period of years from 1933 to 1942 (157, 211).

In 1934 ample records were obtained to demonstrate that seeds of the standard Line 1A of *D. stramonium,* when stored under ordinary laboratory conditions, give increased mutation rates the longer they are stored. Seeds one year old or less gave a mutation rate of less than 1 per cent, while seeds seven to eight years old gave a rate of nearly 9 per cent. When stored under the usual conditions of fluctuating high temperature (70 to 85° F) and dryness that exist in our laboratory storage rooms, *Datura* seed loses its ability to germinate after about 10 years. The data from which these mutation rates were derived were assembled from pollen-abortion records. Later, chromosomal and breeding tests verified the pollen records. On the average, there was an increase of nearly 1 per cent in the number of plants with aborted pollen for each year of additional storage. In progenies grown from plants from the seven- to eight-year-old seed at least 11 visible morphological mutant types were recovered (94, 100).

That other factors besides age may have been responsible for these increases in mutation rates obtained from laboratory-stored seed was indicated by results obtained in 1934 and again in 1941. In 1934 seed was obtained that had been buried in soil for 22 years. When tested by the same methods as had been used for the seed stored in the laboratory, plants from the 22-year-old seed showed no higher rate of mutation than 1-year-old Line 1A controls. In 1941 a quantity of *Datura* seed that had been buried in the ground for 39 years was received from the U. S. Department of Agriculture. These were part of a large variety of crop, flower, and weed seeds that had been buried near Washington, D.C., in 1902 at the start of an experiment to determine the duration of viability of seed of some common species. A total of 367 seeds was received and planted for further testing. Although the seed was nearly 40 years old, it germinated exceedingly well; 359 seedlings (97.5 per cent) were obtained. These plants were examined for pollen abortion and only a very few with significant amounts of pollen abortion were found. $F_2$ progenies of 78 of the plants from this 39-year-old seed were grown and four (5.1 per cent) were found to segregate for new morphological types, presumably due to gene mutations. While this rate is considerably higher than for controls, it is far less than that obtained from seed "aged" under laboratory conditions (106, 157).

The low mutation rates obtained from the 22-year-old and 39-year-old buried seed indicate that age alone has little if any part in causing an increase in the rate of mutation in *Datura*. The high mutation rate manifest in plants grown from seed stored in the laboratory was apparently caused by environmental factors rather than age alone.

Heat and moisture are two of the factors that were obviously different in the case of the buried seed from that stored in the laboratory. It may be suggested also that the probable reduction in the amount of oxygen surrounding the buried seed may also have been a factor in keeping down the rate of mutation. This latter possibility has not been experimentally tested in *Datura*.

An elaborate series of experiments to test the effects of heat and moisture on the mutation rate was begun in 1934 in cooperation with the Boyce Thompson Institute. Line 1A seeds at controlled moisture contents from 2 to 15 per cent were treated at temperatures from 45° to 80° C for periods ranging from 2 hours to 5 days. The results of these experiments were published in 1936. Mutation rates were measured, as in other experiments, by determining the percentages of plants showing high proportions of aborted pollen. The highest mutation rates, about 5 per cent, were obtained from plants grown from seeds with 5 per cent moisture content heated at 75° and 80° C for 14 to 18 hours. In general the mutation rate increased with higher temperature, moisture content, and with the prolonged duration of treatment. While the mutation rates obtained in these experiments were higher than from controls, they were not so high as from seed "aged" in the laboratory (115).

Since "aging" of seed had been found to increase the mutation rate as shown by pollen abortion and the appearance of recessive gene mutations, it seemed advisable to test the effects of aging of pollen. Accordingly, in 1935, a series of tests was made on the aging of pollen from normal Line 1A plants. It was found under the conditions of the experiment that pollen kept for about two weeks was still viable in crosses. Plants grown from pollinations with the aged pollen showed consistently high mutation rates as shown by pollen abortion. From pollen aged from 4 to 13 days, 29 pollen-abortion mutations were recorded in 193 plants tested, giving a mutation rate of 15.0 per cent. Experiments made in 1936 in which better controls of temperature and moisture were maintained during the storage of the pollen failed to show a similar increase in occurrence of mutations (107).

It has not been possible to conclude with certainty what the agent, or agents, are that have been responsible for the apparent increase in mutation rates obtained in these "aging" experiments. The results are not unlike some following x-ray and radium treatments. Perhaps it may be found that the effects of "aging" can be attributed to some form of natural radiation. For that reason a review of the experiments with aging seed or pollen has been included here.

**Comparison of the Effects of Different Kinds of Radiation.** The work of Conger and Giles (1950) on the effects of thermal neutrons on plant tissues suggested that this form of radiation was even more effective in producing genetic changes than x-rays or gamma rays. Since the relative biological effectiveness of slow neutrons appears to be different from that of x-rays or gamma rays, it seemed important to determine the results of exposure to this radiation in producing both chromosomal abnormalities and gene mutations in *Datura*.

The studies of the genetic effects of radiation in *Datura* have differed from most other radiation studies with plants in that the seeds have been exposed and the results determined by examination of the effects on the germ cells or other tissues of the mature plant. Obviously many cell generations intervene between the actual exposure and the observation and recording of the effects of the radiation. As already noted, earlier radiation experiments were conducted in order to obtain new mutations that could be used as labels or markers for chromosomes, or parts of chromosomes, in order to extend the genetic analysis of the chromosomes. The experiments to be reported here were carried on especially to determine the effect of different radiations on *Datura*. The method used with *Datura* does not give information on the effects of radiations on the whole plant, as in the extensive studies of chronic irradiation with the Brookhaven gamma field (Sparrow and Singleton, 1953; Mikaelsen, 1956). Nor does it demonstrate the immediate effects in the production of chromosome abnormalities, as in the many accurate determinations of the results of irradiation of pollen or pollen mother cells of *Tradescantia* by Thoday and Reed (1947), Sax (1950), Kirby-Smith and Swanson (1954), or Conger (1954). The method of exposure of seed to radiation has been used also with barley and wheat (Caldecott *et al.*, 1952; Caldecott and Smith, 1952; Ehrenberg *et al.*, 1952; Ehrenberg and Nybom, 1952) and has given rise to many strains of practical value. Although the method does not give a complete record of all the changes produced by radiation, it does give comparable data on the mutations that survive into mature plants and that can be used in further breeding work. It is therefore an excellent method for comparing the genetic effects of different kinds of radiation.

As already described, a quick and easily comparable index of the quantitative effects of any radiation on *Datura* seeds was discovered in the amount of pollen abortion shown by the plants that were grown from the seeds. As early as 1934 it had been found that data on pollen abortion could be utilized as a reliable measure of mutation rate. The use of such an index makes it unnecessary to grow $F_2$ or later generations in order to discover mutations and obtain a measure of their frequency.

In 1952 the Atomic Energy Commission requested this station to undertake a study, using these special techniques, of the effect of thermal neutrons on the mutation rate in *Datura*. As in subsequent tests with other radiations, seeds of *D. stramonium* Line 1A in plastic bags at a constant moisture content of 4.9 per cent were subjected to the radiation, germinated in flats in the greenhouse, and later transferred to permanent positions in the field. These field-grown plants were then studied for pollen abortion and for chromosomal aberrations. The next year, 1953, this work was extended to test the effects from a nuclear detonation. Here the seeds were exposed at varying distances from the detonation and shielded from blast, heat, and primary gamma radiation by being enclosed in a temperature-controlled chamber capped with a lead hemisphere 7 inches in thickness. More detailed information of the techniques employed and the problems involved were given in a symposium on the biological effects of radiation from nuclear detonations and especially by Plough (1954) in his introduction to that symposium. After irradiation, the seeds were germinated, grown, and examined as before. For comparison in these experiments other seeds from the same capsules used in the nuclear detonation tests were exposed to gamma rays or to x-rays. In 1954 and 1955 the work was further extended to include not only the effects of x-rays and radiation from the nuclear detonation but also the effects of neutrons from the Oak Ridge National Laboratory cyclotron and thermal neutrons in a thermal column at the Brookhaven National Laboratories.

Two main lines and one subsidiary line of approach were used in this study on *Datura*. The pollen mother cells were examined at first meiotic metaphase for gross chromosomal aberrations, the pollen grains were examined for extent of genic or chromosomal abnormality, and finally the morphologically aberrant plants were examined to see if there was any evidence that periclinal or mixochimeras had been formed.

CHROMOSOMAL STUDIES. Buds from plants whose seeds had been exposed to the various radiations were picked in the field and brought into the laboratory where the anthers were crushed and the p.m.c. stained in iron-acetocarmine on slides and examined for chromosomal aberrations.

At the first meiotic metaphase the 12 pairs of *Datura* chromosomes normally appear as bivalents. When, through radiation or some other cause, two or more chromosomes have been broken, there is the possibility of reciprocal interchange, which will give rise to chains or circles of four, six, eight, etc., chromosomes, depending upon the number which have been broken. There is also the possibility of the loss of chromosomal material leading to deficiencies or the accumulation of extra-chromosomal material leading to duplications and inversions within the chromosome. Reciprocal translocations, large deficiencies, and large duplications can be recognized; but small deletions, duplications, and inversions cannot be accurately determined by the method used. This does not interfere with the validity of the work, however, because the same kind of aberrations were counted regardless of the type of radiation, and the final comparison of the effects was based on the same scoring scheme (*10, 219*).

Table 13 shows the various types and frequencies of aberrations found in 1953 and 1954 with the different kinds of radiations. The order of frequency is as follows: circle of four, chain of four, deficiency, duplication, circle of four plus circle of six, necktie, unequal bivalent, and necktie plus circle of four. As is usually true in irradiated plants at metaphase, circles of four are by far the most common type of interchange found, constituting in this series slightly more than half of the total aberrations.

TABLE 13

COMPARISON OF ABERRATION TYPES FROM DIFFERENT RADIATIONS

| Exposure | Plants Examined | Total Aberrations | Cir. of 4 | Chain of 4 | Necktie | Def. | Dup. | Cir. 6 and Ch. 4 | Neck. and Cir. 4 | Unequal Bivalent |
|---|---|---|---|---|---|---|---|---|---|---|
| X-rays, 10,000 r .. | 104 | 16 | 9 | 2 | 1 | 2 | – | – | 1 | 1 |
| Cyclotron neutrons, 650 rep ....... | 75 | 2 | – | – | 1 | 1 | – | – | – | – |
| Thermal neutrons from Brookhaven pile, $7.82 \times 10^{12}$ ion pairs per cc | 14 | 9 | 4 | 1 | – | – | 1 | 3 | – | – |
| Fast neutrons from detonation, 760 rep .......... | 104 | 21 | 12 | 3 | – | 3 | 2 | – | – | 1 |
| Totals .... | 297 | 48 | 25 | 6 | 2 | 6 | 3 | 3 | 1 | 2 |

Although the types of chromosomal abnormalities found in plants from seed exposed to thermal neutrons were the same as those in plants following other kinds of radiation, the frequency of a circle of four plus a circle of six was much greater in these plants. This was thought to be due to the greater effect of the given dosage of thermal neutrons. However, Caldecott et al. (1952) also found a larger percentage of circles of four plus circles of six in thermal neutron-treated barley, a plant apparently not damaged to as great an extent by high dosages of thermal neutrons. In neither case, however, have sufficient plants been analyzed to determine whether or not this difference is statistically significant.

The deficiencies listed in column 7 of Table 13 were of various kinds and degrees and are classified together under this heading for convenience. For example, the two deficiencies following x-ray treatment were losses of a whole or large portions of a translocated chromosome, resulting in metaphase plates showing 10 bivalents plus a chain of three rather than the normal complement of 12 bivalents. The three deficiencies from detonation radiation included one plant with 11 bivalents plus a univalent, one plant with 10 bivalents, a chain of three, and a small free fragment; and, finally, one plant with 11 bivalents, a univalent, and a small free fragment. The deficiency following exposure in the cyclotron was the loss of a whole chromosome, resulting in 11 bivalents and a univalent at metaphase. The duplications were extra fragments of chromosomes present with 12 bivalents. The unequal bivalents might have been either duplications or deletions and so were included under a separate heading.

The results, as shown in Table 14, indicate that the relative biological effectiveness (RBE) for fast neutrons from a nuclear detonation in relation to x-rays or gamma rays in producing chromosomal aberrations in *Datura* was about 14. These results agree well with those obtained from an investigation of the induced pollen lethals found in the same material and with the results reported by Kirby-Smith and Swanson (1954) from experiments with *Tradescantia*. The agreement with the *Tradescantia* work is rather remarkable considering the difference in

TABLE 14

COMPARATIVE EFFECTS OF VARIOUS RADIATIONS ON CHROMOSOMAL ABERRATIONS

| Exposure | Dose | Per Cent Aberrations |
|---|---|---|
| X-rays | 10,000 r | 15.3 |
| Gamma rays | 10,000 r | 19.1 |
| Cyclotron neutrons | 650 rep | 2.6 |
| Thermal neutrons from Brookhaven pile | $7.82 \times 10^{12}$ ion pairs per cc | 64.0 |
| Fast neutrons from detonation | 760 rep | 20.1 |

radiation sensitivity of the two plants, the fact that one irradiated cell was haploid and the other diploid, the fact that one cell was in an active condition and the other dormant, and, finally, the fact that one set of results was obtained from the chromosomes of the same cell that was irradiated and the other obtained from cells many generations removed from the irradiated cells (225).

Strangely enough, the neutrons from the cyclotron did not, in the one exposure that was made, demonstrate nearly as effective aberration-producing powers as did the neutrons from the detonation or even the 10,000 roentgens of x-rays or gamma rays. The reason for this is not apparent and resolution of the problem must await more comprehensive testing of neutron-treated seeds.

The results with thermal neutrons indicated their great efficiency in causing aberrations, although no definite RBE could be established. The dosage of thermal neutrons used in this experiment were quite damaging to the plant generally, as demonstrated by the low germination and survival rates in Table 15. With the exception of the thermal neutron treatment, none of the exposures decreased either germination or survival of the plants to any extent.

One point that should be made in regard to the results is that the kind of chromosomal aberration induced by the neutrons, regardless of their source, is the same as that produced by the gamma and x-radiations.

Neither the neutrons nor the high intensity x-rays tend to produce any hitherto unobserved chromosomal changes.

POLLEN-ABORTION STUDIES. By the appearance of pollen it has been found possible to distinguish between chromosomal and gene mutations affecting pollen abortion in *Datura*. The method was described in 1934 and has been found reliable in determining increased mutation rates from aged seed and from various treatments. Two types of pollen abortion are usually readily distinguishable. In one, the chromosomal type, the pollen grains abort at an early stage, resulting in small, shriveled, and empty grains. The other is marked by subnormal to very small size grains and usually by differences that were interpreted as degenerative changes in their contents. Pollen grains from anthers of plants

TABLE 15

GERMINATION AND SURVIVAL FOLLOWING RADIATION OF SEED

| Exposure | Total Seeds | Germination | | Mature Plants | |
|---|---|---|---|---|---|
| | | No. | % | No. | % |
| X-rays, 10,000 r ...................... | 300 | 270 | (90.0) | 258 | (86.0) |
| Cyclotron neutrons, 650 rep ........... | 300 | 272 | (92.0) | 252 | (84.0) |
| Thermal neutrons from Brookhaven pile, | | | | | |
| 7.82 × 10¹² ion pairs per cc ........... | 300 | 149 | (49.6) | 17 | ( 5.7) |
| Fast neutrons from detonation, 760 rep .... | 400 | 360 | (90.0) | 330 | (82.5) |
| Control ............................. | 300 | 274 | (91.3) | 265 | (88.3) |

grown from irradiated seeds were examined and classified as: (1) normal, (2) "chromosomal mutations"—small, shriveled, and empty, and (3) "gene mutations"—subnormal to small size. Ten plants listed as belonging to the gene-mutation type were all found to be free from obvious chromosomal abnormalities, thus confirming the genic nature of the mutations. Of 11 classified as chromosomal types, all except 3 showed chromosomal abnormalities. It was suggested that the discrepancies might be due either to error in predicting the type of mutation causing the pollen abortion or to failure to delimit the mutant sector correctly. A more likely explanation now seems to be the early activity of lethal genes, causing abortion at a very young stage. However, it appeared that in the majority of cases it was possible to distinguish between these two types of pollen abortion; and the results, as shown in Table 16, indicate a constant ratio of chromosome to gene type of abortion with the various treatments (*94, 209*).

Ratios of chromosomal types of pollen lethals to gene types are the same (about 4:1) for the x-irradiated and fast-neutron treated materials but quite different (3:2) for the thermal-neutron dose. Biologically different responses for thermal neutrons as compared with x-rays have been noted by other investigators (Caldecott *et al.*, 1952). Unlike other observers, who have noted gross morphological changes as different qualitative responses, we have observed no external structural aberra-

TABLE 16

TYPES OF INDUCED POLLEN LETHALS FOUND FOLLOWING RADIATION

| | Flowers Tested | Per Cent Flowers with Pollen Lethals | Pollen Lethal Types Found in Individual Flowers (Per Cent) | | |
|---|---|---|---|---|---|
| Exposure | | | Empty (Chromosomal) | Small (Gene) | Empty and Small (Chromosomal and Gene) |
| X-rays, 10,000 r .......... | 1,537 | 43 | 31 | 7 | 5 |
| Cyclotron neutrons, 650 rep | 1,520 | 27 | 19 | 5 | 3 |
| Thermal neutrons from Brookhaven pile, 7.82 × 10¹² ion pairs per cc ........... | 29 | 86 | 41 | 17 | 28 |
| Fast neutrons from detonation, 760 rep .............. | 1,955 | 56 | 39 | 8 | 9 |

tions unique for thermal-neutron exposures. The differences detected and recorded were for pollen lethals (209, 225).

Estimates and comparisons of relative mutation rates may be furnished by data on pollen lethal sectors induced in *Datura*. These sectors generally develop from aberrant initials in the second layer of the embryonic plumule and occur as limited regions of the plant at maturity. At times the entire plant may be involved. Inasmuch as mature *Datura* plants may bear scores or even hundreds of flowers, the amount or degree of sectoring uncovered depends, to a large extent, on the size of the sample analyzed. Therefore, an attempt was made to obtain one flower from each half-plant and one and four flower collections from each quadrant. When the sample is increased from two flowers per plant to four flowers, the sectoring found is approximately doubled, as can be seen from Table 17. An increase to 16-flower-per-plant samples shows a relatively small

TABLE 17

POLLEN LETHAL SECTORS FOLLOWING RADIATION

| Exposure | Plants with Pollen Lethals | Plants with Same Pollen Lethals in All Flowers No. and % [*] | Normal and Chromosomal Types | Normal and Gene Types | Chromosomal and Gene Types |
|---|---|---|---|---|---|
| X-rays, 10,000 r ............ | 135 | a–76 (56.2) | 28 | 11 | 5 |
| | | b–39 (28.8) | 42 | 20 | 9 |
| | | c–30 (22.2) | 44 | 22 | 11 |
| Cyclotron neutrons, 650 rep .. | 78 | a–56 (71.7) | 21 | 6 | 1 |
| | | b–30 (38.4) | 43 | 16 | 3 |
| | | c–24 (30.7) | 46 | 19 | 4 |
| Fast neutrons from detonation, 760 rep ................ | 223 | a–143 (64.1) | 25 | 8 | 3 |
| | | b–66 (29.5) | 42 | 18 | 6 |
| | | c–54 (24.2) | 47 | 21 | 8 |

[*] a—based on 2-flower-per-plant sample; b—based on 4-flower-per-plant sample; c—based on 16-flower-per-plant sample.

increase in sectoring. Apparently most sectors on plants with both good and bad pollen areas involve approximately one-fourth to one-half of the plant. Sectors smaller than one-fourth of a plant are comparatively rare. The small number (17) of thermal neutron treated plants which reached maturity (Table 15) precluded an extension of this sectoring study to these plants. The similarities among percentages of sectoring of x-irradiated and fast neutron types show that different qualitative responses or biological differences are not induced in *Datura* by these dosages.

MUTATION OF VISIBLE GENES. Tabulation of the numbers of visible morphological mutants was not attempted in these experiments. Facilities did not permit the growing of large numbers of $F_2$ cultures in which segregation of new types could be observed. However, sufficient numbers of $F_2$'s were obtained to demonstrate that these several sources of radiation do produce mutations of this sort as well as chromosomal and pollen-abortion mutations.

Of the plants grown from seed treated with thermal neutrons, 83 were tested by offspring. Twenty-three of these were found to give cultures segregating for various types of obvious morphological characters. Eighty-four plants from seed exposed to neutrons in the cyclotron were similarly tested and 15 were found to give segregating cultures. Of those exposed to the fast neutrons in the nuclear detonation, offspring were obtained from 143 plants selected at random. Of these, 21 segregated for distinct types.

These figures all indicate a very high rate of mutation to distinct forms, which may be assumed to be mostly of the simple gene type. It has been possible to continue breeding work with only a few of these new types. Those that have been investigated show typical Mendelian inheritance. The new types that appeared in these experiments were of the same nature as those that had appeared following earlier exposures to x-rays, radium, and other treatments. Albinos, pales, and seedling types were the most common. New leaf, floral, and habit characters were nearly as frequent and, as usual, few mutations affecting capsule size or shape were recorded. Two new white-flowered forms were recorded, one of which had purple stems; there also appeared a new type with inermis capsules. No distinction could be made between the nature of new types appearing from the different sources of radiation, nor was it possible to obtain sufficient data to determine whether there were significant differences in the rates of particular mutations caused by radiation from the several sources.

MORPHOLOGICALLY ABERRANT PLANTS. Numerous morphologically aberrant plants were produced directly by these various radiations with no apparent relationship between the degree or character of the abnormalities and either chromosomal aberrations as detected in the pollen mother cells or pollen grain abnormalities. These abnormalities were of several sorts; and the degree of abnormality ranged from extremely weak plants, which did not survive the seedling stage, to plants only slightly abnormal. The most frequent sort of abnormality that appeared following these treatments was a condition in which the leaves and stems appeared pale green instead of a purplish green as normally. Other recurrent types were recorded with rough or puckered leaves, narrow or broad leaves, and a few with yellowish leaves. A few plants were found with distinctly darker stems. No particular radiation source was responsible for any specific sort of irregularity. No recognizable $2n + 1$ type appeared following any of these treatments.

As shown in Table 15, the exposures given, with a single exception, had no ill effects on germination. The exposure to thermal neutrons reduced the germination to 50 per cent and, of the 149 seedlings obtained, only 17 reached maturity. As might be expected from an exposure so severe, many of the adults also showed extreme abnormalities. The plants obtained from seed exposed in the cyclotron were the least abnormal of any in the series of experiments. Of 252 adult plants in the field, only one was recorded as being slightly abnormal.

No aberrant types had been recorded among plants grown from x-ray-treated seed in previous experiments. In the 1954 experiments 11 plants were recorded as being not quite normal among 270 field-grown adults. A much more careful examination was made of all plants in these recent experiments than in earlier years. About one in ten of the adults obtained from the seed exposed to the detonation fast neutrons showed abnormalities to some extent.

The cytological investigations that were conducted were not conclusive concerning the reason for the appearance of the different types of abnormalities recorded. Many of the irregularities noted involved only a sector, large or small, of a plant. This is in agreement with the other effects found after seed treatment. None of the abnormalities reappeared in a succeeding generation grown from selfed seed. It is suggested that some, if not most, of the aberrant types that have appeared in plants grown from treated seed may be caused by small chromosomal deficiencies brought about by the irradiation.

**Sectorial and Periclinal Chimeras.** Other work with *Datura* has demonstrated that sectorial and periclinal chimeras often occur following the treatment of seed with certain mutagenic agents (Chapter 8). Since chromosome unbalance often produces morphological abnormalities, it was considered advisable to examine the plants to determine if there was any evidence of ploidy in the epidermis or internal tissue.

The epidermal layer was stripped and the size of the stomata observed directly with the microscope. *Datura* plants with tetraploid or octoploid epidermis have larger stomata than normal $2n$ plants, as do some $2n + 1$ plants. By this method a rapid determination of ploidy in epidermal cells was possible (99).

Some modifications of the technique for the observation of chromosomes in bud meristems were necessary, since the usual hydrochloric or acetic acid hydrolysis rendered the material unsuitable for staining. Since the somatic chromosomes are quite long and tend to become entangled at mitosis, pretreatment with para-dichlorobenzene was necessary. A new method was therefore developed and applied to the buds. These were treated in para-dichlorobenzene for 3 hours, then fixed overnight in a mixture of 5 parts glacial acetic acid, 5 parts commercial formaldehyde, and 85 parts of 70 per cent ethyl alcohol. A 5-minute hydrolysis in hydrochloric acid (10 per cent) followed by an overnight soaking in a 5 per cent pectinase solution softened the tissue sufficiently so that the application of pressure on the cover slip would flatten the cells in the acetocarmine on the slide.

Using these procedures, a number of the morphologically abnormal plants showed enlarged guard cells and stomata, indicating ploidy in the epidermal layer at least. A few of the plants whose bud meristems were so examined had extra chromosomes. Several of these plants showed ploidy in the epidermal hairs and a normal $2n$ chromosomal complement in the underlying tissues, while at least one was apparently reversed with a normal $2n$ epidermis and extra chromosomes in the interior tissue.

Since the Genetics Experiment Station was discontinued before this part of the project could be completed, it was not possible to make conclusive studies. However, enough evidence was gathered to indicate the presence of either periclinal or sectorial chimeras in some of the morphologically aberrant plants.

**Summary.** In *Datura*, as in so many other organisms, radiations have been very useful as inducers of genic and chromosomal mutants, and these in turn have been helpful in clarifying the answers to many questions of morphogenesis and physiology. On the other hand, it has been possible to use the knowledge gained from irradiated plants in the comparison of the effectiveness of different types of radiations—thermal and fast neutrons from various sources. To a great extent the conclusions seem clear-cut. All the radiations so far tested seem to cause the same types of both genic and chromosomal aberrations, but the effectiveness of the different radiations is quite different. Neutrons cause much greater effects, both genic and chromosomal, than do either x-rays or gamma rays for equivalent energies.

# 10

# Sporophytes and Gametophytes

SOPHIE SATINA

The transition from the sporophyte generation to the gametophyte generation in plants has long been a problem of special interest. Among the vital and dynamic processes that prepare the plant for reproduction, the most important phase is meiosis, by which the diploid sporophyte forms the haploid gametes. A vast amount of data has been obtained from studies of the cytology, histology, and morphology of the megasporangium and microsporangium and of the formation of the female and male gametophytes. Among numerous other plants, *Datura* also has been a subject for such studies. Therefore it is desirable to present here a brief outline of the growth and activity of the tissues and organs involved in these stages of development.

**Megasporangium.** The initiation and early development of the megasporangium, or ovule, is discussed in Chapter 8. Its growth in early stages depends primarily on the activity of the innermost germ layer (L III) (Fig. 41a). In early stages the ovule is always erect (Fig. 41b), but its shape changes during development. The ovule begins to curve with the development of the integument at the base of the megaspore mother cell (Fig. 41d). Its inversion increases during meiosis and, when the functional megaspore is formed and divides mitotically, the ovule is either anatropus or campilotropus (Fig. 37d, e) or, most frequently, it becomes intermediate between these two types. The form varies considerably within the same capsule in all species.

The nucellus develops first. The growth of the integument begins only after the differentiation of the archesporial cell (Fig. 41b, c). As in most angiosperms, this sporogenous cell does not divide before it increases in size and becomes the megaspore mother cell (m.m.c.). Apparently a number of nucellar cells are potentially sporogenous. It is not unusual to find from two to five archesporial cells located in the subepidermal layer of the nucellus. Less frequently one or two additional archesporial cells appear in the hyposubepidermal layer also. These cells are easily distinguished from other nucellar cells by their larger

168

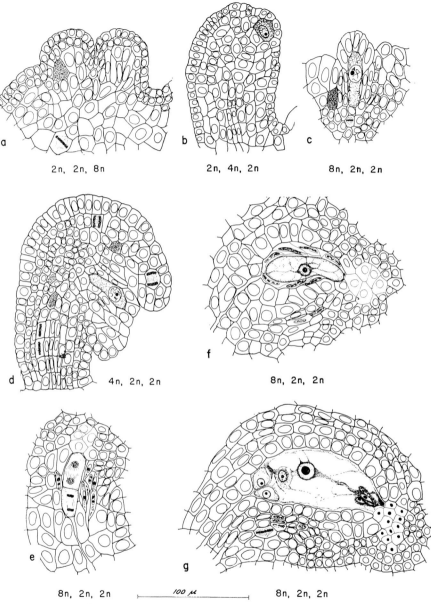

2n, 2n, 8n      2n, 4n, 2n      8n, 2n, 2n

4n, 2n, 2n      8n, 2n, 2n

8n, 2n, 2n      *100 μ*      8n, 2n, 2n

FIG. 41. Development of the ovule in periclinal chimeras of *D. stramonium*.
(a) Participation of an 8*n* L III in early development of two ovules; (b) nucellus
with an archesporial cell. Dividing diploid epidermal cells initiate the growth of
integument; (c) prophase in a 2*n* m.m.c.; (d) curving ovule. Growth of the integument; (e) deterioration of nucellar cells adjacent to m.m.c.; (f) disorganized
nucellar cells; (g) embryo sac. Endothelium open at the chalazal end.

size and stronger affinity for stains. Cases have been observed in which they became megaspore mother cells and reached the metaphase and even the anaphase stages of the first meiotic division. An ovule with three dividing megaspore mother cells is shown in Fig. 42a. This was found in normal diploids, in plants carrying the "dyad" gene, and particularly in the developing ovules of *D. stramonium* triploids. However,

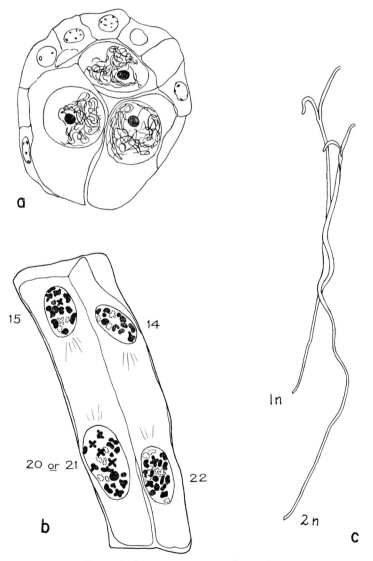

Fig. 42. (a) Nucellus with three m.m.c. at prophase; (b) meiosis in twin m.m.c. Each nucleus with a different number of chromosomes; (c) twin seedlings; one is diploid, the other haploid.

as a rule only one of the archesporial cells becomes the megaspore mother cell. The others gradually lose their contents and are absorbed like the rest of the nucellar cells lying around the functioning megaspore mother cell. The fate and function of the large nucellar portion located beneath the base of the archesporial cell are quite different and will be discussed later in connection with the development of the ovular coat.

The formation of additional archesporial cells explains the appearance of twin seedlings in *Datura*. Twin megaspore mother cells found in triploids at first metaphase and anaphase in meiosis when chromosome counts could be made indicated that both megaspore mother cells developed independently; each daughter cell contained different numbers of chromosomes (Fig. 42b). The same conclusion has been drawn from records of the twin seedlings that have developed from single seeds. None of those observed were "identical twins." One of the seedlings of one pair was a normal diploid, the other a haploid (Fig. 42c). In another case when one of the parents was heterozygous for a recessive gene, "curled," the two seedlings that developed from one seed were both diploids but different—one was normal and the other "curled" (97).

**The Female Gametophyte.** The megaspore mother cell divides meiotically; both meiotic divisions are always transverse and are followed immediately by cytokinesis (Fig. 41e). As a result of these two divisions a linear tetrad of four megaspores is formed. Each megaspore contains the reduced number of chromosomes, but in all *Datura* species it is always the lower cell lying at the chalazal end of the ovule that survives and gives rise to the embryo sac (Fig. 41f). The three upper megaspores disintegrate early and turn into a shapeless mass. In some cases the disintegration of the two upper megaspores occurs still earlier, before or during an abortive second meiotic division.

As described by Guignard (1902), who reported the double fertilization of *D. "laevis" (D. stramonium)*, the gametophyte, or functional megaspore, in *Datura* species follows the common and well-known course of development. After three successive mitotic divisions the so-called normal type of an eight nucleated embryo sac contains at its micropylar end the egg cell and two synergids, at the chalazal end three antipodal cells, and near the center of the embryo sac the central nucleus, which appears after the fusion of two polar nuclei (Fig. 41g). The fusion of these nuclei in *Datura* always occurs before fertilization (169).

**The Ovular Coat.** Incomplete information on the ovular coat of *Datura*, with particular reference to its epidermal structure, is found in a number of early works (Chatin, 1874; Lohde, 1874; Marloth, 1883; Holfert, 1890). The literature on this subject has been covered by Souèges (1907) in his studies of the structure of the ovular coat in the SOLANACEAE, including five *Datura* species (*D. stramonium, D. quercifolia, D. ferox, D. meteloides,* and *D. metel*). Most of Souèges' findings as reported in this fundamental and well-known work were confirmed in the present studies on *Datura*.

The ovular coat in all *Datura* species has a dual origin. Its distal end is formed by the single integument and the basal part by the cells of the nucellus. As has been indicated in Chapter 8, only cells of epidermal origin participate in the formation of the integument. Its initiation occurs soon after the differentiation of the archesporial cell. One or two periclinally dividing epidermal cells first appear near the top of the convex side of the curving ovule (Fig. 41b). These divisions are soon followed by periclinal divisions in other epidermal cells which are located near the archesporial cell, on its sides, but only in those lying at the level with the archesporial cell and *never* beneath it (Fig. 41c, d). The developing integument covers only the cells of this upper portion of the nucellus and does not invest its basal portion. The growth of the distal end of the ovule depends entirely on the elongation and growth of the megaspore mother cell, of the megaspore, and the integument. The latter alone participates in the formation of the micropylar end of the ovular coat. The nucellar cells located between the megaspore mother cell and the developing integument deteriorate (Fig. 41e, f). They disappear completely soon after the meiotic divisions of the megaspore mother cells and the megaspore then comes in direct contact with the innermost layer of the integument (Fig. 41g).

The essential properties and functions of the tissue forming the integument are the same in all ten species of *Datura*. As was shown by Souèges, the tissue differentiates into three layers. The outermost and the innermost layers each have only one tier of cells. The median layer is divided into two zones—the outer and the inner. Each zone is composed of several tiers of cells. The species differ slightly in the width of the cells, in their shape, and in the number of tiers in each zone. The function of each layer is the same in each species. It is protective in the outermost layer. It is nutritive in both zones of the median layer, the cells of which contain a large amount of starch. The function of the innermost layer, called the endothelium or the tapetal layer, depends on the stage of development. At the early stages, when it replaces the completely disorganized nucellar cells around the megaspore, its function is protective. With the growth of the megaspore and the formation of the embryo sac, and particularly after fertilization, its function becomes digestive. The endothelial cells are easily recognized by their shape, larger size, and by their orderly arrangement. This layer almost completely encircles the embryo sac, which is ready for fertilization, leaving only a narrow open space at the micropylar end and a larger one at the chalazal end. The latter never closes and serves as contact between the embryo sac and the basal portion of the ovular coat (Fig. 41g).

As has been mentioned, the basal portion of the ovular coat is formed by the nucellar cells located in the lower portion of the ovule. A comparatively small number of nucellar cells near the chalazal end of the megaspore are digested by the latter, or sometimes later by the antipodal cells (Fig. 41f, g). This results in the formation of the chalazal pocket. But most of the nucellar cells forming the basal region of the ovule remain and take an active part in the formation of the chalazal portion of the ovular coat. They multiply considerably and add primarily to its width and thickness. Their function is protective and nutritive and, like the cells of the median layer of the integument, they contain starch.

Without the use of periclinal chimeras it would not be possible to determine which cells of the ovular coat are nucellar and which are formed by the integument. Observations made on numerous *D. stramonium* chimeras, such as an 8*n*, 2*n*, 2*n*, with polyploid epidermis, indicated clearly that about two-thirds of the ovular coat of an ovule ready for fertilization is formed by the octoploid integument (Fig. 37e). The remaining basal portion is formed by the diploid nucellus. The use of a chimera with 2*n* epidermis and polyploid subepidermal layer showed, as was expected, the reverse, namely, that the larger portion of the ovular coat was diploid and the basal portion polyploid. Both tissues in the coat lie side by side with cells somewhat intermingled where they meet; there is no clearly defined line between the integumental and nucellar tissues of the coat. In ovules the portion of tissue supplied by each is variable. The convex side of the ovule is predominantly covered by the integument and the opposite side by the tissue formed by the nucellus, as is shown in Fig. 37d. The nucellar end of the ovular coat is connected beneath the chalazal cavity with the vascular bundle and the funicle (*169*).

**Microsporangium.** The origin of the stamen primordium and its early development until tissue differentiation in *D. stramonium* is discussed in Chapter 8. The further development of the stamen, its anther and filament, was first studied in detail by Warming (1873). His observations were supported later by Mascré (1921) as well as by our work with other *Datura* species. Like most angiosperms, the anthers of *Datura* contain four microsporangia, or anther sacs. The differentiation of archesporial cells in the young stamen begins at the stage when the latter's outline becomes slightly four-lobed. It is then that a number of archesporial cells located in the subepidermal layer, L II, of the lobes in the stamen can be distinguished from adjacent cells by their distinct increase in size, the presence of larger nuclei, and by their deeply stained contents. They are more numerous in the tall species (*D. metel, D. meteloides, D. innoxia*) than in the smaller species (*D. leichhardtii, D. pruinosa*). The archesporial cells divide periclinally and give rise to two primary layers. Dividing cells in the inner layer produce the sporogenous cells. Cells in the outer primary layer form, by subsequent periclinal divisions proceeding in the centrifugal direction, a number of parietal layers that form the wall of the microsporangium. Its innermost layer of cells develops into the tapetal or nursing layer.

The growth and structure of the microsporangium wall was studied in a number of species of SOLANACEAE by Mascré (1919, 1921). He paid particular attention to the formation, contents, and function of the tapetum. His conclusions on the uniformity in the processes of wall development are based on observations made upon 21 species belonging to 15 genera of SOLANACEAE, including *D. "tatula"* (*D. stramonium*) and *D. "arborea"* (*Brugmansia candida*). Since our studies of the *Datura* species support most of Mascré's observations on the growth of the sporangium wall and on its uniformity in all species studied, the account of our observations will be brief.[1]

The microsporangium wall covered by a single-cell layer of epidermis is formed by four to five, or a few more, parietal layers. The tapetum is adjacent to the outer surface of the crescent-shaped sporogenous layer. The density of the contents of the tapetal cells at various stages of growth indicates their physiological significance. Their increase in size is quite evident at early meiosis of the pollen mother cells. The growth reaches its peak at the end of the second division of the pollen mother cells and the formation of the microspores. The tapetal cells divide by normal mitosis and not by fragmentation, as was suggested by O'Neal (1920). At early stages the cells are uninuclear. Due to the lack of cell-plate formation many cells in later stages contain two, three, or four nuclei. The fusion of nuclei, which results in the appearance of giant nuclei reported by Mascré and other investigators in a number of plants (for references see Schnarf, 1929; Maheshwari, 1950), has not been observed in *Datura*. The formation of the giant nuclei occasionally seen in tapetal cells occurs rather as a result of disturbances in mitosis or incomplete division as suggested by Cooper (1933). It is possible that some fusion of nuclei would be seen if the work were continued; however, since the giant nuclei were seen only in late stages and were lying among degenerating tapetal cells, it seems more likely that their formation is connected with degenerating processes in the tapetum.

All these facts observed in the structure of tapetal cells adjacent to the *outer* surface of the sporogenous tissue were found also in tapetal cells lying in immediate contact with the *inner* surface of the sporogenous tissue which faces the axis of the stamen. The inner and outer tapetal cells do not differ in structure and function, but they do differ in origin. The latter is produced by the primary outer layer, the former by the primary inner layer. The inner layer is apparently derived from sterile cells cut off by the sporogenous tissue, as was observed by Coulter (1898) in *Ranunculus* and noted in other plants by Schnarf (1929). This is in conflict with Mascré and Thomas (1930), who stated that the inner tapetum layer originates from cells belonging to the connective tissue. *Datura* periclinal chimeras prove without doubt that the tapetal cells located on the inner side of the stamen locules are descendants of the subepidermal layer, L II, while the connective tissue of the stamen develops from the layer lying immediately beneath L II, the L III (Chapter 8).

Summarizing the results of these studies on the development of the microsporangium wall, it becomes evident that the differences observed

---

[1] The nature of the cell contents and details on chondriosomes and nutrient substances studied by Mascré were not investigated in our work.

among *Datura* species are not fundamental. The variability found in the number and size of tapetal cells, the number of parietal layers, and the length of time necessary to complete the development of the wall are characters that are dependent on the habit of a species and are influenced by the size of the plant and its vigor of growth.

The same uniformity was found in the development of the pollen mother cells from the sporogenous tissue, which results eventually in the formation of the microspores. The growth of pollen mother cells coincides with that of the tapetum. The primary sporogenous cells divide mitotically to form a number of pollen mother cells, each having one nucleus with a large nucleolus. Their growth is accompanied by a rounding up of the cell. On entering the prophase stage the cells remain attached to each other. Their connection breaks usually at the end of the prophase. At diakinesis the shape of the pollen mother cell is oblong and the cell wall becomes clearly unequal in thickness. It is considerably thicker at both poles than on the sides of the cell. *Datura* is unfavorable material for studying the prophase in meiosis. No method has been found that would allow us to observe clearly the details in the transition phases from leptotene to diplotene.

In general, meiosis in *Datura* proceeds in the usual and normal way and the meiotic divisions follow in quick succession. Since this process is well known in plants and animals, it will be sufficient to give here only a brief account of meiotic divisions in pollen mother cells. The chromatin becomes gathered on slender threads in the nucleus at the onset of prophase. The appearance of well-defined chromosomes of various lengths is followed by the pairing of homologous chromosomes which synapse and split longitudinally, forming four chromatids that remain held together by chiasmata. The split in some chromosomes may be seen at diakinesis, but it becomes much clearer at anaphase. At diakinesis 12 pairs of chromosomes connected at both or at one of their ends appear as bivalents scattered in the pollen mother cell. At metaphase the bivalents become arranged on the equatorial plate of the bipolar spindle. They separate and pass to the poles at anaphase. At telophase a nucleolus appears in each daughter nucleus, as do the nuclear walls. A very short interkinesis is followed by the equational division, which results in the formation of four haploid nuclei. Cytokinesis in all *Datura* species is of the simultaneous type. It occurs after the second telophase when furrows appear at the periphery of the pollen mother cell and move toward its center, dividing the cell into the microspore tetrad or quartet.

The only differences observed among the *Datura* species in the process of microspore formation were in the varying numbers of microspores and in the length of the period necessary for the pollen mother cell development. It is shorter in the species with small flowers and anthers than in the species with large flowers and anthers. No species was found with anthers having more than two, or rarely three, phases of the whole cycle of meiosis simultaneously.

**Mutant Genes Which Cause Irregularities in Sporogenesis.** There are certain recessive genes which cause irregularities in sporogenesis. Some affect the first meiotic division, others the second division, or the cytokinesis. Some of these mutants were found in nature and others appeared following radiation or other treatments. A race carrying a gene affecting the first meiotic division was found in nature near Baltimore, Maryland. The gene was located by trisomic ratios in the $21 \cdot 22$ chromosome. When homozygous it prevents or disturbs the pairing of homologous chromosomes. The 24 univalents lie scattered on the spindle and fail to form a normal genome. About 90 per cent aborted pollen is formed due to irregular distribution of chromosomes. The gene affects the division of the megaspore mother cells in the same way (*85, 88*).

Another mutant was found among $F_1$ offspring of plants pollinated by radium-treated pollen grains. This gene is responsible for the failure of the second meiotic division in the megaspore mother cells as well as in the pollen mother cells. Cytokinesis begins soon after the first telophase and bisects the megaspore mother cell and the pollen mother cell into dyads instead of tetrads of megaspores and microspores. The lack of equational division results in the doubling of their chromosome numbers. This gene, called "dyad," is located in the $9 \cdot 10$ chromosome (*108*).

A gene which appears following the exposure of seeds to x-rays causes the failure of cytokinesis after telophase II in pollen mother cells. This results in the formation of compound microspores containing two to four nuclei. The gene is carried through both the pollen and eggs and has not been located in a specific chromosome (*110*).

Another mutant gene carried by a wild race found in Hungary is located in the $11 \cdot 12$ chromosome. Twin nuclei are formed by homozygous plants causing the doubling of the chromosome number in pollen mother cells. Such doubling is sometimes repeated and nuclei with as many as 96 chromosomes may be formed. Some cells contain only bivalents at diakinesis, instead of tetravalents, and form the so-called "double diploids" (*68*, Chapter 7).

**The Male Gametophyte.** The male gametophyte generation begins after meiosis with the formation of the microspores, or pollen grains. Proper knowledge of the growth and structure of the male gametophyte is of prime importance in genetics, particularly in problems of hybridization. Irregularities in the pollen or pollen-tube divisions, which affect in some way the formation of the male gametes, might be the basis of self-sterility or of incompatibility in crosses. Studies of the details of pollen germination, of pollen-tube growth in the style, or of the time after pollination necessary for the formation of gametes in different species might give information of use in overcoming some of the barriers to fertilization. For example, a knowledge of the time of division of the generative nucleus in the pollen tube growing in the style helps to perfect the technique of style shortening by indicating the proper points at which to cut the style to insure the presence of the dividing generative cell. These are some of the reasons why particular attention has been paid for years to studies of the pollen and pollen tubes in *Datura*.

The accounts of work by other investigators on the male gametophyte reveal a number of conflicting observations. Reports on the growth of pollen and pollen tubes in different species disagree on the mechanisms of both divisions in the gametophyte. Normal mitotic division, the presence of a spindle and of some cytoplasm around the nucleus of the gametes, and the formation of a cell plate following the division of the nucleus were known in a number of plants and were denied or doubted for years in others. The failure to observe normal mitosis in the dividing pollen and in the generative cell has been attributed recently to shortcomings in the methods of fixation and particularly to the use of a nuclear stain instead of a cytoplasmic stain in tracing the presence of cytoplasm in the male gamete. Proper techniques used with suitable material proved that normal mitosis, which had been previously denied in a number of species, does actually occur. It has also been shown that the male gametes are complete cells and not naked nuclei (Finn, 1935; Johnston, 1941).

In working on these problems with *Datura* it has been found necessary to modify the carefully selected fixatives and stains according to the stages of growth and to the particular species being studied. A method that gave good results with some species could not be used without changes with other species. For example, in using the Feulgen reaction for the study of pollen division in *D. stramonium* or *D. leichhardtii*, the hydrolysis process was applied for only 12 minutes, but it was necessary to extend the time for the same process to about an hour in working with *D. ceratocaula, D. innoxia*, and certain other species. The use of a strong acetocarmine solution with a certain amount of chloral hydrate was good in all species for clearing the walls of pollen tubes, in observing the dissected pollen tubes in full length, or for locating the vegetative nucleus or the generative cell. But this solution could not be used in studying details of division in the pollen or in pollen tubes. It was necessary in such cases to use smeared anthers or dissected pollen tubes fixed in Allen-Bouin (B-15) solution and stained in crystal violet with orange G, according to Newton's method (La Cour, 1931). The presence of the sheath of cytoplasm around the nuclei of gametes could be best observed by staining the pollen tubes with Delafield's hematoxylin.

The growth of the young gametophyte begins while the microspore is still within the p.m.c. The round-shaped microspores slip out of it only after producing their own cell walls. Normal mitotic pollen division with a metaphase plate, spindle formation, etc., has been observed in all *Datura* species. In each the generative cell, which is considerably smaller than the vegetative cell, is cut off by a membrane from the latter. When stained by Feulgen reaction, the generative cell can be easily distinguished by the bright purple color of its nucleus as compared to the pale pink color of the vegetative nucleus. The latter appears diffused and contains a very large nucleolus. The difference in their affinity for stain

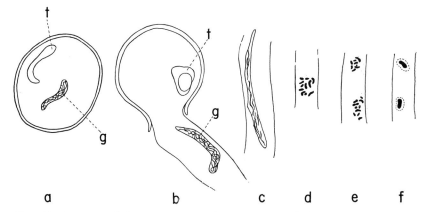

FIG. 43. Division of the generative nucleus in *D. meteloides*. (*g*—generative nucleus; *t*—tube nucleus.) (a) Pollen grain. Prophase in the generative nucleus; (b) pollen and pollen tube. Prophase in the generative nucleus in a pollen tube; (c) pollen tube. Late prophase in the generative nucleus; (d) pollen tube. Metaphase, 11 hours after pollination; (e) anaphase, 11 hours after pollination; (f) two male gametes, 11 hours after pollination.

in both nuclei increases in later stages.[2] With the continued development of pollen the wall between the two cells is no longer visible. The generative cell changes its lateral position and appears in the central region of the pollen.

Mature pollen in all *Datura* species contains two cells. No three-celled pollen, as reported in some other plants, has been observed in *Datura*. Pollen taken from flowers in full bloom showed the generative nucleus beginning to divide. In some species it was at the onset of prophase; in others the prophase was already in an advanced stage. The granular structure of chromatin in the nucleus, which is typical of interphase, was no longer seen. The presence of thin interlaced threads in the oblong generative nucleus proved that it was the prophase stage of the second mitosis in the gametophyte. It was found that in *D. metel, D. meteloides*, and possibly in some other species, division in pollen begins about a week before dehiscence.

Prophase in the generative nucleus was observed also in germinating pollen. The second mitosis of the generative nucleus in the pollen and pollen tube of *D. meteloides* is shown in Fig. 43. The early prophase is shown in a pollen grain before germination and in a pollen tube soon after germination (*a, b*). A late prophase 7 hours after pollination is shown (*c*). A metaphase, anaphase, and two male gametes 11 hours after pollination are also shown (*d, e, f*). *Datura* pollen germinates

[2] This character, seen so clearly when the Feulgen reaction is used to stain mature or germinating pollen, can be used as the best criterion for recognition of the generative cell. It avoids the mistake made in earlier work with *D. metel* pollen in which the generative nucleus was taken for the vegetative in pollen stained with iron hematoxylin (*109*).

readily on the stigma and within an hour after pollination the pollen tube appears through one of the germ pores. In all cases examined the precocious prophase stage was already well advanced. It is of long duration because in all *Datura* species the mitosis in the generative nuclei is completed later in the pollen tube (*186*).

The generative cell and the vegetative nucleus enter into the pollen tube either at the same time or one may follow the other. This order was found to vary in pollen tubes growing on the same stigma and it does not seem to have any influence on further development of the pollen tube. With its growth down the style the chromosome threads contract, become thicker and shorter, and at metaphase well-defined chromosomes are formed. Some are crowded together, others are scattered or aligned along the long axis of the nucleus, but metaphase plates are present in *Datura* species, though some of the plates seem to be rather oblique because of the limited width of the generative cell. Very narrow spindles with thin threads only faintly stained have also been observed. The metaphase stage, which is of a short duration, is rapidly followed by the anaphase and telophase. No attempts have been made to ascertain whether a cell plate is laid down after mitosis or if the gamete cells divide by constriction. Guignard (1902) reported the presence of cytoplasm in the male gametes of *D. "laevis"* (*D. stramonium*). If properly stained, the sheath of cytoplasm around the newly formed nuclei of gametes may be observed in all species. In pollen tubes stained by Feulgen reaction or acetocarmine the cytoplasm remains unstained and a wide clear zone appears around the nucleus.

The species differ considerably in the length of time between pollination and the formation of gametes. Table 18 gives the approximate time of division in the generative nuclei of the ten species. These figures are from observations of pollen tubes in styles of flowers emasculated the day before pollination and kept in tubes with a small amount of water. These were then held for the required time at a controlled tem-

TABLE 18

DURATION OF METAPHASE TO TELOPHASE STAGES IN GENERATIVE NUCLEI IN POLLEN TUBES OF SELFS

| Species | Length of Style (mm) | Hours After Pollination |
|---|---|---|
| D. leichhardtii | 30 | 5–7 |
| D. ferox | 38 | 5–7 |
| D. quercifolia | 40 | 5–7 |
| D. pruinosa | 40 | 4–8 |
| D. stramonium | 70 | 5–7 |
| D. metel | 120 | 12–14 |
| D. ceratocaula | 135 | 6–10 |
| D. discolor | 140 | 9–11 |
| D. innoxia | 150 | 8–10 |
| D. meteloides | 190 | 10–12 |

perature of 26° C. In this table the species are arranged in order of style length. The divisions are completed about 4 to 8 (mostly 5 to 7) hours after pollination in the group of species with styles 30 to 70 mm long. The range of times varies in the remaining five species in which the lengths of styles are 120 to 190 mm. In *D. metel*, with the shortest style in this group, division is accomplished 12 to 14 hours after pollination. It takes less time in those species with longer styles, such as *D. meteloides* and *D. innoxia* (186).

The information obtained from this work with selfs was later used in investigations of various incompatible species crosses to see if the difference in time necessary for the gamete formation would not become a block for fertilization in some combinations. Additional observations on mitosis in pollen tubes were also made in some compatible and incompatible crosses. This work indicated that the division of the generative cell occurred in each cross examined regardless of the length of styles of the species selected. But it became evident from these preliminary tests that in addition to the data on mitosis obtained from selfs, other factors must be taken into consideration in the work with crosses, such as the rate of pollen-tube growth as affected by temperature, and vitality of pollen. The time of mitosis as possibly influenced by the foreign style must be considered. In some species combinations the style would seem to accelerate and in others to delay the end of mitosis; in some crosses division occurred within the same range of time as had been found in selfs. Too few crosses were made to permit any definite conclusions, but there is some indication that in crosses with a high degree of incompatibility the division of the generative cell may be delayed. This work should be continued, since more information is necessary. If these preliminary data are supported by further tests, many interesting questions will arise in connection with the effect of the female tissue (style) on the male gametes, and on their growth, vitality, and division in incompatible crosses.

# 11

# Seed Development

SOPHIE SATINA AND J. RIETSEMA

The comparative study of seed development in selfs of the ten *Datura* species was made for two purposes: to get new information of general botanical interest and to inquire into the possibility of finding some essential differences in seed formation among the *Datura* species. It was hoped that the comparison of observations made on the developing embryo, on the endosperm, and on the tissues forming the seed coat in species might lead to a better understanding of the problem of incompatibility in species crosses.

**Fertilization.** The formation of the female and male gametophytes is discussed in Chapter 10. The double fertilization described first in *D.* "*laevis*" (*D. stramonium*) by Guignard (1902) has been studied in detail only in our Line 1A of *D. stramonium* and in its tetraploid race. The fertilization process could be best followed by using the Feulgen reaction on sectioned material that had been fixed in alchohol–formaldehyde–acetic acid solution. It is stated in Chapter 10 that the division of the generative nucleus in the pollen tube and the formation of two haploid male gametes occur in *D. stramonium* about 5 to 7 hours after pollination at 26° C. Several hours later the pollen tubes reach the ovary and the tube that enters the embryo sac ruptures and releases both male gametes. The male nuclei are at least twice as long as broad. They are smaller in size, contain more chromatic material, and stain much darker with the Feulgen reaction than the large spherical egg and the central nucleus. The shape of the male nuclei is variable. It is oblong on entering the embryo sac but becomes contracted or pear-shaped when it approaches the egg and the central nucleus. It again becomes elongated, tapered, and sharp-pointed at one of its ends when it comes in contact with the haploid female nucleus and the diploid central nucleus. During fusion the male nuclei lying on the surface of these nuclei become gradually incorporated within them. The male nuclei remain visible in the egg and central nucleus for a considerable time and appear as oblong and dark-purple-stained areas at the periphery

181

of the pink-stained fertilized egg and central nucleus. The outline of each male nucleus becomes increasingly vague and the fusion seems to be completed when the fertilized nuclei are again uniformly and faintly stained (*109, 155*).

The fusion of both pairs of nuclei may occur at the same time, but frequently the contact and fusion of nuclei in one of the pairs may precede these processes in the other pair, and either the zygote or the primary endosperm be formed first. It remains unknown whether the cytoplasm that envelops the egg nucleus takes part in fertilization, but the two synergids do not take any visible part. One of them is usually ruptured by the pollen tube entering the embryo sac; the other synergid remains visible until the zygote is formed.

The process of fertilization in other *Datura* species appears to be essentially similar to that of *D. stramonium*, differing only in the length of time that elapses between pollination and fusion of the gametes. This depends on the length of the style of the species, on the rate of pollen germination and of pollen-tube growth, and the resulting earlier or later division of the generative nucleus in the pollen tubes in different species (*105, 186, 202*).

**Formation of the Zygote and Proembryo.** The fusion of the nuclei in fertilization is always followed by a fairly long period of "reorganization" of the substances composing the zygote. The frequently used term "resting period" of the zygote should be avoided. The zygote containing mixed paternal and maternal material with a doubled haploid chromosome complement does not rest. It actually enlarges in size while it is preparing for division. The fusion of nuclei undoubtedly must be followed by some vital and complex actions. Unfortunately nothing is known about the cytochemical processes that must accompany the formation of the zygote. This is true also about the primary endosperm, but the process of reorganization in its triploid nucleus takes less time than in the diploid zygote and the division of the former always precedes by a day or two the division of the zygote in all *Datura* species.

The zygote divides only after the formation of 30 to 40 cells of the endosperm. The earliest division of the zygote, only two days after fertilization, was observed in *D. leichhardtii* and in rare cases in *D. pruinosa*. In *D. stramonium, D. quercifolia, D. ferox*, and usually in *D. pruinosa* it occurs normally 3 or 4 days after pollination. It takes 1 to 2 days more in other species (Fig. 44a, i, p). A few cases of a further delay of zygote division—8 days after pollination—were observed in a race of *D. metel*. Environmental conditions, such as temperature, the age of the plant, moisture, etc., have a considerable influence on the time necessary for the maturation and division of the zygote. By keeping the plants under favorable conditions it has been possible to get earlier zygote division in *D. ceratocaula, D. meteloides*, and *D. discolor*.

Souèges' well-known system of classification of embryonic development in plants is based on the sequences and directions of cell divisions

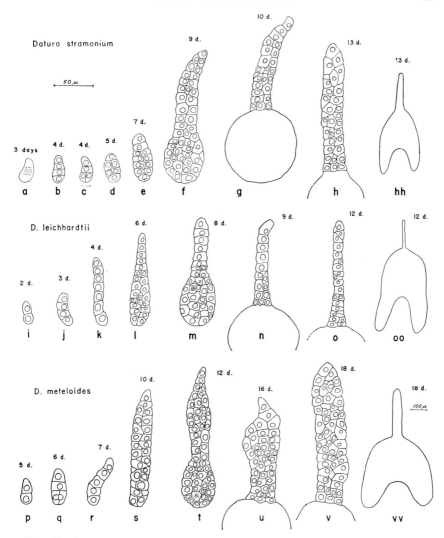

Fig. 44. Successive stages of proembryo development in three species. Each differs in time needed to reach corresponding stages. Note the three types of suspensors.

in proembryos. His work on SOLANACEAE included *D. stramonium*. He followed the growth of the proembryo from the zygote division until the formation of the globe-shaped proembryo and its axillary transition into a bilaterally symmetrical embryo. Because of the inconsistency and variability in the planes of cell divisions in the developing proembryo of *D. stramonium*, Souèges refrained from tracing in this species the origin of some cells forming the globe-shaped proembryo. The lack of a definite pattern in cell divisions is, according to Souèges (1922, 1934), the most striking difference between *Datura* and all the other genera of SOLANACEAE studied. Since we found in other *Datura* species a similar variability in the planes of cell division in the proembryos, as had been reported by Souèges, we made no attempt to follow the mode of segmentation in the growing proembryos after the formation of the octant stage. A brief outline of the proembryo development in *D. stramonium*, Line 1A, will be given here, with the necessary data on the time elapsing between various stages of growth in other species.

As in Souèges' material the zygote in each *Datura* species always divides transversely and forms an apical cell, which lies toward the central portion of the embryo sac, and a basal cell, which lies toward the micropyle. Cells derived from the basal cell later form the suspensor and the root cap. Cells derived from the apical cell form the major portion of the proembryo—the embryo proper with cotyledons, epicotyl and hypocotyl with the primary root.

The basal cell divides first (in contrast to other SOLANACEAE studied by Souèges) and always transversely, but the division of the apical cell is either transverse or longitudinal. In the first case a linear tetrad is formed. In the second case the shape of the tetrad is different. Its distal end contains two sister cells lying side by side and the proximal end has a pair of cells lying one over the other. Both types of tetrads have been observed in the proembryo of *D. stramonium* and of all other species with the exception of *D. leichhardtii*, in which only the linear type was found (Fig. 44b, c, j, q). The proembryo in the latter species is still linear when it reaches the eight-celled stage of growth. The variability in the mode of segmentation starts in other species with the formation of the tetrad proembryo (Fig. 44d, k, r). It causes diversity in the pattern of cell wall orientation, which becomes quite apparent in the octant proembryo, increasing with further development of the latter (Fig. 44e, l, s).

Various stages of growth of *D. stramonium* proembryos and embryos are shown in outlines in Fig. 45 a–j. The 7- to 11-day-old oval, globe-shaped proembryos and the proembryo with a flattened top are axially symmetrical (Fig. 44 a–e). The formation of a bilaterally symmetrical embryo begins when a pair of cotyledonary projections appears on the sides of the embryo body with the flattened top, forming a heart-shaped embryo. It usually occurs when the embryo is about 12 to 13 days old (f, g). The embryo reaches the so-called torpedo stage when the cotyledons are about one-quarter the length of the embryo. With further growth the cotyledons bend in adjustment to the available space within the seed (h, i, j).

It is known from numerous observations made during the years of our *Datura* breeding work that the species differ in their rate of seed development and maturation. This has been observed in natural (field) conditions of growth and in special experiments in which plants of each species were kept, as much as it seemed to be practical, under uniform conditions.

In *D. stramonium* and in the two closely related species, *D. quercifolia* and *D. ferox*, the tetrad is formed normally 4 to 5 days after pollination, the octant 1 or 2 days later, and the oval-shaped proembryo 6 to 7 days after pollination. At this stage of development longitudinal and oblique planes of division predominate in the distal end of the proembryo. This leads to its increase in width. The proximal end elongates because of more frequent transverse divisions and thus forms the suspensor. A 10-day-old globe-shaped proembryo with a well-differentiated suspensor is shown in Fig. 44g. The diameter of the globe-shaped body continues to increase for a day or two until it reaches its last stage of development and becomes a bilaterally symmetrical embryo with initial cells for further growth in differentiation (Fig. 44hh).

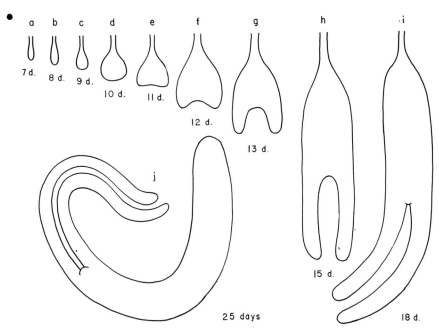

FIG. 45. *D. stramonium.* Various stages in the growth of proembryos (a–e) and embryos (f–j).

A more rapid development is found in *D. leichhardtii.* The linear tetrad is usually formed 3 days after pollination, the linear octant 1 day later. The shape of the proembryo is oval 5 to 6 days after pollination and becomes global about 8 days after pollination (Fig. 44m, n). Two days later it becomes a bilaterally symmetrical embryo with cotyledons (Fig. 44oo).

The greatest variability in the speed of proembryo development may be observed in *D. pruinosa.* Five days after pollination some of the seeds contain only dividing zygotes, small proembryos formed by a few cells, or already well-developed oval-shaped proembryos may be found in other seeds of the same capsule. Depending on the early rates of growth, some proembryos reach the global-shaped stage in about 8 days after pollination, as does *D. leichhardtii;* the slower developing proembryos reach the corresponding stage 2 or 3 days later.

In the remaining five species, *D. discolor, D. ceratocaula, D. meteloides, D. metel,* and *D. innoxia,* the tetrad is rarely formed before the sixth or seventh day and the octant before the seventh or eighth day after pollination. The transition into an oval structure occurs on the tenth or eleventh day. The growth in width and length continues a few days more and global-shaped proembryos in these species usually appear 13 to 17 days after pollination (Fig. 44t, u). The greatest variability in the rate of growth of the proembryo in this group of species occurs in *D. ceratocaula* and *D. metel.* The former has a tendency to develop more rapidly, while the latter shows a distinct tendency toward a lower rate of development. These observations indicate that some species need a longer period of time to develop bilaterally symmetrical embryos than other species. It takes about 3 to 5 days more for these five species than for *D. stramonium, D. quercifolia,* and *D. ferox,* and about a week more than for *D. leichhardtii* and, in most cases, for *D. pruinosa* (Fig. 44vv).

**Differentiation of Cells and Embryo Development.** The differentiation of cells and the formation of various tissues is closely connected with the stage of development and depends entirely on the rate of growth of the species. All species follow the same pattern of differentiation. The first sign of tissue differentiation in the proembryo of *D. stramonium* appears in a 9-day-old proembryo when its oval-shaped body becomes more or less global. The cells of the outermost tier stop dividing periclinally, become arranged in an orderly manner, and differ from the inner mass of cells in size, shape, and staining capacity. This histogenetically distinct peripheral layer (Hanstein's dermatogen) will become the epidermis of the embryo (Fig. 46a).

The differentiation of inner cells begins in the global-shaped proembryo. The loss of homogeneity in the inner tissue is observed first in the density of the cell contents and in the staining capacity of the cells, some staining darker, others lighter (Fig. 46b).

The transition of the proembryo into the embryo is accompanied by a change in the shape of the globe. As a result of subsequent anticlinal divisions of cells located in a few upper tiers of the proembryo's body, its top grows broader and appears flattened. At this stage of growth the differentiation of the inner mass of cells becomes quite evident. Its central portion forms the axial or central core, which appears triangular in sections and contains elongated and narrow cells. The cells forming the tissue surrounding the axial core are different. They are wider and contain larger nuclei but less cytoplasm and stain lighter than the cells of the core. They form the cortex of the body (Fig. 46c). This differ-

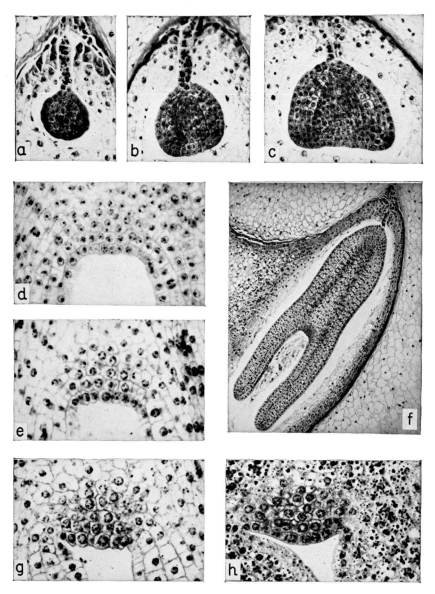

FIG. 46. *D. stramonium.* Longitudinal sections; (a) Ten-day-old proembryo with differentiated peripheral layer; (b) differentiation of inner tissue in an 11-day-old proembryo; (c) 12-day-old proembryo. Differentiated central core; (d) differentiation of the epicotyl in a 13-day-old embryo; (e–h) growth of the epicotyl in 15- to 25-day-old embryos.

entiation of tissues is followed by the initiation of cotyledons. A few subepidermal cells located at opposite sides of the flattened top of the embryo divide periclinally and initiate the formation of two small lateral primordia. Each primordium produces a lateral projection—the cotyledon. With the formation of these two projections the flattened top appears slightly concave and the heart-shaped embryo becomes bilaterally symmetrical. The cotyledons grow rapidly because of intensive cell divisions in their apices. Narrow, elongated procambial cells in the cotyledons and the parenchymal cells on their sides are continuous with the dichotomously branched procambium column and with the cortex in the hypocotyl. Whether the procambium in the cotyledons results entirely from the acropetal growth of the hypocotyl into cotyledons or whether a portion of these cells is derived from tissue differentiation in cotyledons remains unknown. When the embryo reaches the torpedo stage, the cotyledons begin to grow nearly parallel until their apices reach half of the long axis of the embryo sac. They soon begin to bend and become parallel to the curved outlines of the endosperm. When their tips reach the end of the long axis of the embryo sac the cotyledons fold over and grow toward the base of the primary root.

Growth measurements in *D. stramonium* have shown that the relative growth rate of the embryo is at a maximum after 13 days. (The relative growth rate is the ratio of the increase in length in 24 hours to the length at the beginning of that period.) The relative growth rate of the hypocotyl, however, is at a minimum at the fourteenth day. It is during this time that the cotyledons are being rapidly formed, becoming faintly visible as small outgrowths on the twelfth day (Fig. 47). In other words, during most rapid cotyledon formation the part of the embryo from the apical meristem to the suspensor shows a temporary reduction in growth rate. When the cotyledons have reached a length almost equal or even greater than that of the hypocotyl, their relative increase in length is the same. Apparently the formative processes leading to new organs affect the growth of the already existing organ, the hypocotyl.

In *D. stramonium* the embryo reaches its full length in about 3 weeks after pollination. The cotyledons and the massive body of the hypocotyl with the primary root at its basal end are unequal in length, the cotyledons being slightly longer. The ratio of the length of the cotyledons to that of the hypocotyl is approximately 10:9. It takes about 3 more weeks for the embryo to reach maturity. During this last period it grows predominantly in thickness, only slightly in width, but it increases markedly in weight, because the cells of the embryo become filled with reserve food.

The differentiation of tissues and the growth of organs in other species begin at the same stages of development as in *D. stramonium*. The time depends entirely on the rate of growth of each species. It occurs earlier in *D. leichhardtii* and in *D. pruinosa*, about the same time as in *D. stramonium*, in *D. quercifolia*, and *D. ferox*, and somewhat later in other species.

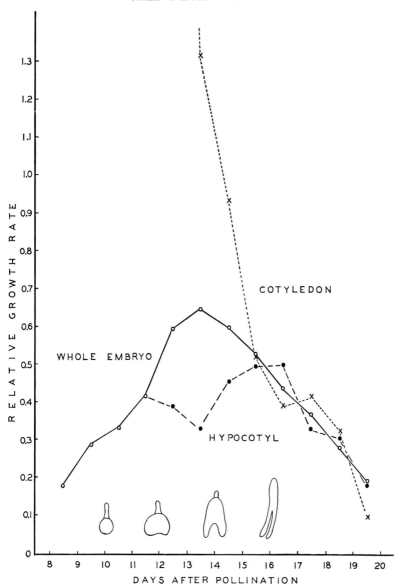

Fig. 47. Relative growth rate of *D. stramonium* embryos.

**Initiation and Development of the Epicotyl.** Neither the growth of the hypocotyl nor the formation of the primary root at its base have been studied in *Datura*. The initiation and development of the epicotyledonary primordium have been followed only in *D. stramonium*. A few small and isodiametric cells appear soon after the formation of the cotyledons. They are located between these two lateral formations and appear at the top of the hypocotyl in the slightly concave part of the heart-shaped embryo. One might fail to recognize these initial cells of the primordium at these stages. But a day or two later a group of cells differing from other cells by their smaller size and smaller nuclei can be easily identified. They form the primordium of the epicotyl (Fig. 46d). Due to subsequent and rapid cell divisions of the meristematic cells the concave outline of the primordium straightens out, becomes wider, and increases in bulk, and the epidermal and subepidermal tiers of cells become orderly arranged (Fig. 46e, f). These can be recognized by their stronger staining capacity. The top of the primordium remains straight for about a day or two longer, but as a result of the continuous increase in the size and number of cells the primordium soon becomes protruded from the embryo body (Fig. 46g). The size of cells and nuclei are considerably larger in the primordium than in the cortex and cotyledons. They also stain much darker. The primordium in an 18-day-old embryo forms a mound that rises above the top of the embryo body and contains about four tiers of orderly arranged cells. The lack of order in the lower portion of the primordium of a 25-day-old embryo indicates that cell divisions and the growth of the epicotyl is not yet accomplished (Fig. 46h). Counts of the total number of cells forming the epicotyledonary primordium made at various stages of development showed the following: a primordium of a 13-day-old torpedo with straight cotyledons contained 77 cells; a primordium of a 15-day-old embryo with curving cotyledons had about 230 cells; a 16- to 17-day-old embryo contained about 400 cells. The increase in the cell number in the primordia of the epicotyl is slower in later stages. The primordium of an 18- to 19-day-old embryo in this series was composed of about 480 cells.

The cells forming the primordia in mature dormant seeds look essentially the same. To learn whether some of these would respond differently to treatment with water, primordia taken from seeds kept 3 to 5 days in water were fixed and cut longitudinally into from 35 to 46 sections, each $6\mu$ thick and stained. The cells located in about two-thirds of each primordium seemed to remain inactive. But cells in the median portion of each primordium seemed to be quite different. They were considerably larger, filled with cytoplasm, and seemed to be prepared for division. This region extended only through 10 to 12 sections in the median portion of each sectioned primordium. This portion was about 60 to $70\mu$ thick, while the total thickess of the primordium was 216 to $276\mu$. Most of the cells forming the three upper tiers in this seemingly active region invariably appeared different from the rest. Their larger dimension, the nature of their contents and nuclei showed that they no longer were dormant or resting. This was particularly clear and appeared first in the cells of the subepidermal layer. The cells located on the sides of these three upper layers and all cells in the layers below seemed to remain inactive.

**Growth and Structure of the Suspensor.** The suspensor plays an important part in the growth of the proembryo. Its function is primarily nutritive; it not only brings the proembryo into a favorable position among endosperm cells containing food supply, but the cells forming the suspensor are also filled with nutritive material and provide oil to the proembryo in its earliest stages of development. The growth of the suspensor in *Datura* begins very early; it is usually completed in a heart-shaped embryo. It is still present in a 2-week-old embryo of *D. leichhardtii*, in a 3-week-old *D. stramonium*, and a 4-week-old *D. meteloides*, but the cells of such old suspensors contain only a very small amount of oil and have apparently begun to deteriorate. In more advanced stages the suspensors disappear entirely.

*Datura* species differ in the shape and size of their suspensors. The ten species can be roughly divided into three groups according to the structure of their suspensors. The first group is intermediate between the other two. The suspensor in these species is two to three cells in width, i.e., it is less slender than in group II and less massive and broad than in group III. This type (I) of suspensor is found in the majority of species: *D. stramonium, D. quercifolia, D. ferox, D. pruinosa, D. metel,* and *D. innoxia* (Fig. 44g, h). In type II the suspensor is long and very slender. Its larger portion at the proximal end remains linear and is about 12 to 14 cells in length. Its smaller portion, which lies close to the club-shaped proembryo, contains two or three pairs of cells. Such a slender suspensor is formed only in *D. leichhardtii* (Fig. 44n, o). The suspensor in species belonging to type III is massive, broad, and shorter. Its cells divide in various planes and it frequently becomes irregularly shaped with a tendency to increase in width near its proximal end (Fig. 44t, u, v). Such suspensors are found in *D. meteloides, D. discolor,* and *D. ceratocaula* (217).

**Oil and Aleurone Grain Formation in Embryo and Endosperm.** The developing seeds of all *Datura* species contain as food sugar, starch, oil, and aleurone grains. The food that is deposited in the embryo sac and in the seed coat plays an important part in seed development. In connection with the comparisons made on the rates of growth of embryos in different species it was essential to learn the exact location of each nutrient substance and to determine at which stage of embryo development it appears first.

Starch is present in the seed coat only and it is consumed during the growth of the seed.

Oil is present in the suspensor, the proembryo proper, in the embryo, and in the endosperm. Fresh material was used in determining the presence of oil in cells. Very young seeds were crushed on slides, cleaned from cell debris, and the tissue stained in a saturated alcohol (80 per cent) solution of Sudan IV. In more advanced stages the fresh seeds were hand-sectioned or dissected on slides and the same stain used. In each species the presence of oil was first observed in the basal cells of the proximal end of the proembryo which forms the suspensor. It soon appeared in other cells of the proembryo and in the endosperm cells near the micropylar end. In later stages cells of the central portion of the endosperm also contained a considerable amount of oil. This substance is apparently supplied through the micropyle and the suspensor plays an important role in growth by transporting and by depositing it in its cells to supply food to the developing proembryo. It was found that oil appears earlier in species with rapidly developing proembryos than in those with slower growth (Table 19). Oil is found 2

TABLE 19

Time at Which Oil Drops and Aleurone Grains Were Detected in Seeds

| Species | \multicolumn{19}{c}{Days After Pollination} |
|---|---|---|---|---|---|---|---|---|---|---|---|---|---|---|---|---|---|---|---|
| | 2 | 3 | 4 | 5 | 6 | 7 | 8 | 9 | 10 | 11 | 12 | 13 | 14 | 15 | 16 | 17 | 18 | 19 | 20 |
| D. stramonium | | X | | | | | | | | | | A | | | | | | | |
| D. quercifolia | | X | | | | | | | | | | A | | | | | | | |
| D. ferox | | X | | | | | | | | | A | | | | | | | | |
| D. pruinosa | X | | | | | | | | A | | | | | | | | | | |
| D. leichhardtii | X | | | | | | A | | | | | | | | | | | | |
| D. discolor | | | | | | | X | | | | | | | | | | | A | |
| D. ceratocaula | | | X | | | | | | | | | | A | | | | | | |
| D. meteloides | | | | | X | | | | | | | | | | A | | | | |
| D. metel | | | X | | | | | | | | | | | | | | | | A |
| D. innoxia | | | | | X | | | | | | | | | | A | | | | |

X = oil; A = aleurone grains.

to 3 days after pollination in the cells of *D. leichhardtii* and *D. pruinosa* proembryos and it appears about 2 days later in *D. stramonium, D. quercifolia,* and *D. ferox.* In the five slow-growing species (with the exception of *D. ceratocaula*) oil was detected in the suspensor and the proembryo cells 7 or 8 days after pollination. In globe-shaped proembryos the cells of the suspensors were usually packed with oil.

In contrast to oil, the aleurone grains appear first in the cells of the central region of the endosperm. Aleurone is present in later stages in other zones of the endosperm but is either missing or found in very limited amounts in the cells of its peripheral tiers. No aleurone is present in proembryos but a large amount is deposited in the hypocotyl and in the cotyledons of embryos when they reach the torpedo stage. Aleurone, like oil, appears earlier, 9 to 13 days after pollination, in the five species with rapid embryo growth, while in the slow-developing species it appears 16 to 20 days after pollination (Table 19). This indicates that both oil and aleurone formation is correlated with the rate of seed development. Neither oil nor aleurone have been observed in the cells of the seed coat (*217*).

**Development of the Endosperm.** The endosperm in all *Datura* species is of the cellular type and every nuclear division in the endosperm is immediately followed by the formation of the cell wall. The enlargement of the endosperm tissue is rapid and it increases in volume several times during seed development. As stated by Guignard (1902) and by Glišič (1928), the primary endosperm precedes the division of the zygote and divides transversely to the long axis of the embryo sac. The plane of the next division is not constant. There is also no constancy in the order of dividing cells. Either the cell of the micropylar end or that at the chalazal end may divide first. At earlier stages the triploid endosperm cells do not differ much in their size and shape and are more or less uniformly distributed in the embryo sac. They are large and stain light because of comparatively small amounts of cell contents. The cell walls are thin and no intercellular spaces are noticeable. But such uniformity does not last long; the cells begin soon to differ in size, shape, contents, and function. A tissue is formed with at least three different but not sharply separated regions. At earlier stages cells divide throughout the entire endosperm tissue. In later stages constantly perpetuating cells are found predominantly in cells located at the periphery of the endosperm. They divide periclinally and form a region of a few superposed tiers of narrow rectangular cells, which resemble and act like cambial cells with the exception of the outermost tier of cells whose function is digestive. Such an arrangement of cells in radial rows resembling active cambial cells which form secondary tissue was found in the peripheral zone of endosperm in maize (Randolph, 1936). The outermost tier of cells consumes the disintegrating cells of the endothelium and replaces them by absorbing the median layer of the integument. The outermost tier of the endosperm is soon absorbed and replaced by the tier of cells lying directly under it. Such replacement of the outermost tier is repeated a number of times during the growth of the seed. The cells in this region do not contain oil. Aleurone is also generally absent; if present, the grains are few and extremely small. Counts made of chromosomes in developing seeds of *D. stramonium* and *D. innoxia* proved invariably that the cells in this peripheral region are triploid.

The cells at the micropylar end form another region and differ from others in their staining capacity. These cells stain dark because of the large amount of oil in them. As a result of several succeeding divisions they become compact and smaller. In some species (*D. leichhardtii, D. discolor, D. ceratocaula, D. meteloides*) the rapid subsequent transverse divisions are so intense that the cells filled with oil form numerous linear stripes running closely parallel to each other. The function of the cells in this zone is nutritive.

The central zone of the endosperm is the largest. It is formed by large and somewhat irregularly shaped cells. At early stages the amount of oil is small, but it increases rapidly in later stages. It is in this zone that the aleurone grains are seen first. They appear at early torpedo stages. Before long a large amount of aleurone is deposited in all endosperm cells (with the exception of the peripheral zone). The differentiation of cells of the endosperm and the appearance of zones in it indicate that the cells in this tissue have more than one function and that they can change their function during the growth of the seed.

During growth the proembryo and the embryo consume the endosperm cells lying close to them, on their sides and near the top. An empty unstained area around them is found already at early stages—soon after the zygote division. This area increases markedly in length and width during seed development. In later stages it is the tip of each cotyledon that digests its way through the endosperm. The consumption of the endosperm is also continued by the cells of the embryo body.

These observations on the endosperm development in *Datura* species show that it is essentially the same as those of many other higher plants. Observations that are limited to details in histology and cytology are not sufficient for understanding the complex processes during seed development in the embryo sac and in the surrounding tissues. The functions and activity of the endosperm, which are closely connected with the growth of the embryo, need more detailed studies by the methods of physiology, biochemistry, and biophysics. One must learn more about enzymes, various substances present in the endosperm, and the competition for food between the endosperm and the tissues in the seed coat and the embryo.

Better knowledge of the endosperm might possibly help us to understand and explain one of the most curious phenomenon in embryology: the striking differences in growth and destiny of the closely related and genetically similar nuclei, both fertilized by gametes delivered by the same pollen tube. Why does the fertilized haploid egg develop into a highly differentiated body—the embryo, and the fertilized diploid central nucleus grow only into a slightly differentiated tissue—the endosperm? The doubled chromosome number in the central nucleus can hardly be the cause for forming a tissue instead of an embryo, because in $4n \times 2n$ crosses the egg contains the same number of chromosomes as the central nucleus in selfs of diploids; both are fertilized by a $1n$ male gamete, but a normal $3n$ embryo develops from this cross instead of the triploid tissue that develops from the fertilized central nucleus of diploids.

**Development of the Seed Coat.** The structure and growth of the ovular coat has been described in Chapter 10. It was shown that the tissues participating in the formation of the ovular coat differ in their origin and structure, and that the portion of the ovular coat derived from the integument is greater than that derived from the nucellus. After the division of the zygote and formation of the first two proembryo cells we have called the ovule a seed and the ovular coat the seed coat.

The growth of the proembryo and embryo in the seed is accompanied from the earliest stages of development until maturation by digestive and nutritive processes. These processes destroy most of the tissue built during the formation of the micropylar end of the ovular coat, i.e., of the integument. The tiers of cells in the inner zone of the median layer of the integument disappear first. Most of them are completely digested by the endothelium and used as food by the proembryo. The digestive capacity of the endothelium is much stronger in *D. discolor,* *D. ceratocaula,* and *D. metel* than in the other species. Most of the cells of the inner zone in these three species are already consumed soon after fertilization and a wide empty area is found around the embryo sac with no vestiges of digested cells of the integument's inner zone left. The activity of the endothelium does not last long. In a 10- to 12-day-old seed of *D. stramonium* the cells of the endothelium, which were previously orderly arranged and full of cytoplasm, begin to flatten, to break connections with each other, and their nuclei become no longer distinguishable. As has been shown above, the digestive function of the endothelium is replaced by the peripheral tier of cells of the endosperm. In some seeds the endothelium is no longer visible and disappears completely in seeds with embryos that have reached the torpedo stage. In other seeds all that is left of the endothelium is a yellowish sheet of dead compressed cell walls, which remain visible around the embryo sac.

The cells of the outer zone of the integument's median layer continue to multiply for a certain period of time, but this zone is also gradually absorbed by the growing endosperm. No more than two or three tiers of cells of the outer zone are left when the seed reaches maturity. The outer epidermal layer of the integument is the only one that remains undisturbed. Details on its structure in seeds of a number of species are given by Souèges (1907) and by Timmerman (1927b). The latter offers a key for distinguishing species (*D. stramonium, D. "tatula," D. innoxia, D. metel,* and *D. "fastuosa"*) by the characters of the epidermal cells in powdered seed.

It is obvious that the integument cannot participate in the formation of the growing seed coat. It is the nucellar portion of the coat that contributes to its growth. The size and shape of the seed depends a great deal on the activity of the intensively perpetuating nucellar cells.

**Summary.** These comparative studies of seed development in the selfs of *Datura* species made upon living and fixed material have shown that there are no essential differences between the species in the development of the embryo and of the endosperm or in the structure, function, and fate of the endothelium and other tissues forming the seed coat. Species differ in the size and shape of the suspensor, in the rate of the proembryo and embryo development, and in the time necessary for the formation of oil and aleurone grains. These substances appear in some species much earlier than in others because their formation is correlated with the rate of the seed development.

# 12

# Growth Processes in the Embryo and Seed

J. RIETSEMA AND BENIGNA BLONDEL

Throughout the many years of *Datura* research the study of the mechanism of heredity was always a center of interest. In later years much attention has been also paid to the seed and the embryo because they are the vital links between generations. When it was discovered, following certain cross-pollinations, that seed often failed to form or nonviable seeds resulted, the mechanism of seed formation was considered even more carefully. At first seed formation was studied with histological methods, but in later years physiological procedures were also used. The main purpose of these studies was to learn more about incompatibility, but it was early recognized that it would be necessary to study the process of seed and embryo formation in more general terms. So little has been known about physiological changes inside the seed after fertilization that it seemed almost fruitless to study seed abortion only. These physiological studies were often of an exploratory nature and were not sufficiently completed.

Van Overbeek developed the method of embryo culture that was followed by experiments on the growth requirements of isolated *Datura* embryos. The studies on embryo culture and on the growth of seeds have provided us with some understanding of the different phases of seed development and of some aspects of the relationships between the different parts of the seed. This justifies their inclusion here. As is true of many of the investigations described elsewhere in this volume, most of this work was done with *D. stramonium*, Line 1A, the standard strain for breeding and cytogenetic experiments. The high degree of homozygosity of this strain eliminates variations in growth due to genetic differences, an advantage which cannot be overestimated in physiological research.

**Embryo Culture.** The pioneer work of van Overbeek on *Datura* embryo culture brought about the beginning of a period of renewed interest in the culture of isolated embryos. The literature contains many early reports of attempts to grow embryos in vitro, but most efforts were confined to the isolation of mature embryos. In 1941 van Overbeek and Conklin, working with Blakeslee at Cold Spring Harbor, succeeded in growing *D. stramonium* embryos on artificial media, bringing them from early heart stages of 0.15 mm in length to advanced torpedo stages of 5 mm after 6 days of growth. In succeeding years methods were developed whereby such tiny embryos could be transferred to soil and ultimately brought to the flowering stage. The importance of this for the *Datura* studies was realized at once and the method was soon applied with success to dissected hybrid embryos. The first hybrids from incompatible crosses secured by this method were from *D. innoxia* crossed to *D. discolor*. In the years following the initial experiments the methods of dissection and culture were gradually modified and adapted to specific needs, thus providing the tools for genetical studies and at the same time producing valuable information on the physiology of the developing embryo. Since the literature on embryo culture has been reviewed elsewhere (Tukey, 1938; Ziebur, 1951; Rappaport, 1954), it will suffice to limit the present dicussion to the work done in Blakeslee's laboratory with *Datura* (*156, 164*).

TECHNIQUE. The success of the embryo-culture method depends primarily on the removal of an undamaged and sterile embryo from the seed and on the transfer of this embryo to a sterile medium. This was successfully done in the early days of embryo-culture work by Hannig (1904). It presents only a few difficulties when certain precautions are taken. Perhaps most important of all is a room with air as nearly quiet as possible. Air currents carry spores of fungi and bacteria, which may drop into opened culture vials and cause infection.

The young capsule, kept in a closed glass container to prevent drying out, is opened with a scalpel, and the seeds are put in a Petri dish with wet sterile filter paper. The dissection of the seed is made on a sterile slide under the low power of a binocular dissecting microscope. A safety razor blade soldered to a needle inserted into a needle holder, two dissecting needles, forceps, and an alcohol lamp or small gas burner complete the equipment. A wooden box turned on its side with a glass cover extending about 6 inches from the top edge over the open side provides a cover under which the transfers to the nutrient medium may be made with good protection against falling spores. A fluorescent lamp provides light without undesirable heat, which would cause the embryo sac contents to dry out during dissection. The tools are sterilized by dipping them into 70 per cent alcohol and heating them over a low flame.

For dissection a seed is placed between two sterile slides and cut into two unequal parts with the sterile razor blade. The seed is opened with the dissecting needles and the embryo lifted out by one of them. A vial with nutrient agar is quickly opened and the embryo transferred to the surface of the agar. This procedure is very easy with young seeds, but toward maturity the seed coat has to be removed. This is done without difficulty after the seed has been kept in water for about 24 hours.

The composition of the nutrient medium may be varied with the purpose of the experiment, but in most culture work the formula of the inorganic salt mixture is usually the same. There is a considerable latitude in the composition of the nutrient solution, but those most frequently used for *Datura* were a slightly modified formula from Tukey (1934) and the modified mixture of Randolph and Cox (1943). The nutrient formulas used for *Datura* embryos are given in Table 20. Both media

TABLE 20

Formulas of Nutrient Solutions *
(Amounts in grams per liter)

| Salts | Tukey Formula (Modified) | Randolph and Cox (Modified) |
|---|---|---|
| KCl | 0.682 | 0.065 |
| $CaSO_4 \cdot 2H_2O$ | 0.170 | – |
| $MgSO_4 \cdot 7H_2O$ | 0.170 | 0.036 |
| $KNO_3$ | 0.170 | 0.085 |
| $Ca(NO_3)_2 \cdot 4H_2O$ | – | 0.236 |
| $(NaPO_3)_n$ | – | 0.010 |
| $FeSO_4 \cdot 7H_2O$ | – | 0.002 |
| $Ca_3(PO_4)_2$ | 0.170 | – |
| $Fe_3(PO_4)_2$ | 0.170 | – |
| $MnSO_4$ | 0.0004 | 0.0004 |

* Modified from those of Tukey (1934) and Randolph and Cox (1943).

are entirely satisfactory, and some other well-known media such as that of Kniep were equally well suited; however, some media, as that of Knudson (1946), gave very poor results. For young embryos 2 per cent sucrose is added and 0.3 per cent of a Seitz-filtered malt extract. For differentiated embryos nearing the seedling stage a medium with only 0.5 per cent sucrose and no malt extract is sufficient. Media with 0.8 per cent agar are preferable but liquid media also give good results. The *p*H of the medium is adjusted to 5.9–6.0. The culture vials used for small embryos are usually shell vials, 50 mm long and 10 mm in diameter, with 1.5 ml nutrient solution. As the embryos grow they need to be transferred to larger tubes with a nutrient containing less sucrose. Following a suggestion by R. E. Cleland this larger culture vial, 70 mm long and 20 mm wide, is covered by a second, slightly shorter and wider vial. This proved to be much more convenient than using a cotton plug (*164, 194*).

The most critical stage in embryo culture is the transfer of the seedling into soil. The soil used in the greenhouse for growing *Datura* seeds is sterilized with steam or chloropicrin to kill any *Datura* seeds present. The seedlings were protected from strong sunlight and from drying by keeping them for a few days in a terrarium with wet sand on the bottom. The small potted seedlings were partly covered with small glass jars which were usually removed after 4 to 5 days. About a week later the pots with seedlings were transferred into the greenhouse. Even then failures were very common and frequently one had his efforts of many weeks rendered futile by the failure of the young seedlings to establish themselves in soil.

Frequently hybrid embryos, when grown in artificial culture, develop shoots without roots. Such seedlings, of course, cannot be transferred into soil. To overcome this lack of differentiation Blakeslee developed a method of "micrografting" whereby a small gelatine capsule, coated with nail polish to prevent softening of the gelatine in contact with water, is used as a "micro-greenhouse." The capsule is put over the tiny graft and attached to the stock with paraffin (Fig. 48). This method made it possible to bring to maturity many weak or rootless seedlings that otherwise would have died at an early stage (*166*).

THE EFFECT OF THE *p*H. A study on the *p*H requirements of *Datura* embryos from selfs was made by van Overbeek *et al.* (1944). Using a 0.01M $Na_2HPO_4$-$KH_2PO_4$ buffer, they found that during the first 2 to 4 days after isolation *p*H 7 is the optimum but that a *p*H of approximately 5.5 is better when the culture is continued for 6 to 7 days. Using different buffer mixtures, they showed that regardless of the composition of the buffer, growth of embryos at earlier stages is better at *p*H 7 and at the later stages it is better at *p*H 5.5. The number of embryos surviving the first 2 to 4 days was also greatest at about *p*H 7. Numerous tests in following years with selfs of other *Datura* species and with hybrid embryos from incompatible species crosses showed invariably that at early stages of development embryos in culture grew better in media with a *p*H value of 6.2 to 6.5 and that a lower *p*H, 5.2 to 5.5, was better for embryos in later stages.

THE EFFECT OF TEMPERATURE. The optimum temperature, according to van Overbeek *et al.* (1944), is 32° C. At this temperature the rate of increase in length is the greatest. Our general observation is that *Datura* embryos, approaching the seedling stage, grow so rapidly at this high temperature that they often develop into spindling seedlings with long, thin hypocotyls, very small cotyledons, and with poor roots. Such seedlings are exceedingly difficult to transfer to soil and seldom develop into normal seedlings. They seem to lose their capacity for further or normal development and therefore are undesirable. By growing embryos at 26° C this is avoided and yet a reasonably rapid growth is obtained.

THE EFFECT OF SUCROSE. Sucrose is an excellent carbohydrate to add to nutrient media, but fructose, glucose, and mannose can also be used with good results. Glycerol and mannitol are inert as carbon sources.

(a)

(b)

FIG. 48. (a) Dr. Blakeslee making a micrograft; (b) two young grafts.

The extent to which sucrose affects growth of the *D. stramonium* embryo depends largely on the stage of development. Embryos of about 0.15 mm in length grew only in media with 8 to 16 per cent sucrose, but embryos of 1.2 mm elongated considerably in media with 0.1 per cent sucrose (*178, 206*). Unpublished studies by D. Paris and the senior writer have yielded similar information for *D. ceratocaula* embryos.

Well-differentiated embryos grew satisfactorily on media without sucrose. By substituting mannitol for part of the sucrose, the embryos seemed to respond to the mannitol concentration when the sucrose concentration remained constant at 2 per cent, indicating that the osmotic value of the solution was the controlling factor in media with varying sucrose concentrations. A sucrose concentration of 2 per cent seems to be optimum for all embryo stages provided the osmotic value is adjusted by varying the mannitol concentration. It is particularly interesting to notice that Rijven (1952) found that very small embryos of *Capsella bursa-pastoris* were isotonic with higher osmotic values than more advanced ones.

THE EFFECT OF INORGANIC SALTS. The only salts for which the effects of concentration were studied are sodium and iron phosphates. Embryos of *D. stramonium, D. discolor, D. innoxia* II and *D. metel*, and of several species crosses were used at the early heart stage (0.2 mm). The rate of increase in length was found to depend very much on the particular species used, but fundamentally the response is similar in these species. The growth of *D. stramonium* embryos in 0.001 per cent $(NaPO_3)_n$ was twice as fast as in 0.003 per cent, but for the other three species the reverse was true. These species grew better with 0.0002 per cent $Fe_3(PO_4)_2$ than with 0.015 per cent. The response of the embryos to variations in sodium and iron phosphate concentrations depends much less on the stage of development than the response to the osmotic value of the medium (*194*).

THE EFFECT OF AMINO ACIDS. The standard nutrient medium described above contains 0.3 per cent malt extract. The exact composition of this malt extract was not known, but it was reasonable to assume that it added amino acids to the medium. Sanders and Burkholder (1948) stated that *D. stramonium* and *D. innoxia* embryos grow as well on a medium with a mixture of amino acids, e.g., casein hydrolysate, as on a medium containing malt extract. They were not able to select any one particular amino acid as the effective agent in stimulating growth, because no single one could replace the mixture. This is not a property of embryos only but has been encountered in tissue cultures as well. We tried to gather information on the requirements of embryos at different stages of development. As in the case with sucrose, casein hydrolysate had its greatest effect on the growth rate of very young embryos and virtually none on that of embryos longer than 1 mm (*205*). Several amino acids not tried by Sanders and Burkholder were added to the nutrient media: aspartic acid, glutamic acid, asparagine, and glutamine.

Of these, only glutamine had any favorable effect on growth when it was the only nitrogen source, but it did not have the same growth-supporting effect as casein hydrolysate. Nevertheless this effect of glutamine is of interest because Rijven (1952) reported that glutamine can fully meet the nitrogen requirements for growth of isolated *Capsella bursa-pastoris* embryos.

These experiments have made it reasonably certain that a single amino acid cannot replace a mixture of amino acids if growth is to occur. Moreover, there is no apparent need for embryos to grow on one or a few amino compounds, since the endosperm contains a mixture of many free amino acids. If casein hydrolysate is made available to more advanced embryos that have been growing on a synthetic medium for some time, they will grow very fast and become spindling and unsuitable for transfer to soil. They show excessive hypocotyl elongation without an accompanying increase in thickness and differentiation.

Coconut Milk Factor. The very striking effects of casein hydrolysate in the nutrient medium on embryo growth should not cause the growth-stimulating effects of other compounds to be overlooked. It was found that a complex mixture of vitamins and amino acids could not stimulate the growth of proembryos but did so after the addition of sterile non-autoclaved coconut milk. Autoclaving caused the coconut milk to become inhibitory at the higher concentrations (van Overbeek *et al.*, 1944). It was assumed that the liquid endosperm of the coconut contains one or more growth-stimulating factors. It was found that yeast extract, wheat germ, and almond meal also contain similar compounds. Since coconut milk is not always available and varies widely with the source, Seitz-filtered malt extract was tried later with immediate success. In subsequent years 0.3 per cent malt extract was added to most nutrient solutions and satisfactorily replaced coconut milk in all routine experiments with *Datura* embryo cultures (*150, 164*).

Vitamins and Auxins. No particular vitamin other than the coconut milk factor has yet been found that is absolutely essential for the growth of *Datura* embryos. Several vitamins, such as pantothenic and nicotinic acid, have been suggested as important, especially when added to the medium together with coconut milk, but the evidence is limited and needs further careful study (*151, 156*).

As might be expected, the effect of auxins on embryo growth has been investigated. The presence of auxin in coconut milk and its root-inhibitory properties were demonstrated in *Datura*. The autoclaved coconut milk inhibited root growth, prevented differentiation, and caused young embryos to develop into calluslike bodies of 2 to 3 mm in diameter. Auxin was observed to modify the differentiation of older embryos. One to ten parts per million of indoleacetic acid impaired the hypocotyl growth and cotyledons became club-shaped. The change in shape was mainly the result of a change in cell form; the cells became wider and shorter in the auxin solutions. This damaging effect of auxins is certainly surprising when one realizes that the endosperm usually contains auxin (Luckwill, 1948) and *Datura* endosperm is no exception according to our recent experiments. In spite of the auxin content of the endosperm, embryos develop normally and one is led to assume the presence of a counteracting agent in the endosperm, preventing the auxin-induced inhibition (*156*).

Such a controlling agent has been demonstrated to exist in Seitz-filtered malt extract. When indoleacetic acid is added to the medium in the presence of malt extract, the inhibiting effect of auxin is much reduced and is further reduced as the malt concentration is increased. As is the case with coconut milk, malt extract is not effective after autoclaving, but it is after filtration. According to van Overbeek (1942), the inhibitor in coconut milk is auxin, but the nature of the inhibitor in autoclaved malt extract is not known, though quite certainly it is not auxin (*200, 207*).

**Growth of the Seed.** The growth of seeds has never received as much attention as the growth of fruits, except in the case of some economically important seeds, as cereals, oil-containing nuts, and coconut. Usually seeds are taken for granted with the fruit, even though it is well known that fruits without seeds normally do not develop. The *Datura* seed is of particular interest to us because it is the medium of the developing embryo.

Since we knew but little about the growth of *Datura* seeds, the first observations were made on the increase in gross weight of the seed after pollination. This could best be done by weight measurements. It was even possible to determine the weight of ovules at the time of anthesis of the flower. It was found that seeds do not begin to grow immediately after pollination but about 2 days later, or about the time when actual fertilization occurs. From then on the growth is of an exponential type and is completed after 15 to 16 days. At the end of this growth period the final weight has been attained and remains unchanged until maturity of the fruit. As simple as this appears, the growth relations are more complicated when the relation between water uptake and dry matter uptake is considered. Though the young seeds during their growth accumulate much dry matter, as described later, they also take up water, and this at a greater rate than dry matter. Consequently the percentage of dry weight of the ovules decreases from 28 per cent at the time of pollination to 15 per cent nearly 2 weeks later. Only after the full size and weight of the seed has been reached, is water replaced by dry matter, mostly oil and proteins, and this at a constant rate of 0.4 mg of dry matter per day during approximately 3 weeks.

During the last 12 days, before the capsule bursts about 50 days after pollination, no appreciable changes in the proportions of water and dry matter content occur. On this basis, seed growth can be divided into two phases: the first, lasting about 15 days, is a growth phase characterized by water and dry matter uptake; the second is a maturation phase characterized by a loss of water and an uptake of dry matter. This is illustrated in Fig. 49. During the maturation stage the color of the seed changes from ivory white to yellow, then golden brown and dark brown, and finally to nearly black. As Souèges (1907) described, this is the result of color changes in the lignified epidermis with very heavy cell walls, which become hard and dry.

Undoubtedly there is a basic difference in the nature of the dry matter accumulated during the growth and maturation phases. During the

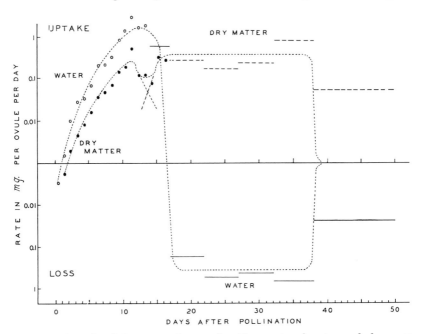

Fig. 49. Growth of *D. stramonium* seeds. Mean rate of water and dry matter uptake. Dry matter uptake: dots and dashed lines. Water increase or loss: open circles and unbroken lines. The dotted lines indicate the general course of water and dry matter uptake.

early growth period tissue proteins and cell wall material are formed, whereas in the later stages oil and protein in the form of aleurone grains are laid down (Chapter 11).

The development of the fruit seems to be closely correlated with seed growth, lasting only as long as the growth of the seeds. It does not slow down before fertilization but continues uninterruptedly from before pollination until its final size has been reached. This is clearly in contrast to seed growth, which is resumed at least one day after pollination.

Weight measurements of embryos are very difficult and impractical, but calculations of the volume based on length and width measurements were possible. These showed that embryo growth is of an exponential type, though growth in length or width alone can be represented by conventional S-shaped curves. The exponential growth character can be expected for a tissue growing at a constant rate of cell division. Only when the embryo begins to bend does the exponential relationship cease; the relative growth rate decreases and eventually becomes zero (Fig. 50). In contrast to the growth of fruit, the embryo growth seems more nearly independent of the growth of the seed as a whole. It completes its growth about 22 days after pollination, at least a week after the capsule and seeds have completed their growth (*224*).

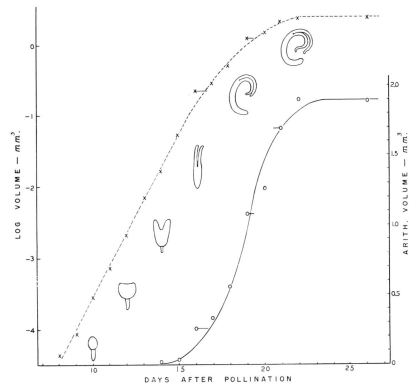

Fig. 50. Growth of *D. stramonium* embryos. Embryo volume at different stages of development. Each point represents ten measurements.

The suspensor is a very remarkable part of the embryo. Only during the first 10 days does it grow at the same rate as the distal part of the embryo; then its growth ceases soon after the embryo begins to differentiate. Its function is not well understood despite several hypotheses (Maheshwari, 1950).

The development of seeds and capsules after pollination with pollen from other species depends upon fertilization of the ovules. Pollination of *D. stramonium* by *D. ceratocaula* gives no viable seeds, but embryos have been dissected from young seeds and grown in culture. The fresh and dry weight measurements have shown that the growth pattern for such seeds is similar to seeds of *D. stramonium* from selfs though much slower. Pollinations by *D. pruinosa* give results similar to those obtained from unpollinated flowers: an early drop of the ovary without any growth of the ovules. *D. pruinosa* pollen tubes only rarely reach the ovules in *D. stramonium* and pollination alone is not sufficient to keep the ovary on the plant (224).

OIL FORMATION. As mentioned earlier, *D. stramonium* seeds are oily, i.e., they contain little or no starch but large quantities of oil (Chapter 11). The first droplets become visible in the suspensor 4 or 5 days after pollination, but most of the oil is deposited during the maturation phase after the thirteenth day. Determination of the oil content by ether extraction, with the total extractable material designated as oil, gave the following information. At first the quantity of oil in the seed is very small, but it begins to increase between the sixth and tenth day (Fig. 51). After the seventeenth day a rather sudden slackening of the rate of oil production occurs, so that from then on only small quantities are laid down in the embryo and endosperm. This means that in a period lasting no more than 7 to 8 days most of the oil is deposited.

By considering the data on a dry weight basis, we observe a relative decrease in oil content immediately before the period of greatest pro-

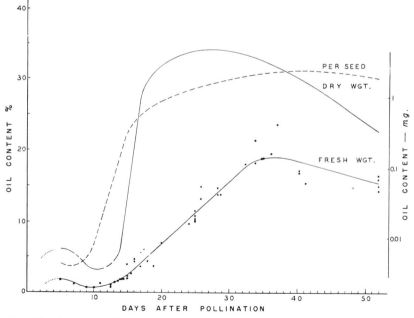

FIG. 51. Oil accumulation in *D. stramonium* seeds. Relation between the age of the seeds and the oil content in per cent of the fresh weight, in per cent of dry weight, and in milligrams per seed.

duction and during the maturation phase. Both decreases probably originate from the same cause. Nitrogen compounds and carbohydrates are supplied continuously to the seed. As soon as more assimilates are taken up by the seed than are transformed into oil, the relative oil content decreases.

The nature of the oil found in the seed of *Datura* has been described by Jamieson (1943). He refers to it as a semidrying oil with a specific gravity of 0.917 to 0.923 at 15° C. He recorded the saponification equivalent as 186 to 202, the iodine number as 113 to 126, and the unsaponifiable matter as 1.0 to 2.6 per cent. The principal acids are oleic acid, linoleic acid, and palmitic acid.

ACCUMULATION OF NITROGENOUS COMPOUNDS. Growing seeds of *D. stramonium* accumulate considerable amounts of proteins in addition to oil. At first the tissue proteins appear to predominate and, later, the reserve proteins, in the form of aleurone grains. As mentioned in Chapter 11, the first aleurone grains can be recognized in *D. stramonium* at the early torpedo stage 13 to 14 days after pollination. They appear first in the endosperm and a day or two later in the embryo. Besides the insoluble nitrogenous compounds in the cells there are also soluble nitrogen compounds, many of them free amino acids. These amino acids are required in the formation of embryo proteins and, as we have seen above, the embryo needs a mixture of amino acids to be able to grow in artificial culture media.

In order to determine the amounts of nitrogenous compounds present in young seeds or their component parts, semimicro Kjeldahl determinations were made. Insoluble nitrogen was determined by precipitation with 10 per cent trichloroacetic acid. The difference between total and insoluble nitrogen was designated as soluble nitrogen.

Young seeds could not be separated into their component parts and were analyzed *in toto*. The bulk of young seeds consists of the seed coat; in seeds 9 days old about 95 per cent of the total volume consists of the seed coat and in seeds 11 to 12 days old this is still as much as 85 per cent. Consequently, analyses of the whole seeds reflect primarily the development of the seed coat, i.e., the integument and the nucellar tissue (Chapter 11). The total nitrogen content of the seeds increases exponentially *after the second* day, as does their total weight (Table 21). Insoluble nitrogen, most of it undoubtedly protein nitrogen, constitutes about 70 per cent of the total. Aleurone grains cannot be observed during the early period, and the proteins are probably tissue proteins.

The rate of water uptake relative to the rate of nitrogen uptake, as shown in the sixth column of Table 21, is of interest. It remains slow at first but subsequently increases rapidly to about 1.8 between the sixth and twelfth days. An explanation may be found if we consider the size of the cells of the seed coat. Initially the cells are small and increase in size only slowly, but they begin to grow rapidly during the second week until they finally become at least 20 times as large as in the beginning. This suggests a drastic change in the mode of seed coat development. During the second week growth by cell enlargement predominates. This is comparable to the growth in some fruits, where cell enlargement is the main process by which the fruit grows, with cell division slowing down to a very low rate shortly after pollination (Sinnott, 1945; Smith, 1950).

TABLE 21

NITROGEN CONTENT OF D. STRAMONIUM SEEDS
AT EARLY STAGES OF DEVELOPMENT

| Age (Days) | Seed Weight (μgr) | Water Content (μgr/seed) | Total N (μgr/seed) | Insoluble N (% of Total Nitrogen) | Ratio of Rate of Water Uptake to 100 × Rate of Total N Uptake |
|---|---|---|---|---|---|
| 0 | 15.6 | 11.2 | 0.31 | 73.5 | — |
| 1 | 15.0 | 11.5 | 0.28 | 68 | — |
| 2 | 18.0 | 13.0 | 0.27 | 87 | — |
| 3 | 30 | 23 | 0.4 | 75 | 0.78 |
| 4 | 60 | 49 | 0.8 | 64 | 0.64 |
| 5 | 100 | 81 | 1.4 | 69 | 0.53 |
| 6 | 185 | 150 | 2.2 | 75 | 0.86 |
| 7 | 400 | 330 | 4.2 | 77 | 1.80 |
| 8 | 665 | 560 | 4.8 | 72.5 | 1.45 |
| 9 | 1080 | 900 | 8.0 | 69 | 1.04 |
| 10 | 2050 | 1750 | 13.0 | 73 | 1.6 |
| 11 | 3500 | 2990 | 20.0 | 69 | 1.8 |
| 12 | 7000 | 5930 | 29.0 | 69 | 3.2 |

As described earlier, the development of the seed can be divided into a growth phase and a maturation phase. The growth of the endosperm can be similarly divided into two phases. The initial development of the endosperm is by cell division. After about the twelfth day it begins to absorb the seed coat parenchyma and a day or two later the first aleurone grains appear. At this stage the endosperm seems slimy, though it actually consists of large vacuolated cells. Gradually it changes to a semisolid state at the nineteenth to twentieth day, becoming dry and hard by the twenty-fifth day. During these stages it increases continuously in weight, but it does so most rapidly during the earlier days (from the eighth until the eighteenth day) and at a much slower rate during the last 10 days before the capsule bursts. The onset and duration of these stages cannot be determined accurately, for they pass gradually from one to the next. The increase in weight of the endosperm is the result of both an increase of its volume and an accumulation of reserve nutrients. The increase in size and weight of the endosperm is clearly shown in Fig. 52. Even though the endosperm increases greatly in size, it is probable that the bulk of the nitrogen deposited after the eighteenth day consists of storage nitrogen. Actual determinations of total nitrogen show that the rate of accumulation from the fifteenth until the thirtieth day is fairly con-

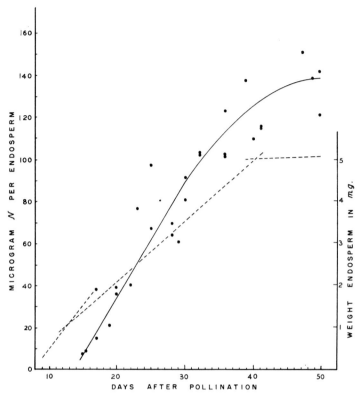

Fig. 52. Nitrogen content (solid line) and fresh weight (broken line) of the endosperm of *D. stramonium*.

stant. Approximately 70 per cent of the total is in an insoluble form (Table 22).

Regarding the embryos, the story is only slightly different. As stated before, the embryo stops growing in size after approximately 3 weeks. Its dry weight, however, continues to increase and also its fresh weight

TABLE 22

PROTEIN NITROGEN CONTENT OF D. STRAMONIUM EMBRYOS AND ENDOSPERM
IN PERCENTAGE OF THE TOTAL NITROGEN FOUND
(The age is given in days after pollination.)

| Embryos | | Endosperm | |
|---|---|---|---|
| Age | Per Cent | Age | Per Cent |
| 18 | 69 | 15 | 72 |
| 20 | 71 | 20 | 72 |
| 30 | 70 | 30 | 71 |
| 39 | 84 | 41 | 85 |
| 50 | 67 | 50 | 67 |

increases slightly during the next 2½ weeks (Fig. 53). The embryo apparently accumulates material that is relatively free of water. Total and insoluble nitrogen determinations showed that the total nitrogen content increases until at least 6 weeks after pollination and that the percentage of insoluble nitrogen is nearly constant at about 70 per cent (Table 22). Since the embryo stops growing in size after three weeks and the rate of nitrogen accumulation begins to slow down shortly thereafter, the period of maximum reserve protein formation must be from about the twenty-second to the twenty-fifth day.

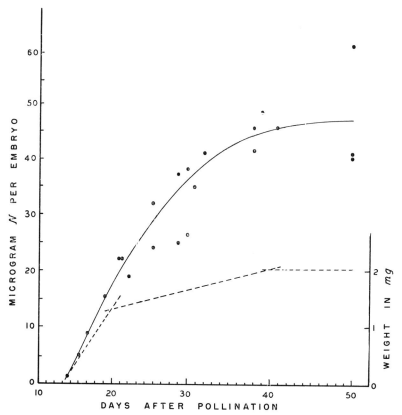

Fig. 53. Nitrogen content (solid line) and fresh weight (broken line) of embryos of *D. stramonium.*

**Free Amino Acids in *D. stramonium* Seeds.** The limited information that we have about the nutritional requirements of *D. stramonium* embryos has made it clear that very small embryos are not able to synthesize their own constituents from a few basic nutrients but need a rather complex nutrient medium. This, as we have seen before, is seemingly different from older embryos, which will grow on media without amino acids, malt extract, or coconut milk. This does not mean that these older embryos can synthesize all their constituents from the nutrients, for they already contain fairly large amounts of proteins and fats, from which they can draw for their metabolic requirements. This also implies that our studies with older embryos may not have given reliable information about their nutritional requirements, and that the demands of the embryos in culture are not necessarily the same as those *in vivo*. Direct evidence about the nutrition in the seed is obtained by analyses of the endosperm and other parts of the seed at various stages of development. We know already that the endosperm contains many amino acids, carbohydrates, growth-stimulating substances, etc., but most of this information comes from analysis of mature seeds (Crocker and Barton, 1953). Nothing is known about the changes in the composition of the endosperm of *D. stramonium* during its development from fertilization to maturity.

The endosperm is not an independent structure, but it receives its nutrients from the parent plant through the seed coat and it would be of interest to know the nature of the relationship between seed coat and endosperm. The embryo takes up nutrients from the endosperm, but probably it can absorb only low molecular compounds, such as amino acids, mono- and disaccharides, inorganic ions, and vitamins. From this material the embryo synthesizes its carbohydrates, fats, and proteins. Here again, the relationship between embryo and endosperm would be better understood if the chemical constituents of both were better known.

The only chemical compounds of which we have learned anything are the free amino acids that have been separated and determined with the aid of the paper-chromatographic method as will be described briefly. The endosperm, embryos, seed coats, or young ovules were ground in 80 per cent alcohol and extracted. The total available quantities were very small, sometimes no more than 40 mg of fresh tissue. The extracts were dried at 40° C and redissolved in a known amount of water. This water solution was applied to Whatman No. 1 filter paper, prepared according to the method of Thompson and Steward (1951). Phenol water (*p*H 5.2) was used for the first run and butanol–acetic acid water (4:1:1) for the second run, both descending. After drying of the chromatograms the spots were developed with ninhydrin for 30 minutes and washed with 50 per cent alcohol after which the concentrations of the acids were measured with a Beckman DU spectrophotometer at 570 m$\mu$ (asparagine and proline at 330 m$\mu$) and read against standard curves. The qualitative determination of the amino acids was done according to the methods described in the literature on the subject of chromatography. All determined amino acids were run together with chromatograms of pure compounds to compare their $R_f$ values in various solvents. The available technical facilities allowed only a moderate degree of accuracy and the following results have to be regarded as semiquantitative and indicative of trends rather than of absolute and accurate concentrations.

In unfertilized ovules several amino acids were found but in low concentrations. Shortly after pollination a sharp rise in the concentrations was observed with maximum concentrations 1 to 3 days after pollination. Thereafter a gradual decrease sets in, which continues until the twelfth to thirteenth day, when the concentrations of most amino acids are well below the original concentrations. This pattern was most pronounced for aspartic acid, serine, glutamine, and asparagine, and less distinct for glutamic acid and arginine. It was not observed for alanine, lysine, or threonine (Table 23). Proline, leucine, and gamma-amino-butyric acid

TABLE 23

Some Free Amino Acids Found in Young D. stramonium Seeds
at Various Stages of Development

(Concentration in millimoles per gram fresh weight)

| Age of Seeds (Days) | 0 | 1 | 3.5 | 5 | 10 | 12.5 |
|---|---|---|---|---|---|---|
| Fresh Weight of Seeds in mg | 0.0156 | 0.0154 | 0.047 | 0.10 | 2.9 | 7.4 |
| Aspartic acid | 3.0 | 9.9 | 8.8 | 6.0 | 4.2 | 0.9 |
| Glutamic acid | 2.5 | 3.9 | 4.3 | 4.0 | 3.0 | 1.3 |
| Serine | 4.3 | 10.0 | 5.2 | 6.1 | 1.3 | 0.7 |
| Asparagine | 0.6 | 2.7 | + | 0.3 | 0.2 | + |
| Threonine | 2.8 | 2.9 | 1.5 | 0.8 | 1.1 | 0.3 |
| Alanine | 2.6 | 2.2 | 1.4 | 1.5 | 0.7 | 0.7 |
| Glutamine | 10.0 | 19.0 | 4.0 | 4.5 | 3.1 | 4.0 |
| Lysine | 0.4 | 0.5 | 0.1 | 0.2 | 0.5 | + |
| Arginine | 1.7 | 2.4 | 2.9 | 2.0 | + | + |

were found in very small quantities. When calculated on a per seed basis, the total quantities rapidly increase as the seed begins to grow, as might be expected because of the exponential growth of the seeds. D. stramonium seeds, as related above, begin to grow at least one day after pollination. During this time the amino acid concentrations increase rapidly, which indicates a great change in metabolic activity very soon after pollination. Synthesis of proteins does not begin until after the second day; in other words, the increase of amino acid concentrations becomes evident before protein synthesis can be observed. There is no evidence that indicates the origin of these amino acids, viz., whether they result from protein hydrolysis or are supplied by the female parent.

The seed coats of older seeds could be separated from the embryo sac and extracted separately. When the seed was still white and soft, the whole seed coat was ground and extracted; but when the epidermis became hard and dark brown, it was removed and only the soft parenchymous tissue was extracted. This soft parenchymous tissue is slowly digested by the growing endosperm until at the end of the period of seed growth the remaining parenchyma is very thin.

All free amino acids, in so far as they could be determined, remain at fairly low and constant concentrations. The only observed exception was asparagine, which showed an increased concentration when the seeds became brown and hard (Table 24). Other amino acids probably present in the seed coat are valine, leucine, and gamma-amino-butyric acid.

TABLE 24

SOME FREE AMINO ACIDS IN THE SEED COAT OF D. STRAMONIUM
AT VARIOUS STAGES OF DEVELOPMENT

(Concentration in millimoles per gram fresh weight) *

| Age in Days | 11.5 | 15 | 20 | 25 | 32 |
|---|---|---|---|---|---|
| Aspartic acid | 1.2 | 0.2 | 1.4 | 1.0 | 1.0 |
| Glutamic acid | 0.7 | 0.2 | 0.7 | 0.5 | 0.4 |
| Serine | 0.6 | 0.2 | 0.7 | 0.8 | 0.6 |
| Asparagine | + | 0.2 | + | 0.2 | 1.6 |
| Threonine | 0.5 | 0.2 | 0.2 | 0.2 | 0.9 |
| Alanine | 0.6 | 0.7 | 0.9 | 0.9 | 0.7 |
| Glutamine | 0.7 | 0.5 | 1.6 | 0.3 | 1.1 |
| Lysine | — | + | 0.3 | 0.4 | + |
| Arginine | + | 0.1 | 1.1 | 0.7 | + |

* Only the parenchymous tissue without the epidermis was used for analysis of seed coats 20, 25, and 32 days old.

The endosperm fulfills a dual purpose. First it provides the proper environment for the embryo and later accumulates large quantities of protein and oil, which are used by the embryo after germination. These functions can hardly be separated in time, for they overlap to a great extent. It was not practical to isolate endosperms from young seeds in quantities sufficient for extraction, so we have information only about the stages of endosperm development that coincide with the maturation phase, and we have none about the early stages in which accumulation of the proteins and oil has not yet begun.

The most characteristic features are the high concentrations of serine, aspartic acid, glutamic acid, alanine, and arginine in the third week. After that all concentrations drop but by the sixth and seventh weeks the asparagine concentration increases again. Table 25 lists the concentrations at various endosperm stages. The maximum concentrations in the third week coincide with the termination of endosperm growth. During

TABLE 25

SOME FREE AMINO ACIDS IN ENDOSPERM OF D. STRAMONIUM SEEDS
AT VARIOUS STAGES OF DEVELOPMENT

(Concentration in millimoles per gram fresh weight)

| Age in Days | 12.5 | 15 | 20 | 27 | 33 | 40 | 50 |
|---|---|---|---|---|---|---|---|
| Fresh Weight of Endosperm in mg | 1.5 | 1.2 | 1.4 | 1.9 | 4.3 | 6.2 | 7.4 |
| Aspartic acid | 2.6 | 5.0 | 1.2 | 0.9 | 1.2 | 1.9 | 1.9 |
| Glutamic acid | 3.0 | 3.7 | 3.6 | 2.1 | 0.8 | 0.5 | 0.4 |
| Serine | 0.9 | 2.7 | 1.1 | 0.4 | 0.2 | 0.1 | 0.6 |
| Asparagine | 0.7 | 0.5 | — | + | 0.6 | 2.2 | 1.5 |
| Threonine | 1.2 | 1.3 | 1.5 | 0.7 | 0.1 | — | + |
| Alanine | 0.9 | 9.9 | 8.5 | 1.9 | 0.3 | 0.1 | 0.2 |
| Glutamine | 6.7 | 4.6 | 5.8 | 0.3 | 0.5 | 0.3 | 0.7 |
| Lysine | 0.6 | 1.1 | 0.9 | 0.2 | — | + | + |
| Arginine | 3.2 | 3.2 | 6.3 | 0.4 | — | — | — |

the following 17 days the rate of protein synthesis remains unchanged, whereas the amino acid concentrations decrease. When all synthesis has ceased, asparagine increases. Similar maxima in amino acid concentrations in the seed have been found in wheat and corn (Koblet, 1940; Duvick, 1952).

Free amino acids found in the embryos are listed in Table 26. Here again, as in the endosperm, there is a maximum concentration of several amino acids, but now it is in the fourth or fifth week, somewhat later than the time of maximum concentration in the endosperm. Though aspartic acid and glutamic acid occur in abundance, the most striking are the two basic amino acids, lysine and arginine. They occur together in large quantities in the apical meristems of *Adiantum* and *Lupinus* (Steward *et al.*, 1954) and their occurrence in embryos may have a similar physiological explanation though we can only speculate as to what that is.

TABLE 26

Some Free Amino Acids in D. stramonium Embryos
at Various Stages of Development

(Concentration in millimoles per gram fresh weight)

| Age in Days | 15 | 19 | 23 | 29 | 33 | 40 | 50 |
|---|---|---|---|---|---|---|---|
| Fresh Weight of Embryos in mg | 0.1 | 0.7 | 1.2 | 2.1 | 1.7 | 2.4 | 2.1 |
| Aspartic acid | 0.2 | 3.7 | 2.6 | 5.0 | 1.5 | 0.2 | 0.4 |
| Glutamic acid | 0.5 | 3.3 | 4.8 | 4.6 | 2.0 | 0.5 | 2.1 |
| Serine | 0.2 | 0.8 | 1.8 | 0.8 | 0.4 | 0.1 | 0.4 |
| Asparagine | — | + | + | 0.1 | 2.1 | 2.6 | 0.8 |
| Threonine | + | 1.1 | 1.9 | + | — | + | + |
| Alanine | 1.5 | 2.1 | 3.6 | 1.2 | 2.4 | 0.2 | 0.4 |
| Glutamine | 0.2 | 3.1 | 2.5 | + | 2.3 | 0.5 | 0.5 |
| Lysine | 0.1 | 2.1 | 7.0 | 1.5 | 0.2 | 0.1 | — |
| Arginine | 1.1 | 6.3 | 26.0 | 8.8 | — | — | — |

The peak concentrations coincide with the end of the growth of the embryo and the time of maximum rate of reserve protein formation. A similar situation is found in the endosperm. As in the endosperm the asparagine concentration, very low in the beginning, increases during the maturation period. Other amino acids that have been recognized are proline, valine, leucine, and gamma-amino-butyric acid. The latter is most prominent after 4 weeks.

Young isolated embryos grow only on a medium with several amino acids, but older embryos can grow on a medium containing only nitrate. From the endosperm analyses we learn that the embryo is provided with the larger concentrations in the third week, at a stage when isolated embryos can grow very well without amino acids. Though this appears contradictory, it is likely that the growth *in vitro* is supported by accumulated proteins in the embryo used up because of starvation. Glutamine, a very important amino acid in culture media, occurs in abundance in most parts of the seed. Only in very young seeds immediately after fertilization is it found in very high concentrations. This may be a result of protein hydrolysis or a sudden supply from the placenta. The seed coat never shows great changes in concentration nor is it engaged in an accumulation of proteins or in active cell division. Only at the last stages does it show larger asparagine concentrations, as does the endosperm and embryo. The endosperm and embryo show great changes in amino acid concentrations at the time when a fundamental change in growth pattern takes place: for the endosperm the beginning of the maturation phase, or the final stages of the milky state, for the embryo the final stages of its growth. These transition periods are characterized by changes in a pattern of the utilization and perhaps production of amino acids, expressed by changes in the amino acid concentrations. The accumulation of asparagine toward the end is typical for tissues being dehydrated or going into a rest period.

**Internal Atmosphere of the Capsule.** *Datura* seeds, like other angiosperm seeds, develop within a fruit and are separated from the atmosphere by the fruit wall. In capsules of normal *D. stramonium* diploids the total number of seeds varies between 500 and 1,000. They are packed closely together, leaving only small spaces among and between them and the inside of the capsule wall. From these air pockets the seeds must derive oxygen for their respiration and into them release carbon dioxide. An uninterrupted oxygen supply for the seeds is only possible by a continuous gas exchange between the outer and inner atmosphere through the wall. If this gas exchange is based upon diffusion of oxygen to the inner part of the capsule and of carbon dioxide from the inner to the outer atmosphere, the oxygen concentration inside must be lower than that outside and the carbon dioxide concentration inside must be greater than that outside. Inside the seeds one may expect to find an even lower oxygen concentration and a still higher concentration of carbon dioxide.

Although several studies on the internal gas composition of fruits have been reported (Dowd, 1933; Wardlaw, 1936), few reports pertaining to dehiscent fruits like the *Datura* capsule are to be found (Ullrich, 1949). In this light, verification of the above assumptions on the internal gas composition of the *Datura* capsule seemed worth while not only for their general interest but also because embryo culture studies have always been made in ordinary air with a very low carbon dioxide concentration and 21 per cent of oxygen. It is by no means certain that these are the optimum conditions for embryo development.

First the air inside the capsule, in the spaces between the seeds, was analyzed by making use of a simple technique described by Berg (1946). Samples of the internal atmosphere of the capsule were withdrawn with a syringe filled with saturated LiCl. A hollow glass needle glued to the syringe was pushed through the capsule wall while the capsule was still attached to the plant. To prevent leakage or contamination with air the capsule was held under water during the process (*214*).

It became clear at once that in the capsule of *D. stramonium* the composition of the atmosphere does not undergo the radical changes that have been observed by Wardlaw and Leonard (1936) in fleshy fruits like the cucumber and papaya during ripening. The carbon dioxide concentration is fairly low at first but rises gradually to about 6 per cent 19 days after pollination, followed by a slight decrease to a level of 4 per cent, which is maintained until nearly the time of maturity of the fruit. The oxygen concentration inside the capsule initially is about 18 per cent but drops to 15 to 16 per cent when the carbon dioxide concentration is maximum and then rises again to around 17 per cent for the remaining growth period (Fig. 54). The nitrogen concentration is highest shortly after fertilization but seems to remain fairly constant at about 80 per cent for the greater part of the growth period.

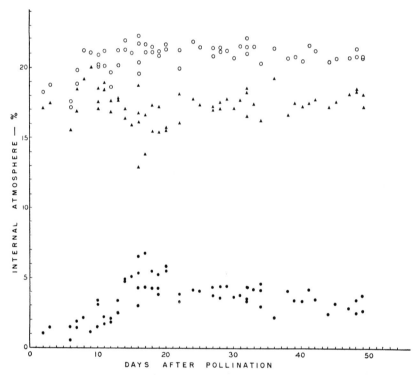

Fig. 54. Composition of the internal atmosphere of *D. stramonium* capsules. Nitrogen: open circles; oxygen: triangles; carbon dioxide: solid dots.

Inside the seeds the oxygen concentration will probably be lower than in the cavities around the seeds, whereas the carbon dioxide concentration will be higher. How much lower the oxygen concentration in the embryo sac is we can only guess, but because the seed coat of very young seeds is very thin it is not unreasonable to assume that in early stages the embryo does not suffer from a shortage of oxygen. In later stages when the seed coat becomes brown and hard, passage of gases to the embryo may become increasingly slow. Several reports have been made on the difficult passage of gases through the seed coat (Brown, 1940; Crocker and Barton, 1953). The carbon dioxide should increase in the seed when the seed coat becomes more impermeable and hard, but, again, at the very early stages the concentration around the embryo may not be much higher than in the fruit cavity.

A few words may be said about the possible factors that influence and control the internal gas concentrations in the fruit. The internal carbon dioxide concentration is maintained by production and release of $CO_2$ by the seeds and the tissues of the fruit and by the loss of it through the fruit wall to the outside air and possible fixation. The oxygen concentration is determined by the rate of intake through the fruit wall and its consumption by the seeds and fruit tissues. We know little about the passage of these gases through the wall. The exchange of gases depends on the thickness of the fruit wall, on its anatomical structure and chemical composition, and on its respiration and photosynthetic activity. None of these variables have yet been measured with the exception of the thickness of the capsule wall and its water content (Fig. 55). Any evaluation

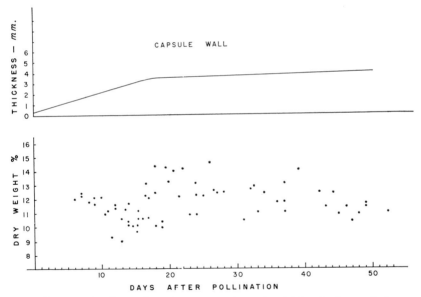

FIG. 55. Growth of capsules of *D. stramonium*. (top) The thickness of the capsule wall; (bottom) dry weight of capsule wall.

of this limited information for the purpose of determining the passage of gas through the wall would certainly be premature, though one may point out that the increase in thickness of the wall after pollination parallels the increase in carbon dioxide concentration and the decrease in oxygen concentration. The movement of gases through the capsule wall may be expected to be inversely related to the thickness of the wall.

**Seed Respiration.** The next step was to examine the respiration of seeds at various stages of development. For this we used the conventional Warburg technique. Table 27 shows that oxygen uptake of the seeds per unit of fresh weight is high at the early stages of seed growth but decreases sharply after one week. The oxygen consumption per seed, however, shows an increase for 2 weeks after pollination and decreases only toward the end of the maturation period. The respiratory quotient (RQ) of the seeds also changes considerably during development. The RQ of very young seeds is lower than one, but after a few days it rises to unity and after 2 weeks even to values close to 1.5. At the last stages of seed growth the RQ decreases again to values of about one or slightly less. The increasing uptake of oxygen per seed can be explained from the increased weight and seed size as a result of growth.

TABLE 27

OXYGEN CONSUMPTION AND APPARENT RESPIRATORY QUOTIENT (RQ)
OF D. STRAMONIUM SEEDS *

| Age (Days) | Oxygen Uptake per Seed | Oxygen Uptake per Microgram Fresh Weight | RQ |
|---|---|---|---|
| 3 | 0.07 | 2.14 | 0.60 |
| 5 | 0.36 | 2.96 | 1.05 |
| 7 | 1.00 | 1.54 | 1.04 |
| 10 | 3.27 | 0.90 | 0.96 |
| 14 | 6.73 | 0.80 | 1.14 |
| 20 | 5.38 | 0.47 | 1.31 |
| 24 | 6.93 | 0.60 | 1.39 |
| 32 | 4.29 | 0.30 | 1.17 |
| 46 | 0.87 | 0.07 | 0.96 |

* Age in days after pollination. Oxygen uptake in microliters per hour. Measurements made within one hour after removal of the seeds from the fruit.

More difficult to understand are the changes in the respiration rate on a fresh weight basis. As indicated above, the initial 2 weeks of seed development mark a period of growth and the following 5 weeks a period of maturation. During the growth period the dry matter content (largely cell walls and protoplasm) decreases from 28 per cent to 15 per cent and this decrease is nearly sufficient to account for the decrease in respiratory activity. During the maturation period the respiratory activity of the seed continues to decrease though the amount of protoplasmic material probably undergoes little change. The seed coat gradually becomes less permeable, the seed tissue dries, and meanwhile the seed gradually passes into a state of dormancy and the metabolic pattern of the tissue changes from growth to the formation of fats and proteins. How much each of these factors contributes to the decrease of the seed respiration cannot be estimated at this time.

The changes in the RQ value also merit some attention. Only at the beginning of seed growth is the RQ lower than one, but it soon becomes about unity. This change occurs less than a week after pollination. The large amounts of starch in the seed coat of a young seed could serve as a respiratory substrate, though immediately after pollination other substrates may have been used and be responsible for the low RQ value. The rise in RQ after 2 weeks also suggests a change in substrate. The rate of oil accumulation has decreased considerably by this time and some of the compounds used for oil formation may now become available for respiration. Finally, one must inquire whether the measured RQ presents a true picture of the respiration or only an "apparent" one. Seeds contain large amounts of carbon dioxide, either chemically or physically bound, as shown by the figures of Table 28. The analyses have been made according to the method of Willaman and Brown (1930). The storage of carbon dioxide in the seeds must have influenced the value of the observed RQ, making it lower than it actually is by preventing release of carbon dioxide from the seeds. However, according to the figures, the

TABLE 28

TOTAL CARBON DIOXIDE FOUND IN D. STRAMONIUM SEEDS

| Age (Days) * | Carbon Dioxide Content (Micrograms per Seed) |
| --- | --- |
| 11 | 0.9 |
| 14 | 5.6 |
| 17 | 4.4 |
| 20 | 6.0 |
| 27 | 5.4 |
| 34 | 4.5 |
| 40 | 8.3 |
| 47 | 11.5 |
| 52 | 13.7 |

* Age in days after pollination.

carbon dioxide content of the seeds increases only near the end of the maturation period and the decrease in RQ sets in much earlier. Therefore, the RQ must present a true relationship between consumed oxygen and released carbon dioxide except for the last week when more carbon dioxide is fixed by the seeds. It would be very interesting to know to what extent dark fixation of carbon dioxide and anaerobic oxidation take part in the metabolism of the seed.

**Conclusion.** The material presented above offers only a starting point for more detailed investigations into the physiological processes that go on in the growing seed. In spite of the fragmentary character of the work it must be clear that these processes are very complex and changing continuously. A great number of different activities occur concurrently. It can easily be imagined that any small disturbance might disrupt the orderly sequence of activities and cause aborted seed to result. The disturbance need not be very great, but to learn what constitutes a disturbance that will result in incompatibility we need to have more information on the normal development of the seed from fertilized ovule to mature, viable seed.

# 13

# Segmental Interchanges and the Species Problem

SOPHIE SATINA

The nature and evolutionary relationships of the *Datura* species have been especially important problems in the *Datura* studies since 1930. The taxonomy, the development of embryos in selfs and crosses, the incompatibility between species in crosses, and other subjects related to the species problem are discussed separately in Chapters 2, 11, 14, and 15. The present chapter deals with the analysis of chromosomes of the species and races in relation to species separation and with the outward appearances of some hybrids.

There are no numerical chromosomal changes in the evolution of the *Datura* genus. The haploid number of chromosomes in every species is 12, but each species differs in its chromosome-end structure. It has been stated by Blakeslee "that species may have arisen in nature by the same processes as have produced our artificial species" [1] (*80*) and that "The frequency of interchange of chromosomal fragments in *D. stramonium* and the relation of this phenomenon to the formation of new pure-breeding types has led to the hypothesis that segmental interchange has accompanied the changes responsible for the formation of species in the genus *Datura*" (*83*). These assumptions have been supported by the finding of 35 different chromosomal types among the 1,058 races of *Datura* collected in nature and subsequently analyzed. Cytological studies have given ample evidence that segmental interchanges between nonhomologous chromosomes in races and species have taken place and that these have resulted in structural changes in the chromosomes which have been preserved in different naturally isolated groups of species (*75, 121, 159, 177, 208*).

**Occurrence of Prime Types in Species.** A number of cryptic or prime types (PT's) differing from other races in some of their chromosome-end

[1] The term "artificial species" was used by Blakeslee in referring to the synthesized pure-breeding types (*86*).

220

arrangements have been found in nature among races of *D. stramonium*. Their modified chromosomes have been derived through segmental interchanges (Chapter 4). It seemed probable that this process of modifying chromosomes is of widespread occurrence in nature and that it might play an important part in species evolution. Thus, in accordance with Blakeslee's plans, studies of the species problem involved a survey of prime types, or chromosomal types, among races of all *Datura* species. This was followed by studies of chromosome-end arrangements in all species. It seemed desirable to obtain data on segmental interchanges between chromosomal types within a single species, and between the species, in order to compare the interchanges in species with those occurring in races.

The method used in this work was similar to that applied in studies on *D. stramonium*. Each available race of a species was crossed to the tester selected for that species and to each other, and dividing pollen mother cells of the hybrids were used for the chromosomal studies. In the homozygous condition the chromosomes of all prime types are arranged in pollen mother cells at metaphase I as 12 bivalents. In the heterozygous condition, as a result of segmental interchange between nonhomologous chromosomes, the pollen mother cells of hybrids contain bivalents and a configuration involving a single interchange of two nonhomologous chromosomes which form a circle of four. Less frequently two interchanges are found in hybrids from chromosomal types within the same species and dividing p.m.c. of such hybrids contain two circles of four.

The chromosomal type selected as the tester in each species is designated as Type I. To avoid confusion the term "prime type" or the abbreviation PT, with an Arabic number, is used in the text and illustrations only in reference to *D. stramonium*. Roman numbers are added to the species names to designate the chromosomal types in other species: *D. ferox* I, *D. ferox* II, etc. For brevity in the text the word *chromosome* is used instead of "chromosome-end arrangements."

Eleven PT's were found among the 875 races of *D. stramonium* collected and tested (Chapter 4). The total number of races tested in the other nine species was considerably smaller—only 183 races. In 19 races of these the analysis of the chromosome-end arrangements was not completed. Chromosomal types with modified chromosomes have been found in all species except *D. pruinosa* and *D. discolor*. Apparently too few races (only four of each) were available for tests in these two species. Three chromosomal types have been found among 12 races of *D. quercifolia*, two among 16 races of *D. ferox*, two among 7 races of *D. leichhardtii*, two among 3 races of *D. ceratocaula*, four among 31 races of *D. meteloides*, six among 61 races of *D. metel*, and three among 45 races of *D. innoxia*.

**Racial Differences.** As is true for the prime types of *D. stramonium*, most of the chromosomal types in other species cannot be distinguished by outward appearance. Some morphological differences were found in the shape and size of flowers and leaves of *D. ceratocaula, D. meteloides,* and *D. metel.* Races of the last-named species differ considerably in growth habit, flower color and form, some having single and some double flowers. These and other characters are probably merely the product of particular genes and not dependent on the chromosomal type involved.

Other well-expressed racial differences in crossability were observed between some types within a single species. *D. leichhardtii* I × *D. discolor* crosses produced viable seeds, but crosses of *D. leichhardtii* II with the same *D. discolor* plants gave only empty seeds or seeds containing arrested or deteriorated embryos. The reverse occurs in crosses of *D. leichhardtii* with *D. ceratocaula* I. When *D. leichhardtii* II is used as the female parent, it gives much better results than *D. leichhardtii* I. Thus in crosses with *D. discolor* better results are obtained with *D. leichhardtii* I, but in crosses involving *D. ceratocaula* the race *D. leichhardtii* II is more successful (*185*).

Another kind of racial difference was found in *D. meteloides.* Each of its four types produces normal 2n seeds in selfs. Each type used as a male parent in crosses with *D. stramonium* is strongly incompatible, but *D. meteloides* II differs from the tester and the types III and IV in having a mixture of 1n and 2n pollen. In summer the amount of 2n pollen is small, no more than 1 per cent, but it becomes as high as 25 per cent in the fall, due to irregularities in microsporogenesis, presumably caused by low temperature at night. When such pollen was used in crosses with 21 various *D. stramonium* races, the formation of viable seeds invariably resulted. The type *D. meteloides* II thus becomes compatible with *D. stramonium* under certain conditions. However, none of the dissected embryos or the germinated seeds developed into the expected diploid plants.

As shown in Table 29, the capsules from crosses of 21 PT's of *D. stramonium* × *D. meteloides* II were divided into two groups: 49 capsules were picked and opened 3 to 4 weeks after pollination and 40 capsules were harvested when ripe. In each group over 400 large seeds contained embryos. Of the 53 dissected embryos grown in culture media 16 reached maturity. Each plant was a triploid. Of the mature seeds 30

TABLE 29

OFFSPRING OF CROSSES OF 21 PT's OF D. STRAMONIUM × D. METELOIDES II
(Fall, 1949)

|  | Dissected Embryos | Mature Seeds Sown |
|---|---|---|
| Number of crosses ............... | 49 | 40 |
| Number of large seeds ........... | 438 | 467 |
| Embryos transferred to soil ........ | 53 | 30 |
| Mature plants ................... | 16 | 27 |
| Number 2n ...................... | 0 | 0 |
| Number 3n ...................... | 16 | 27 |

germinated and all the 27 plants that reached maturity were triploids. Thus all of the 43 offspring brought to maturity were numerical triploids. Only two $3n$ plants were recorded from many $D.$ $stramonium \times D.$ $meteloides$ I crosses made during a period of several years (195).

Another example showing preferential functioning of $2n$ pollen was observed in diploid $\times$ tetraploid crosses in a race of $D.$ $metel$ I. As many as 1,260 viable seeds were obtained from 50 $2n \times 4n$ crosses, while the same number of $4n \times 2n$ crosses produced only 74 seeds, none of which germinated. All the plants that grew from seeds of the first combination were found to be triploids. Such preferential functioning of $2n$ pollen is contrary to the results of all previous experiments with $Datura$ $2n \times 4n$ crosses. As in the examples mentioned of morphological differences between races, these differences in crossability may be due to modifying genes rather than to the specific chromosome-end arrangements (222).

**Interspecific Hybrids.** The survey of chromosomal types within a single species was followed by detailed studies of the chromosome-end arrangements in the standard testers and in chromosomal types of each species. Belling's hypothesis of segmental interchange, which served as the basis for the method, was developed by Blakeslee and Bergner and used in the chromosome analysis of the ten natural $Datura$ species. The point of chromosome breaks and the length of interchanged segments cannot be detected by the method employed. The structural changes are indicated only with respect to their end arrangements as seen at M I in dividing pollen mother cells. The end arrangements only are determined by this method, described below, and interpreted in terms of the standard PT 1 of $D.$ $stramonium$ (Chapter 4).

For the method used in chromosome analysis it is necessary to secure interracial and interspecific hybrids. The hybrids from crosses between races of single species are obtained easily. But difficulties are encountered in getting interspecific hybrids in certain combinations, because most of the $Datura$ species are incompatible and do not produce viable seeds when crossed. Fig 56 indicates all the crosses that have been made between the testers of the ten species. The solid lines represent species crosses from which viable seeds have been obtained. Incompatible crosses are indicated by dotted lines; in some of these cases hybrids have been obtained by the embryo-dissection method. The arrows at the ends of the lines show which species was used as the female parent. Some crosses are successful in one direction only. There are only four species that give hybrids directly in crosses with $D.$ $stramonium:$ $D.$ $quercifolia,$ $D.$ $ferox,$ $D.$ $leichhardtii,$ and $D.$ $discolor.$ $D.$ $leichhardtii$ gives viable seed when used as the female with seven other species.

An indirect and tedious method was applied to get a $D.$ $stramonium$ $\times D.$ $pruinosa$ hybrid that was necessary for the analysis of the $D.$ $pruinosa$ chromosomes. It took six years to complete this work. The $D.$ $leichhardtii$ I tester which is compatible in crosses with both species has been used as an intermediary or "bridging" species. Successive back-crosses of *D. leichhardtii* I × *D. pruinosa* hybrids to *D. leichhardtii* I brought the chromosomes of *D. pruinosa* into the matrix of *D. leichhardtii* I protoplasm. Apparently the barriers to crossability were removed be-cause a race developed from these repeatedly backcrossed hybrids did replace with success the tester of *D. pruinosa* in crosses with *D. stra-monium* and other species (160). Hybrids necessary for the chromo-some analysis of the remaining four species: *D. ceratocaula, D. metel-*

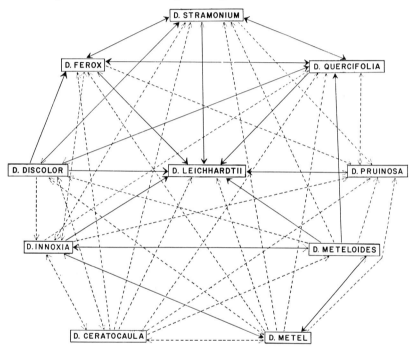

Fig. 56. Crosses made between the tester races of the ten *Datura* species. Solid lines represent compatible and dotted lines incompatible crosses.

*oides, D. metel,* and *D. innoxia,* which are highly incompatible with most other species, were obtained only after the development of the new method of embryo dissection and culture *in vitro* described in Chapter 12.

A discussion of the various degrees of incompatibility encountered in interspecific crosses is given in Chapter 15. Some species crosses pro-duce ample viable seed. Other crosses produce embryos that can be matured only by the embryo-culture method, and still others completely fail to produce embryos although in some cases zygotes are formed. Incompatibility is thus a question of degree for each particular inter-specific cross.

As shown in Fig. 67, of the 90 possible combinations of crosses be-tween testers of the ten species only 17 are compatible and give hybrids with viable seeds. These are indicated by an X. Three other combinations, $X_{sp.}$, may give sporadically one or a few viable seeds. The first three species listed can be used either as female or as male parents. *D. leichhardtii*, which is compatible with all species except *D. ceratocaula* and *D. metel*, gives hybrids only when used as a female. *D. discolor* and *D. meteloides* are successful in crosses with four species but only when used as males. The same is true to a lesser degree for *D. pruinosa* and *D. innoxia;* the former is capable of forming hybrids with at least one species and the latter with two species. *D. metel* gives sporadic hybrids with two species when it is used as the female. *D. ceratocaula* is the only species that does not readily form hybrids with any other species. The 50 incompatible combinations of species crosses marked $\boxed{\text{ED}}$, ED, and E, and methods used in bringing to maturity the arrested growth of hybrid embryos of these crosses are discussed in Chapter 15.

**Characteristics of Hybrids from Incompatible Crosses.** Most of the species hybrids obtained in this work cannot occur in nature due to the presence of various natural barriers to crossability. The securing of species hybrids by the embryo-dissection method provided an opportunity to study many hybrids otherwise unknown. All of the hybrids thus far obtained between the ten species of *Datura* have produced flowers with a high proportion of aborted pollen. The $F_1$'s from compatible crosses have about 40 to 60 per cent of aborted pollen; the percentage of aborted pollen is much higher (75 to 100 per cent) in all hybrids from incompatible species crosses. The highly inbred nine species, when crossed with *D. ceratocaula* I as the male parent, give hybrids, all of which have a very high percentage of aborted pollen, and capsules from selfing these hybrids contain only a few seeds.

Mature plants of all the species hybrids we have grown have shown characters more or less intermediate between the two species involved in the cross. Some particular parental characters may be dominant and appear almost unchanged in the hybrid. Other characters are found to be recessive and nearly or completely disappear. However, by the general aspect of habit, stem, leaf, and floral characters, all hybrids can be recognized as such, and in most combinations the identity of the two species used in the cross is obvious. Hybrids of *D. ceratocaula* with the other nine species may be taken as examples. Some of the dominant characteristics of *D. ceratocaula* were observed in all hybrids: the hollow stem, absence of hairs on the pedicel, purple veins in anthers, and a purple pigment on the inner wall of the capsule, etc. Other *D. ceratocaula* characters were found to be recessive: the deep yellow color of the stigma and absence of spines and hairs on the capsules (Fig. 57). Details on intermediate characters and on the dominant and recessive characters found only in some hybrids have been published (*172*).

Morphological, anatomical, and some physiological characters were also studied in two intergeneric hybrids: *D. innoxia* × *Brugmansia suaveolens* and *D. innoxia* × *B. rosea*.[2] The characters in the hybrids

[2] A discussion of the generic names *Brugmansia* and *Datura* is given in Chapter 2.

were mostly intermediate between the widely different parents. The dominance of *Datura* was observed in the purple pigmentation, dichasial branching, the 10-lobed corolla, early lignification of xylem, and the absence of definite flowering periodicity. The *Brugmansia* characters, such as the woody or semiwoody stems, greater stature, the nature of bark, the trumpet-shaped corolla, hairiness of the latter, and drooping of flowers were present in both hybrids. Due to irregularities in meiosis both hybrids had 100 per cent aborted pollen. The embryo sac in both hybrids degenerated at the 2 to 4 nucleated stages (*167, 187*).

By the embryo-dissection method a hybrid was obtained between *D. discolor* and *D. metel* that was ascertained to be a sterile numerical

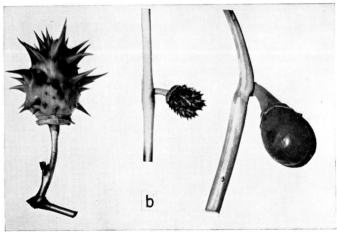

Fig. 57. Two species hybrids and their parents. (a) *D. ceratocaula* ♀, hybrid, and *D. metel* ♂; (b) *D. ferox* ♀, hybrid, and *D. ceratocaula* ♂.

triploid and phenotypically more like the male parent. Some of its apices were treated with colchicine emulsion and eventually developed into numerical hexaploid branches or formed 6n sectors on triploid branches. A number of apices were affected differently. In some cases the chromosome doubling occurred only in one or two germ layers and formed a variety of periclinal chimeras: 3n, 6n, 3n, or 6n, 6n, 3n, or 3n, 6n, 6n. Branches with mixed ploidy in some of the layers were also formed; these mixochimeras soon reverted to the original triploid. The hexaploid branches were fertile, producing a few capsules with some viable seeds. Three of the 10 seeds planted germinated within 5 weeks. The seedlings grew well and were eventually recorded as hexaploid plants. A comparison between the original 3n and the numerical polyploids showed that fertility was partially restored in the 6n plants. The plants grew slower than the triploid hybrids, produced fewer flowers, had thicker leaves and corollas, and contained less aborted pollen (65 to 70 per cent as compared to 94 to 97 per cent). They also produced fewer microcytes (199).

The use of the embryo-dissection method, combined or followed by colchicine treatments, in experimental hybridization should be tested in a larger number of species crosses. The new hybrids resulting from such work have, perhaps, no evolutionary significance in nature but offer excellent material for a variety of studies connected with growth, fertility, physiological and other vital problems.

**Method of Chromosome Analysis.** In analyzing the chromosome-end arrangements in a species it is best to determine first how many chromosomes, if any, of the species (A) to be tested are homologous with the chromosomes of the standard tester D. stramonium, PT 1, and how many are modified. Answers to both questions are obtained from dividing pollen mother cells at metaphase I of the hybrid between PT 1 × A. The unmodified chromosomes in A form bivalents with their homologs in PT 1 at meiosis. The modified chromosomes in A differing in their end arrangements from the chromosomes in PT 1 form configurations in the hybrid. Thus, as shown in Fig. 58a, the 24 chromosomes in the PT 1 × D. meteloides I hybrid are arranged as two free bivalents, a circle of 12, and two circles of 4 chromosomes. One of these circles is large and the other is of medium size. The presence of two bivalents proves that only two chromosomes of D. meteloides I are homologous with two chromosomes of PT 1 and that this species has ten modified chromosomes in terms of the standard tester.

To determine *which* of the chromosomes in A are homologous with some of the PT 1 chromosomes, a number of PT's are crossed to the species A. If the hybrid from a certain PT × A has the *same* number of bivalents as the hybrid PT 1 × A, it indicates that the interchange of chromosomes in A differ from those in the modified chromosomes of the PT used in the cross, that such chromosomes are absent in A, and that other PT's must be tried for the analysis. If the hybrid contains *fewer* bivalents than the hybrid PT 1 × A, the decrease is always accompanied by an increase in the number of chromosomes involved in configurations. This proves that the modified chromosomes in the PT used in the cross are unmodified in A and that some of its chromosomes have the same end arrangements as some of the chromosomes in the standard PT 1. Such a case is shown in Fig. 58b. The hybrid from PT 50 with

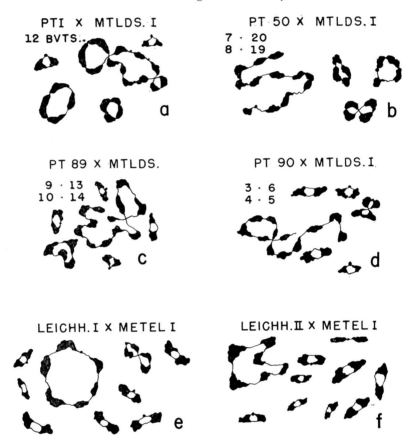

FIG. 58. Configurations of chromosomes found in species hybrids.

two modified chromosomes, $7 \cdot 20$ and $8 \cdot 19$ instead of $7 \cdot 8$ and $19 \cdot 20$, crossed to *D. meteloides* I does not contain any bivalents, but it has three circles of 4 instead of two circles present in PT $1 \times A$. The two bivalents (Fig. 58a) took part in the formation of the extra circle, which could only be made up of the modified $7 \cdot 20$ and $8 \cdot 19$ chromosomes in PT 50 and the unmodified $7 \cdot 8$ and $19 \cdot 20$ chromosomes forming the closed circle configuration:

$$7 \cdot 8 \; - \; 8 \cdot 19$$
$$| \qquad\qquad |$$
$$7 \cdot 20 \; - \; 20 \cdot 19$$

This proves that the two bivalents present in Fig. 58a are the un-modified chromosomes $7 \cdot 8$ and $19 \cdot 20$, which in *D. meteloides* I are homologous with PT 1.

If the hybrid from a certain PT $\times$ A has more bivalents and fewer chromosomes associated in configurations than the hybrid of PT $1 \times A$, some chromosomes in A must have the same end arrangements as the modified chromosomes in the PT used in the cross. Being homologous with them, they form the additional bivalents in the hybrid. Such a case is shown in Fig. 58c. The hybrid of PT 89 $\times$ *D. meteloides* I has four bivalents, a chain of 12 (which is the broken circle of 12), and only one (the large) circle of 4. This increase in the number of bivalents, four instead of two, and the absence of the second (of medium size) circle of 4 in this hybrid as compared to the hybrid PT $1 \times$ *D. meteloides* I proves that two modified chromosomes in *D. meteloides* I are homolo-gous to the modified $9 \cdot 13$ and $10 \cdot 14$ chromosomes in PT 89. They form the two additional bivalents in the hybrid PT 89 $\times$ *D. meteloides* I (Fig. 58c). This also proves that one of the two circles of 4 in the hybrid PT $1 \times$ *D. meteloides* I shown in Fig. 58a is formed by these modified $9 \cdot 13$ and $10 \cdot 14$ chromosomes in *D. meteloides* I and the un-modified $9 \cdot 10$ and $13 \cdot 14$ chromosomes of PT 1:

$$9 \cdot 10 - 10 \cdot 14$$
$$|\qquad\qquad |$$
$$9 \cdot 13 - 13 \cdot 14$$

By use of PT 90 with the modified $3 \cdot 6$ and $4 \cdot 5$ chromosomes (Fig. 58d) it has been found that *D. meteloides* I has the same modified chro-mosomes and that the large circle of 4 in Fig. 58a is formed by the

$$3 \cdot 6 - 6 \cdot 5$$
$$|\qquad\qquad | \text{ chromosomes.}$$
$$3 \cdot 4 - 4 \cdot 5$$

In addition to crosses with PT's the tested species A was also crossed to the testers and chromosomal types of other species. As has been stated, most of the chromosomes in types within a species are homolo-gous and only a few are associated in one or no more than two configura-tions. As shown in Table 30, the tester *D. leichhardtii* I and the type *D. leichhardtii* II have ten homologous chromosomes. The type differs from the species tester in having the $15 \cdot 21$ and $12 \cdot 22$ chromosomes in-stead of the $15 \cdot 12$ and $21 \cdot 22$ chromosomes present in the tester. The species tester *D. innoxia* I and the type *D. innoxia* III have ten homol-ogous chromosomes and the latter differs from the tester in having the $5 \cdot 6$ and $11 \cdot 2$ chromosomes instead of the $5 \cdot 2$ and $11 \cdot 6$ chromosomes present in *D. innoxia* I. In analyzing the chromosomes in species A the comparison of hybrids from A crossed to types within a species are of particular help. For example, the hybrid of *D. leichhardtii* I $\times$ *D. metel* I has a circle of 6, a circle of 4 chromosomes, and seven bivalents (Fig. 58e). The hybrid *D. leichhardtii* II $\times$ *D. metel* I has a circle of

TABLE 30

INTERCHANGED CHROMOSOME ENDS IN TEN SPECIES OF DATURA (27 TYPES) IN
TERMS OF THE CHROMOSOMES OF D. STRAMONIUM, PT 1
(The modified chromosomes are in boldface type. The number of chromosomes
homologous with PT 1 in each type are shown at the bottom of each vertical column.)

*Datura stramonium*

| PT 1 | PT 2 | PT 3 | PT 4 | PT 7 | PT 87 | PT 88 | PT 94 | PT 95 | PT 96 | PT 2+3 |
|---|---|---|---|---|---|---|---|---|---|---|
| 1·2 | **1·18** | 1·2 | 1·2 | 1·2 | 1·2 | 1·2 | **1·14** | **1·2**[20] | 1·2 | **1·18** |
| 3·4 | 3·4 | 3·4 | **3·21** | 3·4 | **3·12** | 3·4 | 3·4 | 3·4 | 3·4 | 3·4 |
| 5·6 | 5·6 | 5·6 | 5·6 | 5·6 | 5·6 | 5·6 | 5·6 | 5·6 | 5·6 | 5·6 |
| 7·8 | 7·8 | 7·8 | 7·8 | 7·8 | 7·8 | 7·8 | 7·8 | 7·8 | **7·19** | 7·8 |
| 9·10 | 9·10 | 9·10 | 9·10 | **9·10**[20] | 9·10 | 9·10 | 9·10 | 9·10 | 9·10 | 9·10 |
| 11·12 | 11·12 | **11·21** | 11·12 | 11·12 | **11·21** | 11·12 | 11·12 | 11·12 | 11·12 | **11·21** |
| 13·14 | 13·14 | 13·14 | 13·14 | 13·14 | 13·14 | 13·14 | **13·18** | 13·14 | 13·14 | 13·14 |
| 15·16 | 15·16 | 15·16 | 15·16 | 15·16 | 15·16 | **15·23** | 15·16 | 15·16 | 15·16 | 15·16 |
| 17·18 | **17·2** | 17·18 | 17·18 | 17·18 | 17·18 | 17·18 | **17·2** | 17·18 | 17·18 | **17·2** |
| 19·20 | 19·20 | 19·20 | 19·20 | **19·20**[10] | 19·20 | 19·20 | 19·20 | **19·20**[2] | **8·20** | 19·20 |
| 21·22 | 21·22 | **12·22** | **4·22** | 21·22 | **4·22** | 21·22 | 21·22 | 21·22 | 21·22 | **12·22** |
| 23·24 | 23·24 | 23·24 | 23·24 | 23·24 | 23·24 | **16·24** | 23·24 | 23·24 | 23·24 | 23·24 |
| 12 | 10 | 10 | 10 | 10 | 9 | 10 | 9 | 10 | 10 | 8 |

| D. quercifolia | | | D. ferox | | D. discolor | D. pruinosa | D. leichhardtii | |
|---|---|---|---|---|---|---|---|---|
| Type I | Type II | Type III | Type I | Type II | Type I | Type I | Type I | Type II |
| 1·18 | 1·18 | 1·18 | 1·18 | **1·21** | **1·11** | 1·18 | 1·18 | 1·18 |
| 3·4 | 3·4 | 3·4 | 3·4 | 3·4 | 3·4 | 3·4 | 3·4 | 3·4 |
| 5·6 | 5·6 | 5·6 | 5·6 | 5·6 | 5·6 | 5·6 | 5·6 | 5·6 |
| **7·20** | **7·20** | 7·8 | **7·20**[16] | **7·20**[16] | 7·8 | 7·8 | 7·8 | 7·8 |
| 9·10 | **9·2** | 9·10 | 9·10 | 9·10 | 9·10 | **9·14** | 9·10 | 9·10 |
| **11·21** | **11·21** | **11·21** | **11·21** | **11·18** | **16·18** | **11·16** | **11·16** | **11·16** |
| 13·14 | 13·14 | 13·14 | 13·14 | 13·14 | 13·14 | **13·10** | 13·14 | 13·14 |
| 15·16 | 15·16 | 15·16 | **15·16**[20] | **15·16**[20] | **15·21** | **15·21** | **15·12** | **15·21** |
| **17·2** | **17·10** | **17·2** | **17·2** | **17·2** | **17·2** | **17·2** | **17·2** | **17·2** |
| **19·8** | **19·8** | 19·20 | **19·8** | **19·8** | 19·20 | 19·20 | 19·20 | 19·20 |
| **12·22** | **12·22** | **12·22** | **12·22** | **12·22** | **12·22** | **12·22** | 21·22 | **12·22** |
| 23·24 | 23·24 | 23·24 | 23·24 | 23·24 | 23·24 | 23·24 | 23·24 | 23·24 |
| 6 | 5 | 8 | 5 | 5 | 7 | 5 | 8 | 7 |

| D. ceratocaula | | D. innoxia | | D. metel | D. meteloides | |
|---|---|---|---|---|---|---|
| Type I | Type II | Type I | Type III | Type I | Type I | Type IV |
| **1·11** | **1·11** | **1·17** | **1·17** | **1·17** | **1·17** | **1·17** |
| 3·4 | 3·4 | 3·4 | 3·4 | 3·4 | **3·6** | **3·6** |
| 5·6 | 5·6 | **5·2** | 5·6 | 5·6 | **5·4** | **5·4** |
| 7·8 | 7·8 | 7·8 | 7·8 | 7·8 | 7·8 | 7·8 |
| 9·10 | 9·10 | **9·14** | **9·14** | 9·10 | **9·13** | **9·13** |
| **14·16** | **14·16** | **11·6** | **11·2** | **11·2** | **11·2** | **11·2** |
| **13·18** | **13·23** | **13·10** | **13·10** | 13·14 | **10·14** | **10·14** |
| **15·21** | **15·21** | **15·21** | **15·21** | **15·21** | **15·21** | **15·21** |
| **17·2** | **17·2** | **16·18** | **16·18** | **16·18** | **23·18** | **23·16** |
| 19·20 | 19·20 | 19·20 | 19·20 | 19·20 | 19·20 | 19·20 |
| **12·22** | **12·22** | **12·22** | **12·22** | **12·22** | **12·22** | **12·22** |
| 23·24 | **18·24** | 23·24 | 23·24 | 23·24 | **16·24** | **18·24** |
| 6 | 5 | 4 | 5 | 7 | 2 | 2 |

6 chromosomes, no circle of 4, and nine bivalents (Fig. 58f). The presence of two additional bivalents in this hybrid proves that *D. metel* I has two more homologous chromosomes with *D. leichhardtii* II than with *D. leichhardtii* I. These can only be the **15 · 21** and **12 · 22** chromosomes, which are present in *D. leichhardtii* II and absent in *D. leichhardtii* I. By the use of various PT's and other testers in crosses with *D. meteloides* I, it was possible to determine that the circle of 12 present in the hybrid of PT 1 × *D. meteloides* I is formed as follows:

$$1 \cdot 17 - 17 \cdot 18 - 18 \cdot 23 - 23 \cdot 24 - 24 \cdot 16 - 16 \cdot 15$$
$$\vert \qquad\qquad\qquad\qquad\qquad\qquad\qquad\qquad\qquad\qquad \vert$$
$$1 \cdot 2 \; - \; 2 \cdot 11 - 11 \cdot 12 - 12 \cdot 22 - 22 \cdot 21 - 21 \cdot 15$$

By the application of similar reasoning it has been possible to determine the end arrangements of nearly all the chromosomes in other species. Such a practice leads to a reduction in the number of hybrids needed and in the amount of cytological work.

**Chromosome-End Arrangements.** The analysis of chromosome ends was completed for 27 chromosomal types found in nature. In eight more wild types: *D. innoxia* II (six races), *D. meteloides* II and III (one race in each), and *D. metel* II, III, II + III, IV, and V (11 races of *D. metel* in total), the chromosome analysis has not been completed. Crosses have shown that *D. meteloides* III differs from the tester, *D. meteloides* I, by two interchanges. *D. innoxia* II, *D. meteloides* II, and each of the four *D. metel* types, II, III, IV, and V, differ from their respective testers by a single interchange, the type II + III by two interchanges. It was also found that only five chromosomes are involved in the interchanges among the *D. metel* types with their tester (*158*).

The end arrangements of all the analyzed chromosomes in terms of PT 1 of *D. stramonium* are shown in Table 30. The 27 chromosomal types have a total of 57 chromosomes differing in their end arrangements. Each of the 12 chromosomes of the standard *D. stramonium* tester (PT 1) has its ends rearranged at least twice. The 5 · 6 chromosome is modified the least often. It is found unmodified in 24 types, being modified only in *D. innoxia* I and the two *D. meteloides* types. The 3 · 4 and 23 · 24 chromosomes remain unmodified in 23 types. The 7 · 8 is present in 22 types and the 19 · 20 in 20 types, etc. Modifications in chromosomes are apparently racial and not specific in character. Certain chromosomes, such as 1 · 2, 5 · 2, 3 · 12, 11 · 12, etc., are found in some of the chromosomal types of the species but modified in other types within the same species. On the other hand, none of the chromosomes found in *D. metel* I are present only in this species. For each modified chromosome there is a similar one in another species. This is true also in *D. leichhardtii* II. Too few types were analyzed in *D. meteloides* to make any valid conclusion about the 3 · 6, 4 · 5, 9 · 13, and 10 · 14 chromosomes found only in the two types of this species. It appears that the species of *Datura* have no individual chromosomes that could be considered to be specific by being present in all types of a species and absent in all other species.

The frequency in which each of the 24 individual ends of the 12 chromosomes has been involved in interchanges with other ends is different. Some were combined only with three different ends, others with four, five, six, or seven ends. The largest number of different segmental interchanges, seven for each, occurred with the · 1, · 11, and · 18 ends. As stated in Chapter 4, the secondary chromosome 1 · 1 is the largest of all the chromosomes in *D. stramonium;* of the 11 · 12 chromosome the · 11 arm is of medium size; the · 18 arm of the 17 · 18 chromosome is one of the smallest. It is obvious that the sizes of the arms have no direct influence on the frequency of exchanges of their ends. This is also true in respect to the presence or absence of a secondary constriction in the chromosome. For example, the frequency of exchange in the · 9 and · 10 ends is equal, both being combined with five different ends, but the · 9 arm has no secondary constriction, and the · 10 arm has the largest satellite of any of the chromosomes of *D. stramonium.* The frequency of exchanges in the 11 · 12 chromosome is almost twice as great in the · 11 arm, which has no satellite, as in the · 12 arm with a satellite. However, the reverse is found in the 21 · 22 chromosome in which the frequency of segmental exchange is greater in the · 21 half carrying the satellite. The reason for these differences in the frequency of exchange in individual ends remains unknown.

The comparison of the end arrangements in chromosomes of PT 1 with those in other species shows a wide range in the number of homologous chromosomes. The *D. stramonium* PT 1 tester has as many as eight homologous chromosomes with two types of two species, *D. quercifolia* III and *D. leichhardtii* I. There are seven homologous chromosomes in three other types, six in two, five in six, four in one, but there are only two, the 7 · 8 and the 19 · 20 chromosomes of PT 1, in both the *D. meteloides* types (Table 30).

Further comparison of chromosomes of other species with PT 1 reveals the interesting phenomenon that there are more homologous chromosomes in PT 1 and the two highly incompatible species *D. metel* I and *D. ceratocaula* I (seven and six, respectively) than in PT 1 and the compatible species *D. ferox* I and II, or *D. quercifolia* II. These two latter species are taxonomically the closest to *D. stramonium*, but each has only five chromosomes homologous with PT 1. There are also several compatible and incompatible species that have equal numbers of chromosomes homologous with PT 1. There is no apparent connection between the similarity or dissimilarity of chromosome arrangements and compatibility or incompatibility in species crosses. This conclusion is further supported by other evidence: PT 50 and *D. meteloides* I have *no* homologous chromosomes and the hybrid between them show all the chromosomes associated in configurations (Fig. 58b). However, this cross yields a large number of seeds with good dissectable embryos. The cross of PT 89 to *D. meteloides* I (Fig. 58c) indicates the presence of four homologous chromosomes; however, such a pollination repeatedly results in the production of capsules with only two or three seeds containing small, dissectable, but undifferentiated embryos (*208*).

The number of homologous chromosomes present in other species is quite variable (Table 30). The 12·22 chromosome is the only homologous one in the types tested of *D. ferox* and *D. meteloides*. This is also true in *D. quercifolia* I and II as compared with the *D. meteloides* types. The largest number of homologous chromosomes in *D. meteloides* with any other species is six (with *D. metel* I and *D. innoxia* III). Each of the other eight species has as many as ten homologous chromosomes with at least one of the other species. They appear in *D. quercifolia* and *D. ferox*, in *D. discolor* and *D. leichhardtii* II, *D. ceratocaula* I or *D. pruinosa* and *D. leichhardtii* II, *D. metel* I and *D. innoxia* III. Thus in each of these pairs the two species differ from each other by only one interchange. This indicates that in respect to their chromosome-end arrangements the difference between two species may be in some cases no greater than that found between the chromosomal types within a species. In addition there is this striking fact: the chromosomes in certain races in two different species collected in nature have similar end arrangements. This occurs in a chromosomal type of *D. stramonium* from Peru with the associated PT 2 + 3 and the *D. quercifolia* III found in Mexico. Both of these have the same four modified chromosomes, 1·18, 11·21, 2·17, 12·22, and in each the remaining eight chromosomes are unmodified and homologous with those of PT 1 (*159*).

**Discussion.** It is obvious that there is no direct correlation between speciation and the number of homologous chromosomes in species and we may quote Blakeslee's conclusion that, "Although segmental interchange has apparently not been the cause of differentiation of species, it has accompanied such differentiation and in some ways appears to be a factor in evolution" (*152*). The evidence given above was obtained by using an arbitrarily chosen tester, PT 1, of *D. stramonium;* this is the most common type in the United States, the first type obtained, and is the one most intensively studied, both genetically and cytologically. Now that the chromosome-end arrangements are known there is no doubt that the comparisons could be made more easily if a different tester were used. A tester like PT 2 + 3, which has more chromosomes in common with other species and types, would be better. It has no unusual chromosomes as 1·2, 11·12, 17·18, which are found only in PT 1 and in a few other *D. stramonium* PT's but are absent in most types and all other species. The use of such a tester would result in an increase in the number of homologous chromosomes and a corresponding decrease in the number of chromosomes associated in configurations in hybrids. However, the conclusions drawn from work with such a tester would not differ from those made using PT 1 as the standard.

The occurrence of reciprocal translocations between nonhomologous chromosomes may bring a similarity in the chromosome-end arrangements of different species. Such a similarity seems suggestive but does not differentiate species, since it appears also in races within a species. The differences between chromosomes of some species are of the same kind and often no greater than are those that separate and distinguish types within a single species. Some species differ from others by only one interchange between two chromosomes. This, and the finding of chromosomal types of two species with similar chromosome-end arrangements, prove that the visible resemblance in chromosomes do not properly indicate the degree of phylogenetic relationships and cannot be used as criteria for setting apart species. This supports Cleland's (1942) warning that caution is necessary in ascribing to similarity in segmental arrangements any general phylogenetic significance. Nor does similarity of chromosomes in different species have any direct relation to hybridization. In cases where there are no obvious isolation blocks to fertilization the number of homologous chromosomes in species has no direct relation to the degree of incompatibility in crosses.

The widespread occurrence of segmental interchanges as observed in *Datura* has also been reported in other plants. This factor is only one of the links in the long chain of processes involved in the evolution of species in nature. Indeed its relation to speciation is obscure. The apparent similarity of chromosomes observed in such an analysis is not sufficient evidence for considering two different types as identical, nor are two different species always distinguishable by means of chromosome structure. Other information is needed, such as the differences in specific genes, the character and location of chromosome breaks, the size of translocated segments, details of the morphology of chromosomes in each species genome, and additional data on the inversion of segments. Some of these details have been observed in *Datura* but in two or three species only. A high degree of difference between chromosomes was observed in the karyotypes of *D. stramonium*, but nothing is known about karyotypes of other species: their chromosome sizes, the centromeres, secondary constrictions, and other details (*152*).

Apparently the major factors involved in the evolution of species are the genes and especially the particular alleles and their arrangements. The chromosomes are the bearers of genes and any rearrangements of chromosomes or their segments may bring about changes in the gene products or characters. Details on divergencies in chromosome structure are of prime importance. The inversion of segments results in reversing the order of genes in such segments; the shortening of an arm indicates the transfer of genes to another chromosome, thus influencing adjacent genes or affecting the balance of genes. A correct knowledge of the interrelationships between chromosomal structures and genes is necessary in every species. These are all factors of evolutionary significance and the fundamental processes in speciation cannot be properly understood without taking all these factors into account.

# 14

# Barriers to Crossability: Prefertilization

## J. Rietsema

The extensive studies on the genus *Datura* could not have been accomplished without hybridization, both interspecific and between individuals of a single species. This is true also for similar investigations on other groups, as tobacco, corn, wheat, oats, and other economically valuable plants. Some of the various obstacles to successful hybridization have been discovered since the work of the early hybridizers mentioned in Chapter 1. Our studies of the problems encountered in efforts to hybridize *Datura* have yielded some valuable information concerning this important problem. Some of the barriers that make interspecific hybrids difficult or impossible to obtain in this genus have been determined; and methods to overcome certain of these barriers have been developed and will be described in this and the following chapter.

Hybrids between any *Datura* species are rarely found in the wild, even though some species grow in overlapping geographical areas. The only species hybrid definitely identified in collections from the wild is that between *D. stramonium* and *D. ferox*. This has been obtained from several places in South America (39). The rarity of such naturally occurring species hybrids indicates that they are not easily formed. Geographical, geological, and other natural or obvious barriers preventing natural hybridization between species are beyond the scope of this chapter. Those factors that prevent or hinder the forming of viable hybrids after pollination, naturally or artificially made, will be dealt with in this chapter. It will also be shown that some of the problems encountered in obtaining species hybrids are identical to those in certain crosses within a species.

A discussion of these obstacles to crossability soon involves a distinction between prefertilization and postfertilization barriers. This separation is fundamental because the factors involved are basically different.

In the present chapter we are discussing the barriers that hinder or prevent normal pollen germination and pollen-tube growth; in the next, we will discuss some of the barriers preventing normal development of the hybrid embryo and endosperm.

**Failure of Pollen Germination.** Failure of pollen germination and pollen-tube growth was observed in combinations involving races of *D. stramonium* as early as 1921. Before any effective means could be developed to overcome defective pollen-tube growth its nature had to be studied more closely. We owe our knowledge of the physiology of the pollen and pollen tubes of *Datura* largely to the work of Buchholz, who spent many summers at Cold Spring Harbor working on this problem. Interest in this problem was created when it was observed that the Globe $(2n + 21 \cdot 22)$ mutant was transmitted by the pollen to a limited degree (Chapter 6). Study of this particular type of genetic behavior revealed that pollen grains carrying the extra chromosome usually failed to fertilize ovules. Details and further discussion of the peculiar pattern of pollen-tube growth found in $2n \times 2n + 1$ crosses are presented later in this chapter.

Storage of *Datura* pollen over limited periods of time does not offer any serious difficulties. Pollen of most angiosperms can be kept viable for several months under suitably controlled conditions. This is also true for *Datura* pollen, which can be kept at room temperature for 10 to 14 days without losing its vitality. However, by storing over a saturated $CaCl_2$ solution at 5 to 7° C, it can be kept for 6 to 12 months. A very simple method of storing pollen for long periods has been used in this laboratory. The fresh anthers are placed in small shell vials and these are hung by a thread from the cork inside a larger vial, which, at the bottom, contains a saturated $CaCl_2$ solution. The stoppered vial is kept in a refrigerator and opened when pollen is needed. This method has been used with good success and has enabled us to make pollinations between plants belonging to different generations or between plants differing widely in time of flowering.

Pollen of all *Datura* species germinates readily *in vitro*. Significant differences exist, however, between the various species. For instance, on 1 per cent agar with 5 per cent sucrose the pollen of the long-styled species gives much higher germination percentages than pollen of the short-styled species (202). Indications have been obtained that pollen from tetraploid plants (*D. ferox, D. pruinosa, D. innoxia, D. leichhardtii*, and *D. meteloides* I) does not germinate so well as pollen from diploid plants of the same species. Also starchy pollen germinates less well than starch-free pollen of the same species, the presence of starch being determined with Lugol's solution. This is not so unusual, since several workers have reported this difference between starchy and starch-free pollen of other plants (Renner, 1919).

Liquid media were found to be definitely harmful, for *Datura* pollen rarely germinated in such media. Semisolid media are far superior but still do not allow optimum pollen-tube development. In this respect

*Datura* pollen resembles that from many other plants reported as being sensitive to moisture conditions in the medium (Kuhn, 1937; Sartoris, 1942). On agar the pollen tubes have never reached the extreme length that they reach in the styles of the flowers, which indicates that this medium does not entirely satisfy all requirements. In addition, the pollen tubes are often curved, branched, and club-shaped, and growth in general is extremely variable (*202*).

Pollen of any *Datura* species seldom fails to germinate readily and completely on stigmas of compatible species. Pollen grains that are aborted, as in the case of certain chromosomal and genic types, will, of course, never germinate. One case is known in which viable pollen fails to germinate unless specially treated. This is a condition resulting from a recessive mutation causing the pollen to be clumped together in a sticky mass, much as in orchid pollinia. When the pollen grains are separated by mixing with fine starch and then used in pollinations, they germinate readily. It is not known why the clumped pollen does not germinate. Although pollen germination may frequently be slow or poor, in *Datura* it is never a complete barrier to crossability. About 96 per cent of normal *D. stramonium* pollen will germinate on *D. stramonium* stigmas but only a very few pollen grains will germinate on stigmas of *D. innoxia*. However, even with this low percentage of germination, some pollen tubes will grow through the style to the ovules (*105, 166*).

**Normal and Abnormal Pollen-Tube Growth.** In *Datura* the inability of pollen tubes to reach the ovule is a primary cause of many fertilization failures. This was recognized early and many studies on pollen-tube growth in styles have been made under the leadership of Buchholz. The first problem to be solved was to find a method that would permit observation of pollen tubes in the style. This was done by Buchholz, and his method, gradually improved by him throughout the years, has been used with *Datura* ever since (*72*). For other plants this method may or may not be satisfactory and for specific problems other methods have been described (Sawyer, 1925; Straub, 1947).

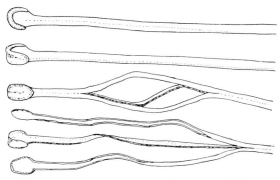

Fig. 59. The slitting of the cortex and the dissection of the transmitting tissue of styles.

The following is a brief description of the method developed by Buchholz. After a suitable interval following pollination (16 hours at 18° C, or 10 hours at 22° C for *D. stramonium*, or at other times and temperatures for special studies) the style is broken off above the ovary. The cortex of the style is slit along the sides (Fig. 59), leaving the stigma untouched. The style is then scalded for 30 seconds to 2 minutes in water at 70 to 75° C and removed as soon as it begins to darken. The style is then placed in 50 per cent alcohol containing 6 per cent formalin for one to several hours before dissection. It is important to note that sometimes variations in technique are necessary depending on the condition of the material, but dissection should not be postponed more than 12 hours after killing. Under a dissecting microscope the cortex is separated from the transmitting tissue with a thin needle. The entire strand of the transmitting tissue may then be removed in one piece. Staining (not later than a day after dissection) is done in a mixture of 8 parts of 1 per cent aqueous acid fuchsin and 2 parts of 1 per cent alcohol or aqueous light green. With this stain the pollen tubes stain a dark violet shade. Staining may require from 3 to 10 hours. The stained strand is taken from the dye and after drying with filter paper is cleared in 80 per cent lactic acid for several hours. After clearing the transmitting tissue is spread, straight and flat, on a slide. Lactic acid is added and a cover glass applied. Gentle pressure makes the tissue spread out into a thin layer 2 to 3 mm wide. Sealing is done by covering the edges of the cover glass with a mixture of gum mastic and paraffin. The slide is then ready for examination.

In order to make a quantitative comparison of pollen-tube growth it was necessary for Buchholz to devise a special system of measurements. By the use of a mechanical stage the ends of the pollen tubes are counted in relation to their distance from the stigma. This is done for each 2 or 3 mm portion of the style, beginning at the stigmatic end. Burst and normal pollen tubes are counted separately. The number of pollen-tube ends in each 2 or 3 mm section of the style is then plotted against the distance from the stigma; the normal pollen tubes are plotted above the horizontal axis, the burst and swollen tubes below. A column at the left of the graph is used to show the number of ungerminated pollen grains remaining on the stigma. The length of the horizontal axis represents the length of the style. The results may be expressed graphically as in Fig. 60.

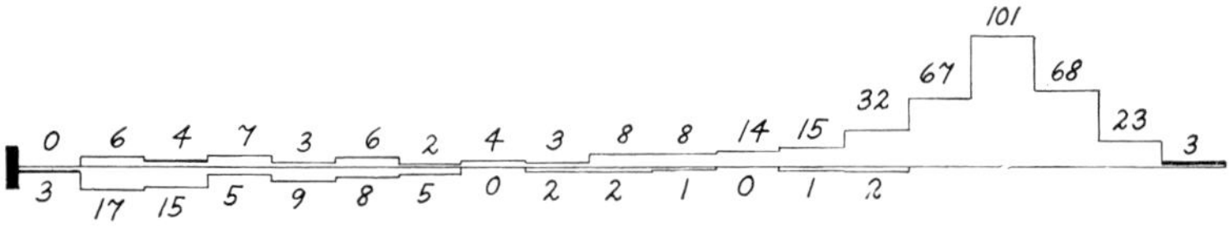

Fig. 60. Diagram of pollen-tube distribution in selfs of diploid *D. stramonium*. Normal pollen tubes are plotted above the horizontal axis, burst and swollen tubes below. The solid vertical bar at the left indicates ungerminated pollen.

All *Datura* species are self-fertile and continuous inbreeding does not affect the vitality nor the growth rate of the pollen tubes. Furthermore, pollen tubes grow equally well in the style of the flower that produced them as they do in styles of flowers of siblings. However, pollen of one *Datura* species often germinates poorly on the stigma of another; and frequently pollen-tube growth in the foreign style is retarded. In some combinations there is surprisingly little effect of the foreign style on the growth rate of the tubes. When *D. stramonium* is pollinated by *D. meteloides* pollen germination is almost perfect and the pollen tubes grow only slightly slower in the *D. stramonium* styles than they would in styles of their own kind. However, in the reciprocal combination with *D. stramonium* as the pollen parent, pollen germination is very poor and the pollen tubes grow very slowly in the *D. meteloides* style. The latter cross is incompatible, therefore, because the pollen tubes are not able to reach the ovary (*51*).

Pollen germination and pollen-tube growth have been measured in selfs of all the ten *Datura* species and in the 90 possible combinations of interspecific crosses. It should be pointed out that only a single race, which had been adopted as the tester of each species, was used (Chapter 13). It is possible that other races might show differences in respect to pollen-tube growth. Fig. 61 represents the results of this work. These diagrams were prepared as described above and show graphically the position and condition of pollen tubes and the impregnated pollen 18 hours after pollination at 19° C. From this compound diagram some interesting observations may be made. In the interspecific crosses between the three closely related species (*D. stramonium, D. ferox,* and *D. quercifolia*) pollen germination is high and pollen-tube growth, as a rule, is good. *D. pruinosa* and *D. leichhardtii* seem to constitute a similar group, with some distinct bimodal curves. The remaining five species, with long styles, also seem to show a certain resemblance to each other, although much less closely than do the other two natural groups (*105*).

In combinations between species from different groups reciprocal crosses always show great differences in the growth of the pollen tubes. The degree of morphological resemblance between the species is reflected by the behavior of pollen tubes. It is also clear that several interspecific combinations are nearly or entirely incompatible because of a failure of the pollen tubes to reach the ovary.

Certain factors are clearly responsible for some of the incompatibilities encountered. There is in *D. stramonium* a type, the product of a recessive gene mutation "tricarpel," which is characterized by the bursting of a very high proportion of pollen tubes carrying the gene. The bursting of such tubes explains the small numbers of recessive individuals recovered in male backcrosses of plants heterozygous for tricarpel (*49*).

The rates of pollen-tube growth and the lengths of the styles are very important. At 19° C *D. innoxia* pollen tubes grow 3.3 mm per hour in

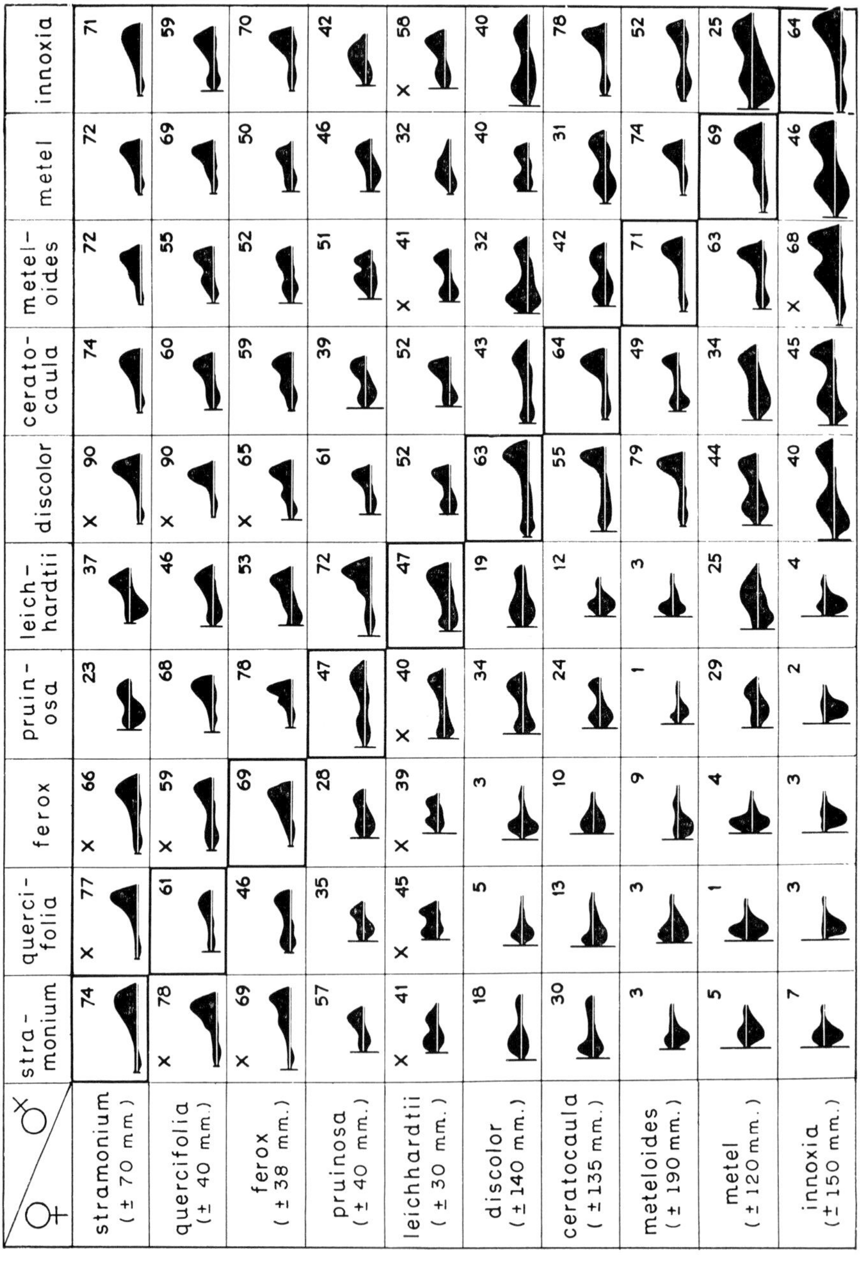

Fig. 61. Pollen-tube growth in crosses between the ten species of *Datura*. The length of the pistils is shown under the species name. The numbers in the rectangles are the distribution index values, i.e., the percentages of pollen tubes that have grown at least half the length of the longest tubes.

*D. innoxia* styles, but *D. quercifolia* pollen tubes grow only 1.9 mm per hour in their own styles. *D. innoxia* styles are about 150 mm long and *D. quercifolia* styles are only about 40 mm long. In other words, there is a correlation between the length of the style and the growth rate of the pollen tubes. Slow-growing pollen tubes of the short-styled plants growing in the long styles of other species may never reach the ovary because they grow too slowly or because they cannot reach the greater length necessary to traverse the entire style. Burst or swollen pollen tubes also occur frequently. Such tubes will not grow any further. In Fig. 67 (Chapter 15) the hybrids that have been obtained without employing special techniques between the ten species of *Datura* are indicated as ($\times$). The combinations in which no fertilization occurs are shown by ($-$). Selfs of each species are indicated by the diagonal row of £'s. It is obvious from this figure that combinations involving a short-styled male parent and a long-styled female parent are unsuccessful because of the failure of fertilization.

The experiments referred to above were conducted at a temperature of 19° C and the diagrams in Fig. 61 are therefore comparable. As was expected, temperature had a marked effect on the rate of pollen-tube growth. The optimum temperature for pollen-tube growth in *D. stramonium* is close to 33° C. The relative humidity also affects pollen-tube growth and it is therefore vitally important to make comparative studies under conditions of constant temperature and humidity. This can be done by cutting in the early morning previously emasculated flowers from the plant and removing them to a room or chamber having a constant temperature and high humidity. Pollination can follow in the evening of the same day and the styles dissected after 12 to 20 hours (50).

**Pollen-Tube Growth in Chromosomal Types.** In *D. stramonium* the cross $2n \times 4n$ is not successful. In an effort to find an explanation for this the pollen-tube growth in this combination was investigated, as were the other possible combinations between the balanced chromosomal types, $1n$, $2n$, $3n$, and $4n$. Earlier, in 1926 and 1927, it was shown that these types produce varying proportions of aborted pollen: 88 per cent from haploid plants, 1 to 1.5 per cent from diploid plants, about 45 per cent from triploid plants, and 3.5 to 8 per cent from tetraploid plants. Aborted pollen can be visually recognized and the following considerations do not concern such pollen (Chapter 5).

Some abnormal pollen-tube growth occurs in all combinations investigated, including selfs. Burst or swollen pollen tubes occur least frequently from pollen with 12 chromosomes. Haploid plants produce about 12 per cent or less good pollen. These pollen grains have 12 chromosomes, mainly the result of nonreduction. About a quarter of this "good" pollen is unable to germinate on the stigma of any of the balanced types. Though the reason for this high proportion of non-germinating pollen is not fully understood, it is possible that chromosomal or gene mutations may be partly responsible. Of the normal-appearing pollen from triploids, about 90 per cent fails to germinate. Probably only pollen grains with the normal 12 chromosomes or with a single extra chromosome will germinate. Haploid pollen from a diploid parent usually shows about 1 to 4 per cent burst or ungerminated pollen on the stigma. In tetraploid plants a high degree of nondisjunction occurs in microsporogenesis, which is reflected in a high percentage of nongerminating pollen or abnormal pollen tubes.

Not only the pollen source but also the styles influence germination and pollen-tube growth. Styles on the $1n$, $2n$, or $3n$ plants are unfavorable for pollen from $4n$ plants. Pollen from $2n$ plants grows well in the styles of all four types. The styles of $4n$ plants are favorable for pollen from $2n$ plants but slightly less so for pollen from $4n$ plants. Pollen tubes from haploid plants grow well in $2n$, $3n$, and $4n$ styles. The nature of this effect of the styles remains unexplained (58).

In unbalanced chromosomal types such as the Globe ($2n + 21 \cdot 22$) mutant we encounter similar phenomena. The pollen from a $2n + 1$ plants consists of 50 per cent (or more) normal pollen with 12 chromosomes and of close to 50 per cent pollen with 13 chromosomes. The pollen-tube diagrams that are obtained when a $2n + 1$ type, such as $2n + 21 \cdot 22$, is used as a male parent are usually bimodal. Evidence has been accumulated to prove that the faster growing and therefore longer pollen tubes are those derived from $1n$ pollen grains and that the shorter tubes are from $1n + 1$ pollen grains. Some style splicing experiments described below give striking demonstrations of these facts (21).

The availability of the large number of trisomic primaries and secondaries ($2n + 1$ types) makes it possible to study the effect of the extra chromosome on pollen-tube growth and on the transmissibility of the extra chromosome through the pollen. The extra chromosome may influence the pollen germination, the rate of pollen-tube growth, or the extent of bursting and swelling. Tests indicate that, of the 12 primaries, 5 may be transmissible through the pollen to some extent. In descending order of pollen transmissibility these are: $2n + 11 \cdot 12$, $2n + 13 \cdot 14$, $2n + 21 \cdot 22$, $2n + 15 \cdot 16$, and $2n + 17 \cdot 18$. Pollen transmission of the $2n + 17 \cdot 18$ type has been obtained only under the most favorable conditions. Of the secondaries the $2n + 2 \cdot 2$ and $2n + 6 \cdot 6$ and possibly the $2n + 15 \cdot 15$ can be occasionally transmitted by pollen. The other secondaries give either poor pollen germination or burst pollen tubes (66, 78).

Somewhat similar is the situation following pollinations with pollen from plants from different genera or even from different families. Pollen from many other solanaceous plants and from plants of several other families was applied to stigmas of *D. stramonium*. Without exception the germination was good; frequently pollen tubes grew to considerable length, though fertilization did not occur. The solanaceous plants gave on the average a better pollen germination and a higher pollen-tube growth rate than pollen of plants from other families (168).

**Overcoming Some Prefertilization Barriers.** On the preceding pages it was shown how incompatibility can result from either bursting or from too slowly growing pollen tubes. No methods are known to prevent the tubes from bursting or to speed up their growth sufficiently to bring about fertilization. In order to secure certain otherwise incompatible combinations special methods must be devised.

Buchholz showed that the $2n \times 4n$ cross is incompatible because the pollen tubes from the $4n$ male parent burst in the $2n$ style. A method of overcoming this barrier may be explained by quoting Blakeslee in reporting some work on the structure of the style by the use of periclinal chimeras:

> The first layer . . . forms the transmitting tissue within the style through which the pollen tubes grow. Hence, the style of a $4n$, $2n$, $2n$ periclinal chimera (the chromosomal numbers of the three layers are indicated from outside in) should act like a pure $4n$ female parent so far as its reaction to pollen tubes from a $4n$ male parent is concerned. As a matter of fact, pollen tubes from a $4n$ male grow readily without bursting in styles of a periclinal chimera of the type mentioned which has a $4n$ epidermis and take part in fertilizing the egg cells which are derived from the normal $2n$ germ layer (*166*).

This statement was based on histological studies of the style and on results obtained from numerous experiments using periclinal chimeras with $4n$ epidermal and $2n$ subepidermal layers crossed to $4n$ plants (Chapter 8). From such crosses 122 capsules were obtained. These contained an average of 123 seeds per capsule, thus proving that fertilization had taken place and that a block to crossability (bursting pollen tubes) had been overcome.

When pollen tubes grow too slowly to reach the ovary or when the slow-growing tubes are left behind by faster growing tubes, it has been possible in some instances to apply the method of style splicing that Buchholz developed for *Datura* (Fig. 62). Style splicing has been re-

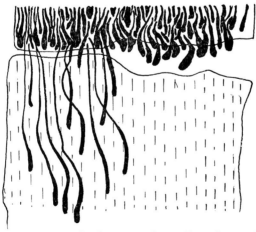

Fig. 62. Result of cutting and splicing a style. Pollen tubes at the left have succeeded in crossing the gap. Where the gap is wider the tubes may be unable to reach the tissue beyond.

ported in experiments with *Iris* (Jost, 1907), *Nicotiana* (East and Park, 1918), and *Petunia* (Yasuda, 1931).

By this method any midportion of a style may be removed and the remaining tip replaced on the cut stump of the same style or placed at any desired point on the style of a different flower. The portion to be removed is determined from known data on the position of pollen tubes at specified times after pollination. In crosses involving $2n + 11 \cdot 12$ and $2n + 15 \cdot 16$ male parents on normal diploids it has been possible to obtain 75 per cent or more $2n + 1$ offspring when that part of the pollinated style was removed which contained the faster growing $1n$ pollen tubes, thus allowing the slower $1n + 1$ pollen tubes to reach the ovary and take part in fertilization. Although the pollen tubes readily cross between the cut surfaces when the portions are "spliced" together, there is no actual union of tissues by meristematic growth (*79*).

In certain interspecific crosses between species having long styles with short-styled species it has been possible to obtain fertilization by cutting out a portion of the long style and replacing the tip portion containing the pollen tubes from the short-styled male parent. In the crosses of *D. discolor* × *D. quercifolia* and *D. innoxia* × *D. ferox*, embryos were obtained by this method. In the cross *D. innoxia* × *D. quercifolia* fertilization takes place but no viable embryos are obtained. The lack of viable seed from these crosses is not caused by the failure of fertilization but is due to factors interfering with the development of the embryo and seed, as will be discussed in the following chapter (*167, 190*).

**Conclusion.** Studies on pollen germination and pollen-tube growth have shown that there are a number of barriers preventing fertilization in a variety of crosses. Some of them, such as the early loss of pollen viability, can be easily removed by applying methods that preserve its vitality for longer periods of time. Among other blocks, the bursting of pollen tubes in styles is undoubtedly the most common factor preventing fertilization. Not all the factors causing the swelling and bursting of pollen tubes are known, but the two methods described above—the use of periclinal chimeras and the splicing of styles—overcome the difficulties in some crosses. Fertilization can be obtained at present in $2n \times 4n$ crosses and in certain incompatible crosses resulting from the slowness of pollen-tube growth or from the length of styles in crosses of long-styled with short-styled species. The factors causing the formation of nonviable seeds containing arrested or deteriorated embryos and methods to bring some of these to maturity are discussed in the following chapter.

# 15

# Barriers to Crossability: Postfertilization

## J. Rietsema and Sophie Satina

The arrest of embryo and endosperm growth leading to abortion of the seed is fairly common in crosses between parents belonging to different species, either with the same number of chromosomes or with different numbers. In combinations of parents that belong to the same species but with different numbers of chromosomes, as $2n \times 4n$ or the reciprocal, seed abortion also occurs frequently. Studies of the factors that are involved in early seed collapse were reviewed by Brink and Cooper (1947). Most of the accounts are descriptive and the observations are limited to the histology and cytology of the hybrid embryo, the hybrid endosperm, and the somatic tissue of the seed. Information on the physiological events leading to seed abortion is insufficient and much needed.

In the course of the years that had been devoted to the study of the genus *Datura* it was found that fertilization occurred in many crosses between species, but that further development of the fertilized ovule into viable seed was often disturbed and only aborted seeds resulted. A detailed study of these aborted seeds and of the processes leading to seed collapse was begun about 1940. At that time van Overbeek demonstrated that immature embryos obtained from selfs could be dissected from seeds and transferred to culture media where they would continue to develop. Embryos are found in many aborted seeds from crosses, and van Overbeek's technique of embryo isolation and subsequent culture has been used with such arrested embryos with good success. Many new hybrids, heretofore unknown, can now be obtained by culturing the hybrid embryos and subsequently getting flowering plants. These results stimulated renewed investigations about the nature of seed abortion. The major results of these studies with *Datura* are described in this chapter.

**Embryo Growth in Incompatible Crosses.** In order to begin to analyze the problem, a thorough knowledge of the extent of seed abortion, either in combinations between species or in crosses within a species, was required. Studies were made of the development of hybrid seeds in comparison with seeds from self-pollinations. The process of fertilization, the histology and cytology, and, later, the physiology of the developing hybrid seeds all received special attention. Although these studies were far from being completed at the time of the termination of our *Datura* research, knowledge of the nature of incompatibility has been considerably increased.

In capsules that have developed from incompatible crosses the seeds are frequently empty. The number and size of the empty seeds depend on the combination of species used in the cross and on the condition of the female parent. In some cases the capsules contain hundreds of seeds, in other cases only a very few. The size of the seeds and the condition of their constituents may often vary within one capsule. This variation in seed size may appear in immature capsules as early as 3 to 4 weeks after pollination. Many of these young seeds are empty, but some may contain embryos, or endosperms, or both.

In some species crosses no correlation could be established between the size of the seed and the presence of an embryo, e.g., *D. stramonium* × *D. metel*. However, in the majority of combinations the embryos are usually found in the larger seeds, some of which are almost twice as large as the small empty seeds in the same capsule. Examples are *D. pruinosa* × *D. quercifolia*, *D. discolor* × *D. quercifolia*, *D. stramonium* × *D. innoxia*, *D. stramonium* × *D. metel* I, *D. stramonium* × *D. meteloides*, and *D. meteloides* × *D. metel* I (167, 182).

These large seeds do not occur in any particular region of the capsule. They are found either at the top, the central portion, or at the bottom of the capsule, sometimes only in one or two locules and other times in each of the four locules, side by side with empty seeds. They are found in interspecific crosses as well as in crosses between diploid and polyploid races of the same species. The smaller fruits have a larger percentage of large seeds than the larger ones, which may contain hundreds of small seeds. If the capsules are left on the plant 1 or 2 weeks longer, most of the large seeds become aborted as well. Further embryo and endosperm development has stopped and the deterioration of the embryo and endosperm follows.

Why do a few larger seeds develop further and what are the factors that, at least temporarily, retard their deterioration? Why do some seeds survive this early collapse even though they develop under apparently the same conditions as the smaller early aborting seeds? Is it the result of competition among seeds for the food supply or are the deteriorating influences less effective in smaller than in larger fruits? The answers to some of these questions are little more than guesses at the present time. The summary just presented is very general and each particular combination of parents has its own distinctive characteristics.

In the combinations *D. innoxia* × *D. discolor, D. discolor* × *D. cerato-caula*, and *D. ferox* × *D. ceratocaula* about 50 per cent of the 3- to 4-week-old seeds contain embryos. In the majority of other incompatible species crosses the number of seeds with embryos is smaller. The embryos are usually small and they differ greatly in size, in shape, and in the degree of differentiation. In some cases there is a considerable delay or a complete lack of differentiation (*D. metel* × *D. innoxia, D. discolor* × *D. stramonium, D. innoxia* × *D. stramonium, D. leichhardtii* I × *D. ceratocaula*, and *D. leichhardtii* II × *D. discolor*). In a number of combinations the embryos are small, round or oval-shaped, and undifferentiated, while in others they are large and globose. In still other cases they form abnormal outgrowths, abnormal hypocotyls or cotyledons, or show the beginning of necrosis (*D. leichhardtii* × *D. metel* I, *D. innoxia* × *D. metel*, and *D. ferox* × *D. ceratocaula*). Sometimes the seeds may contain embryos, in heart or early torpedo stages, that are seemingly normal though transparent. These ghostlike embryos have almost no cytoplasm and any injury by a dissecting needle will cause them to collapse. Some embryos become ghostlike in the culture medium (*164, 172, 182, 228*).

Studies on fixed and sectioned material support the observations made on embryos dissected from living material. Some of the sectioned hybrid embryos appear normal (Fig. 63d, g, h), while in others there is a lack of differentiation (Fig. 63 b, c, i). Abnormally long suspensors and a suppressed development of the proembryo proper are shown in Fig. 63e, f and Fig. 64a and an abnormally short and broad suspensor in Fig. 63a. A ghostlike embryo with almost empty cells is shown in Fig. 64c as compared with the normal *D. stramonium* embryo found in selfs (Fig. 64b). It was found that the hybrid proembryos and embryos contained enough oil but no aleurone grains. The deterioration or arrest of growth occurred invariably before the deposit of aleurone.

In nutrient media the abnormal embryos may continue to grow for weeks or even months. Undifferentiated embryos ultimately form lobes or develop into irregular bodies with twisted or flattened outgrowths and branching cotyledons but with no radicles. Embryos may form seedlings with shoots but no roots or roots without shoots. Frequently variously shaped embryos show multiple growth with two, four, or more embryo-like structures developing from portions of their tissue. Each of these structures, if isolated, may continue to grow and to develop into a seedling and normal hybrid (Fig. 65). In one exceptional case, a cross of *D. ceratocaula* I × *D. metel*, one isolated embryo of less than a third of a mm in diameter formed as many as 106 "buds" in a few months. Many of these "buds" produced roots and shoots and were grown to mature plants. If the experiment had been continued, undoubtedly more "buds" would have been formed. The ability of the undifferentiated embryo to produce unlimited bud-forming meristems is typical of this species combination (*172, 194*).

These observations show that before seed abortion becomes manifest

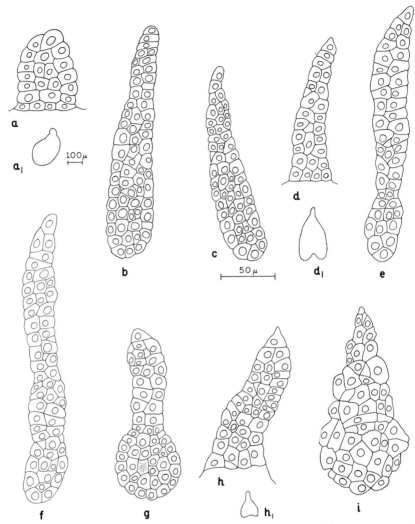

Fig. 63. Hybrid embryos from incompatible species crosses. (a) *D. pruinosa* × *D. stramonium,* 13 days old; (b) *D. stramonium* × *D. innoxia,* 13 days old; (c) *D. leichhardtii* × *D. metel,* 11 days old; (d) *D. ferox* × *D. leichhardtii,* 11 days old; (e) *D. meteloides* × *D. innoxia,* 13 days old; (f) *D. metel* × *D. meteloides,* 16 days old; (g) *D. meteloides* × *D. metel,* 13 days old; (h) *D. innoxia* × *D. discolor,* 16 days old; (i) *D. meteloides* × *D. discolor,* 16 days old.

the embryos are viable and capable of further development, provided the immediate environment fulfills certain nutritional conditions.

**Endosperm Growth and Deterioration in Incompatible Crosses.** The initial development of the endosperm in incompatible crosses does not differ from the development observed in selfs. The fusion of the diploid central nucleus with one of the male nuclei occurs in many ovules at the

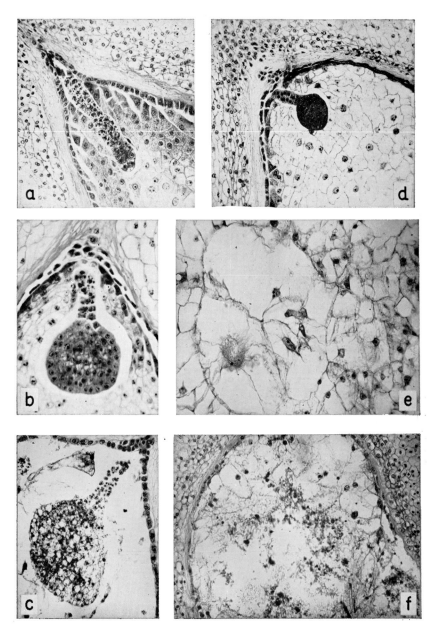

Fig. 64. Abnormal development and deterioration of proembryos and endosperms in hybrids. Longitudinal sections. (a) *D. metel* × *D. meteloides.* Hybrid proembryo 16 days old with abnormally long suspensor, retarded differentiation, normal endosperm; (b) *D. stramonium,* proembryo 11 days old; (c) *D. stramonium* × *D. meteloides,* deteriorating "ghost" proembryo; (d) *D. metel,* proembryo 19 days old, normal endosperm; (e) *D. stramonium* × *D. innoxia,* beginning of endosperm deterioration, giant nuclei and cells; (f) *D. stramonium* × *D. innoxia,* completely deteriorated endosperm, 11 days old.

same time as zygote formation, but it may also precede or follow it. The division of the primary endosperm nucleus precedes the division of the zygote, as it does in selfs. This has been observed in all the combinations of species crosses studied and in the *D. stramonium* incompatible polyploid crosses. The only difference observed between incompatible crosses and selfs during this period is in the time required for the pollen tubes to reach the ovules. This difference depends primarily on the length of the style of the female parent and on the rate of growth of the pollen tubes (Chapter 14).

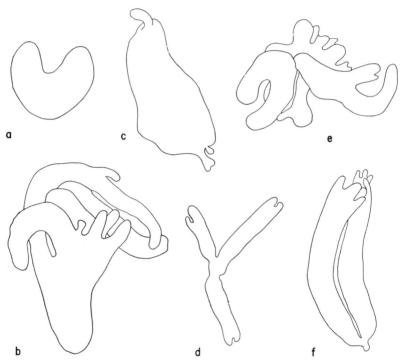

Fig. 65. Hybrid embryos grown in culture media. (a)(b)(c) *D. innoxia* × *D. metel,* 30, 20, and 38 days, respectively; (d) *D. leichhardtii* × *D. metel,* 35 days; (e) *D. innoxia* × *D. ceratocaula,* 42 days; (f) *D. discolor* × *D. ceratocaula,* 20 days.

In early stages of growth the endosperm cells appear normal and contain a considerable amount of oil. Signs of deterioration in seeds which will become empty appear at various stages of development. The first visible symptom is the enlargement of several cells, leading to the formation of groups of very large cells scattered throughout the endosperm but predominantly in its central portion. These are highly vacuolated, with nuclei that are larger than in normal-appearing endosperm cells of selfs (Fig. 64d, e). Some of these large nuclei can still divide and appear to be triploid. In other combinations, "giant" nuclei, with a diameter six times that of normal, are observed. They contain over 140 chromosomes instead of the 36 chromosomes of the normal endosperm. Nuclei with such an increase in chromosome number were observed in the hybrid endosperm of crosses of *D. stramonium* $2n + 1$ forms with *D. ceratocaula* II, in *D. stramonium* × *D. innoxia*, and *D. metel* × *D. meteloides* I. Reduplications in chromosome number (endomitosis) in the endosperm nuclei of maize have been reported by Duncan and Ross (1950). A review of such supernumerary chromosomal reproduction has been made by Lorz (1947). The endomitosis observed in *Datura* differs from that in the endosperm of maize and in tapetal cells of tomato (S. W. Brown, 1949), of spinach (Witkus, 1945), and of some other plants by the presence of well-developed spindle fibers in the dividing giant nuclei and by the apparently normal and complete mitosis. In *Datura* the formation of giant nuclei seems to be connected with the deterioration of cells of the endosperm. The groups of large cells increase in number, their nuclei become pycnotic, their cytoplasm granulated, and the cell walls disappear (Fig. 64f). The deterioration of the endosperm occurs gradually and before the appearance of aleurone grains in its cells. In older seeds no trace of this tissue can be observed. The embryo may show symptoms of degeneration before it can be detected in the endosperm, but in other cases the embryo deteriorates after the endosperm or simultaneously with it (*226, 228*).

The seeds do not always deteriorate simultaneously. Some seeds may collapse later than the majority in the same capsule. This may even happen in advanced stages at which the endothelium and several other cell layers of the seed coat have been digested before the deterioration of the endosperm began. In these cases swollen "giant" seeds result. These round-shaped seeds are about twice the size of other seeds and are filled with a sticky substance and covered by a transparent seed coat. However, in about 5 weeks after fertilization these swollen seeds collapse. Such swollen seeds were found in some *D. stramonium* $2n + 1$ types × *D. ceratocaula* and in a number of other species crosses. They were rarely seen in *D. innoxia* I × *D. discolor* hybrid seeds, but were almost invariably present in *D. leichhardtii* × *D. metel* I and *D. metel* I × *D. meteloides* I (*198, 203*).

**Ovular Tumors.** A peculiar phenomenon often observed in aborting seeds of both interspecific and diploid × polyploid crosses of *D. stramonium* is the formation of the so-called "ovular tumors," or ovular tissue. This tissue develops from the innermost layer of the seed coat, the endothelium, and is therefore somatic in origin and has the genetic constitution of the female parent. As related in Chapter 11, the endothelium becomes absorbed by the peripheral layer of the developing endosperm and disappears 10 to 12 days after pollination in selfs. In many incompatible crosses endothelial cells, instead of degenerating, increase in size and become full of cytoplasm (Fig. 66a). A few of these divide first tangentially to the long axis of the embryo sac and later in other planes.

In this way a tissue develops, consisting of groups of small cells, all of the group having originated from one endothelial cell. These groups of cells form one single compact body, or tumor (Fig. 66d), or may be scattered along the edge of the embryo sac and loosely connected with each other (Fig. 66b, c). The tumoral tissue in *Datura* never occludes the chalazal end of the embryo sac. Neither starch, oil, nor aleurone grains has ever been found in the cells of such tumors.

Sometimes the endothelial cells divide soon after fertilization and in other cases much later. The development of the tumor accompanies the deterioration of the endosperm and in many cases it is not possible to tell which took place first—the enlargement of the endothelial cells or the endosperm degeneration. Outward growth of this tissue has never been observed in *Datura*, nor in any other species (Brink and Cooper, 1947). Proembryos that are enclosed by the tumoral tissue usually do not differentiate, but they may increase in size and remain alive. They can be isolated for further growth in culture media (Fig. 66d).

What role the tumors play in the process of seed collapse has been questioned frequently by those studying the problem of tumor formation. In some crosses in which the early embryo growth is arrested and the endosperm deteriorates very shortly after fertilization, the growth of seeds also stops early. The endothelial cells in such cases may increase in size but divide only sporadically and tumors are either absent or deteriorate very early (*D. pruinosa* × *D. metel* and *D. metel* × *discolor*). In other instances seeds have been found with huge tumors, almost completely filling the embryo sac and often enveloping a large undifferentiated embryo, which seems still to be unaffected. The endosperm in such seeds disappeared later (*D. metel* × *D. ceratocaula, D. ferox* × *D. metel,* and *D. stramonium* × *D. metel*). In crosses of *D. innoxia* × *D. discolor* it has always been observed that the endosperm collapse was complete before endothelial activity could be seen. In a number of cases in other incompatible combinations deterioration of the embryo and endosperm is accompanied by degeneration of the endothelial layer. This, of course, prevents the latter from forming a tumoral tissue (reciprocal *D. stramonium* diploid and tetraploid crosses, *D. stramonium* × *D. metel,* and *D. stramonium* × *D. innoxia*) (155, 181, 198).

The various kinds of aborted seeds are sometimes found in one capsule. Which predominates depends on the combination of parents used in the cross and on the condition of the female parent (226).

Returning to the question of the role of tumors in seed abortion, the fact that tumors sometimes fail to appear or appear after the collapse of the endosperm has been initiated, leads one to suspect that tumors are the result of seed abortion or of a secondary phenomenon accompanying it. They certainly do not cause abortion in those cases in which the endosperm collapse precedes their formation even though it has been found that extracts from ovular tumors can inhibit embryo growth *in vitro*. There are indications that this is because of a high auxin content in the tissue (193, 207).

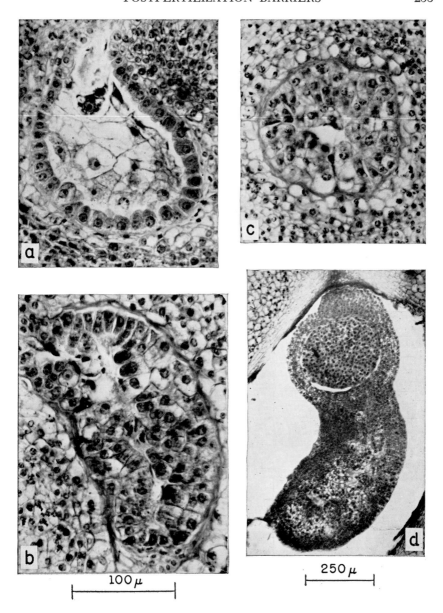

Fɪɢ. 66. Tumors in hybrids from incompatible crosses. (a)(b)(d) Longitudinal sections, (c) transverse section. (a) *D. stramonium* × *D. metel*, embryo sac 7 days after pollination, with enlarged endothelial cells; (b) *D. stramonium* × *D. metel*, 11 days after pollination. Embryo sac filled with tumoral tissue. (c) Same, tumoral tissue; (d) *D. metel* × *D. ceratocaula*, 29 days after pollination, endosperm replaced by a tumor, which encircles the undifferentiated proembryo.

**Crossability and Rate of Embryo Development.** The development of the embryo in selfs has been discussed in detail in Chapter 11. It has been shown that the development of the embryo in all *Datura* species follows an irregular pattern of cell division. The species can be classified into groups according to similarities in the rate of growth and differentiation of the embryo, particularly of its suspensor, and on the time of oil and aleurone appearance in the embryo and endosperm. In each species the development of the endosperm and embryo are integrated to such an extent that the endosperm, changing continuously, always provides the proper environment for the embryo, which in turn differentiates in an orderly manner. With respect to incompatibility, it seems probable that a disturbance in the embryo-endosperm relationship may be at the root of many failures in crosses. The combination of two species with different types of embryo and endosperm development could lead to a seed in which the endosperm and embryo develop disharmoniously, resulting in a subsequent failure of the seed.

## INTERSPECIFIC CROSSES IN DATURA

| ♀ \ ♂ | STRAM. | QUERCI. | FEROX | PRUINOSA | LEICH. | DISCOLOR | CERATO. | METELOID. | METEL | INNOXIA |
|---|---|---|---|---|---|---|---|---|---|---|
| STRA-MONIUM | £ | X | X | E | ED | X | ED | ED | ED | ED |
| QUERCI-FOLIA | X | £ | X | ED | ED | X | ED | X SP. | ED | ED |
| FEROX | X | X | £ | ED | ED | X | ED | E | ED | ED |
| PRUI-NOSA | ED | ED | ED | £ | ED | ED | ED | ED | ED | ED |
| LEICH-HARDTII | X | X | X | X | £ | X | ED | X | ED | X |
| DIS-COLOR | ED | ED | — | — | — | £ | ED | ED | ED | E |
| CERATO-CAULA | — | — | — | — | — | ED | £ | E | ED | ED |
| METEL-OIDES | — | — | — | — | — | E | ED | £ | ED | ED |
| METEL | — | — | — | — | — | ED | ED | X SP. | £ | X SP. |
| INNOXIA | ED | E | ED | — | — | ED | ED | X | ED | £ |

Fɪɢ. 67. Crossability between the ten *Datura* species. Female parents are listed in the left vertical column, male parents in the upper horizontal row. X: crosses giving viable seed. X sp: crosses giving sporadic hybrids. [ E D ]: mature hybrids obtained from dissected and cultivated embryos. E D: dissected embryos that died in culture before maturity. E: zygotes and embryos too small to be dissected. £: selfs. The dashes indicate crosses in which fertilization cannot occur because of the inability of pollen of the short-styled plants to grow through the long styles of the females.

The results of hybridization experiments among the ten species of *Datura* are shown in Fig. 67. Each species has been used both as a female and male parent. Of the 90 combinations of crosses possible, the 20 boxes in the lower left portion marked (—) refer to crosses between five long-styled species as females and five short-styled species used as male parents. Fertilization in such crosses has been obtained only by using the style shortening or splicing method (Chapter 14). It has been applied thus far to five combinations. It has been found that of the other 70 combinations studied only 17 give viable hybrid seeds. These are indicated by X. In three other crosses ($X_{sp}$) a very few viable seeds have appeared sporadically. The remaining 50 combinations studied are all incompatible, but fixed and sectioned material has shown that in each case fertilization may take place. The zygote and the primary endosperm divide and form at least a few cells before the arrest of growth. Early deterioration of the seed has been found in six combinations (E). In 44 combinations the hybrid embryos have been dissected and grown in culture. Mature hybrid plants | ED | were thus secured from 29 incompatible crosses. Dissected embryos died in culture before maturity in 15 combinations, ED. This material provided excellent opportunity for studying and comparing the details of embryo formation and endosperm growth in crosses. By making these crosses we hoped to learn whether certain species induce a higher degree of incompatibility than others. We especially hoped to learn how the rate of development and the size or shape of the suspensor are related to incompatibility in crosses. It appears that no simple set of correlations will explain incompatibility in *Datura*. A great many different factors are involved, and the critical ones differ from cross to cross. Though no single principle was established, the observations are of some general interest and they will be described in some detail.

Reciprocal crosses were made between species differing as follows: (a) Those with slowly developing embryos and late oil formation (*D. innoxia* × *D. discolor, D. meteloides* × *D. metel, D. metel* × *D. meteloides,* etc.); (b) those with rapidly developing embryos and early oil formation (*D. ferox* × *D. leichhardtii* and *D. pruinosa* × *D. leichhardtii*); (c) those with more or less narrow and small suspensors (*D. leichhardtii* × *D. metel* and *D. pruinosa* × *D. ferox*); and (d) those species with very large and irregularly shaped suspensors, such as *D. meteloides* × *D. discolor* and *D. discolor* × *D. ceratocaula* (Chapter 11).

All combinations between representatives of these four groups were also made, such as species from groups (a) with species from groups (b), (c), and (d), and between representatives from group (b) with some of (c) and (d), etc. However, no correlation could be established between any character known to be present in the species and the degree of incompatibility of the particular combination in which they were used. For instance, in the following crosses all species have rapidly growing embryos, early oil formation and the same type of suspensors, but they give different results: *D. stramonium* $\times$ *D. pruinosa, D. querci-folia* $\times$ *D. pruinosa,* and *D. ferox* $\times$ *D. pruinosa.* In the first cross (marked E) the embryo does not form more than four to six cells. The second combination (marked $\boxed{ED}$ ) produces dissectable embryos and the third combination (marked ED) yields only small undifferentiated embryos, which cannot be grown successfully in culture media.

In combinations with *D. discolor* as a male parent (a species with slow embryo development, late oil appearance, and with a large and ir-regularly shaped suspensor) and *D. stramonium, D. quercifolia,* and *D. ferox* as female parents (all species with rapid embryo development, early oil formation, and regular suspensors) the hybrid seeds are viable. But in contrast the cross *D. pruinosa* $\times$ *D. discolor* gives only early arrested embryos (ED) even though *D. pruinosa* in selfs shows de-velopment similar to the three species listed above. Crosses of the fast-developing species (*D. ferox, D. pruinosa, D. stramonium,* and *D. quercifolia*) with species that, like *D. meteloides,* have a slow embryo de-velopment again give variable results indicated as E, ED, $\boxed{ED}$ , $X_{sp}$.

The number of embryos in the crosses marked $\boxed{ED}$ varied greatly. For example, *D. ferox* used as a female parent gave the largest number of viable embryos when pollinated by *D. ceratocaula* but only a very few when pollinated by *D. leichhardtii* or by *D. metel* and none at all when pollinated by *D. pruinosa, D. meteloides,* and *D. innoxia.* In most crosses involving *D. stramonium* as the female parent the number of dis-sectable embryos is small, but in all but one they are viable and can be grown successfully in a culture medium. Only with *D. pruinosa* were no dissectable embryos found. The same diversity of results was ob-tained in crosses with female parents belonging to the group of slow-developing embryos with late oil appearance.

Summarizing the above observations, we reach the conclusion that no correlation exists between the degree of incompatibility and the differ-ences in the rate of development of the embryo, the time of oil appear-ance, and the shape of the suspensor of the parents. It is remarkable, as shown in Fig. 67, that reciprocal crosses are seldom similar: *D. leich-hardtii* is better as a female parent, whereas *D. meteloides, D. discolor,* and *D. ceratocaula* can be used with better success as male parents.

**The Degree of Incompatibility in Crosses.** In the preceding sections evidence is given: (1) that there is no correlation between the differences in the rate of embryo development of the parents and the degree of in-compatibility; (2) that tumor development follows, or accompanies, abortion instead of being its cause; and (3) that within one capsule sev-eral types of aborted seeds may occur side by side. This last observation emphasizes an important aspect of the incompatibility problem. From the characteristics of the various types of aborted seeds we make the suggestion that different stages of seed development are represented. In other words, in one capsule some seeds may be affected earlier than others and this results in different types of aborted seeds in the mature capsule, though in all cases the primary cause of abortion may be identical.

In Fig. 67 three crosses are indicated $X_{sp}$. These were crosses that occasionally yield a viable seed, though the vast majority are aborted. These have characteristics of both compatible and incompatible crosses. Furthermore, compatible combinations ($X$) frequently give only a few seeds or a very low percentage of seed germination. Sectioned material proved the presence of deteriorating seeds among normally developing seeds in compatible crosses.

Study of the data shows that there are degrees of incompatibility; some combinations are extremely incompatible, some quite compatible, and others have a position between these extremes. This gradual transition may be illustrated by the differences in the increase of the average weight of seeds after fertilization. *D. stramonium* was pollinated by the nine other species and the average weight of the seeds determined after 6 days. The weight of *D. stramonium* seeds 6 days after selfing and after crossing to *D. ferox* is the same; it is less after pollination by *D. quercifolia* and *D. discolor*. All three crosses are compatible. After pollination by *D. leichhardtii, D. ceratocaula,* and *D. innoxia* the increase in weight is much less (Table 31). The last two combinations are incompatible though embryos have been isolated and have developed into mature hybrid plants. In these two combinations tumoral tissue appears but not very early. Pollination by *D. meteloides* and *D. metel* results in slow growth, but abortion in the majority of seeds occurs much earlier than in other combinations. After pollination by *D. pruinosa* the ovary drops from the plant after 5 to 6 days because most of the ovules have not been fertilized (*198, 224*).

TABLE 31

FRESH WEIGHT OF D. STRAMONIUM SEEDS SIX DAYS AFTER POLLINATION
BY OTHER DATURA SPECIES

| Male Parent | Weight * (in %) |
|---|---|
| D. stramonium | 100 |
| D. ferox | 100 |
| D. quercifolia | 91 |
| D. discolor | 77 |
| D. leichhardtii | 63 |
| D. ceratocaula | 59 |
| D. innoxia | 59 |
| D. meteloides | 36 |
| D. metel | 27 |
| D. pruinosa | 9 |

* Weights in percentages of the fresh weight of *D. stramonium* seeds 6 days after selfing.

Fresh weight of the ovules at the time of pollination: 15.6 micrograms; weight of seeds in selfs 6 days after pollination: 142 micrograms (142 equals 100 per cent).

These observations indicate that the borderline between compatibility and incompatibility is not very sharp. The figures in Table 31 show another interesting feature. In Chapter 12 we have seen that the initial fresh weight of the seeds of *D. stramonium* is largely made up of the seed coat rather than the embryo sac contents. If this is also true after fertilization of *D. stramonium* by other species and there is no contradictory evidence, then we may conclude that the growth of the somatic tissue of the seed (seed coat) depends a great deal on the activity of the endosperm and embryo. If the endosperm does not develop at all, the growth of the seed coat comes to a stop, as in those crosses where abortion occurs shortly after fertilization, e.g., *D. pruinosa* × *D. metel* and certain other crosses.

No information is available about the processes that cause the endosperm or embryo to collapse sooner or later. Experimentally they are extremely difficult to handle. Slightly more is known about the seed coat and its derivative, the tumor.

**Some Physiological Aspects of Seed Abortion.** Ovular tumors are found in many aborted seeds and occur only after fertilization. The stimuli that induce cell enlargement and cell division in the endothelium are not yet understood, but ovular tumors are frequently found in incompatible combinations after degeneration of the endosperm or embryo has started. They are never found *before* the deterioration becomes noticeable. This indicates that in a seed with a normal, healthy endosperm the stimuli for cell enlargement and cell division of the endothelium and other tissues are kept controlled and correlated. As soon as the endosperm loses its vigor or disappears the endothelium begins to grow without relation to the remainder and tumor formation may begin. An abnormal endosperm can have different effects on the seed, since it can exert or fail to exert direct influences on the seed coat, which still may receive supplies through the funiculus. It should be mentioned that there are some pertinent observations suggesting that endosperm influence on the seed coat may be related to tumor formation.

In connection with the stimuli leading to cell division of the endothelial layer, the attempts made by van Overbeek to induce parthenogenesis with auxins are of significance. By injecting numerous chemicals into the ovaries with unfertilized ovules, he hoped to induce the formation of haploid embryos in *Datura*. All efforts failed; the only compounds having any effect were auxins, which caused growth of the ovary into a capsule with a large number of "seedlike" structures. None of these "seeds" contained an embryo. The embryo sac was always empty except for a small body called a "pseudoembryo." This body developed from the endothelium and was of somatic origin. In every respect these pseudoembryos resembled tumors found in the aborted seeds in incompatible crosses. They were found in unfertilized ovules of *D. stramonium*, *D. metel*, *D. ceratocaula*, and *D. discolor* after injection of one part per million of naphthalene acetic acid into the ovary, 1 or 2 days after anthesis. Here the growth of the ovules into seedlike bodies was not induced by fertilization or by the endosperm, but by the auxin. The ovular tumor, or pseudoembryo, could develop in the embryo sac without the presence of an endosperm or embryo. It is possible that auxin directly stimulated the endothelium, but an indirect stimulation through the seed coat is equally possible.

Even in unfertilized ovules of a developing capsule of *D. innoxia* crossed with *D. ferox* enlarged endothelium cells were observed; their growth was possibly stimulated by the *D. ferox* pollen before the ovule dried out. Here again the activity of the endothelium is not prevented, perhaps because there is no endosperm and embryo. It would be of interest to investigate the presence of cell growth inhibitors in the endosperm (*190*).

Some observations have been made concerning the chemical constituents of the seed coat. It was noted in deteriorating seeds of *Nicotiana* (Kostoff, 1930) and *Datura* that starch accumulates in the seed coat. Starch is also present in early stages in the seed coat following self-pollinations. In mature stages only the outer layers of the seed coat contain starch and the amounts of oil and aleurone grains in the endosperm increase with growth. In aborting seeds large amounts of starch are found in the cells of the seed coat, but very small quantities of oil and aleurone are contained in the endosperm. An obvious explanation, but entirely hypothetical, is that in a "normal" seed assimilates carried to the seed are converted to proteins and oil in the endosperm. If the endosperm does not function normally, these assimilates may accumulate in the seed coat and may be converted into starch by a different mechanism. A similar situation can be expected in regard to proteins if the endosperm does not form aleurone grains (*198*).

Some limited observations are available on the free amino acids found in the seed coat of *D. innoxia* seeds either after self-pollination or after pollination by *D. discolor*. Seeds of the same chronological age were compared with each other, although it must be kept in mind that hybrid seeds are much smaller than seeds from selfs and that the physiological age may be quite different. This is shown in Table 32, where the growth

TABLE 32

GROWTH OF D. INNOXIA SEEDS FOLLOWING SELF-POLLINATION
AND POLLINATION BY D. DISCOLOR

| Seeds in *D. innoxia* Selfs | | | Seeds in *D. innoxia* × *D. discolor* | | |
|---|---|---|---|---|---|
| Age in Days | Fresh Weight (mg) | Dry Weight (%) | Age in Days | Fresh Weight (mg) | Dry Weight (%) |
| 15(3) | 4.3 | 15.6 | 15(4) | 1.9 | 19.2 |
| 18(4) | 17.8 | 16.4 | 18(4) | 8.9 | 17.2 |
| 25(2) | 21.6 | 19.8 | 25(3) | 10.8 | 25.8 |
| 34(2) | 25.2 | 44.8 | 34(2) | 14.4 | 36.7 |

The values represent averages of several determinations, the number of which is given in parenthesis.

of seeds from selfs and from pollinations by *D. discolor* is given. The concentration of free amino acids was calculated on a milligram per gram fresh weight basis. Tables 33 and 34 give some of the analytical data, which, though they are of a semiquantitative nature, are indicative of some important changes within the seed during its development and correlated with viability or abortion (215).

TABLE 33

FREE AMINO ACID CONTENT OF SEED AND SEED COAT OF D. INNOXIA
FOLLOWING SELFS AND CROSSES WITH D. DISCOLOR
(S and X, respectively)

| | | Whole Seed | | Seed Coat | | | |
|---|---|---|---|---|---|---|---|
| | | | | With Epidermis | | Without Epidermis | |
| Age in Days | | 8 | 14 | 18 | 25 | 32 | 35 |
| Aspartic acid | S | 5.7 | 4.3 | 0.3 | 0.2 | 0.1 | 0.45 |
| | X | 7.15 | 4.4 | 0.7 | 4.3 | 2.9 | 0.6 |
| Glutamic acid | S | 4.5 | 3.2 | 0.2 | 0.1 | 0.2 | + |
| | X | 3.7 | 4.0 | 0.6 | 0.9 | 0.6 | 0.2 |
| Serine | S | 3.2 | 3.9 | 0.2 | 0.3 | 0.9 | 0.3 |
| | X | 6.6 | 8.9 | 1.3 | 2.4 | 1.9 | 1.5 |
| Asparagine | S | 0.02 | 0.55 | 2.5 | 0.25 | 1.7 | + |
| | X | 0.05 | 3.3 | 6.0 | 12.0 | 18.9 | 8.6 |
| Glutamine | S | 5.5 | 1.1 | 0.5 | 0.35 | 1.8 | 0.05 |
| | X | 6.6 | 5.4 | 1.5 | 4.3 | 5.1 | 1.0 |
| Alanine | S | 1.0 | 0.9 | 0.5 | 0.3 | 1.7 | 0.5 |
| | X | 1.35 | 1.2 | 1.3 | 1.85 | 1.2 | 0.5 |
| Arginine | S | 0.05 | 0.8 | 0.4 | 1.2 | 1.1 | 0.15 |
| | X | 0.15 | 0.8 | 0.3 | + | 2.0 | 0.8 |

Concentrations given in micrograms per milligram of fresh tissues.

It appeared that there are striking differences in the free amino acids in the seed coat (Table 33). The earliest observed differences became visible after 8 days, when it was noted that serine is more concentrated in hybrid seeds. Two weeks after pollination, asparagine, and to a lesser extent also glutamine, reach high concentrations in the aborting seeds, and later aspartic acid, glutamic acid, and alanine become more concentrated. Generally speaking, the concentrations decrease after the fourth week, but after 5 weeks the differences between the selfs and hybrid seeds are still obvious. The differences between aborted and normal seeds are less prominent when the actual amounts of amino acids are calculated on a per seed basis, but even then they are striking. Other identified amino acids did not show significant differences or could not be determined quantitatively, as threonine, lysine, gamma-amino-butyric acid, leucine, proline, glycine, and valine.

In the tumoral tissues the same amino acids were found to be prominent as in the seed coat, but here the concentrations were even higher
(Table 34). Concentrations of aspartic acid, glutamic acid, serine, and
alanine were especially notable. Asparagine and glutamine are equally
abundant in the seed coat as in the tumor. In the endosperm the situation is somewhat different. Especially during the fourth week after pollination high concentrations of aspartic acid, glutamic acid, alanine, and
arginine were noted. After the fourth week the concentrations decrease
again, which is similar to what was found in *D. stramonium* (Chapter 12).

TABLE 34

FREE AMINO ACIDS IN ENDOSPERM OF D. INNOXIA (ENDOSP.) AND IN
TUMORAL TISSUES OF D. INNOXIA × D. DISCOLOR SEEDS (TUMOR)

| Age in Days | | 18 | 25 | 32 | 35 | 41 |
|---|---|---|---|---|---|---|
| Aspartic acid | Endosp. | 3.0 | 3.0 | 1.8 | 0.5 | |
| | Tumor | | | 4.0 | 1.65 | 1.2 |
| Glutamic acid | Endosp. | 3.9 | 4.45 | 3.7 | 0.3 | |
| | Tumor | | | 7.2 | 1.0 | 1.5 |
| Serine | Endosp. | 0.6 | 1.5 | 0.2 | 0.4 | |
| | Tumor | | | 0.8 | 3.45 | 4.8 |
| Asparagine | Endosp. | 0.7 | 0.9 | + | 0.3 | |
| | Tumor | | | 21.9 | 8.4 | 6.2 |
| Glutamine | Endosp. | 1.9 | 3.2 | 3.7 | 0.2 | |
| | Tumor | | | 4.6 | 1.85 | 1.9 |
| Alanine | Endosp. | 4.0 | 6.6 | 6.0 | 0.9 | |
| | Tumor | | | 6.3 | 2.0 | 2.8 |
| Arginine | Endosp. | 12.8 | 14.1 | 0.6 | 0.1 | |
| | Tumor | | | 0.6 | 0.9 | + |

Concentrations given in micrograms per milligram of fresh tissues.

The most interesting aspect of the amino acid determination is the
fact that an increase in the serine concentration becomes noticeable long
before a tumor can be observed. This is also true in respect to asparagine.
Asparagine usually accumulates in nongrowing tissues. It seems, then,
that the effects of seed abortion on the free amino acids become noticeable before tumor formation is initiated and even early in the endosperm
deterioration phase, lending support to the earlier mentioned hypothesis
that tumor formation is not the cause, but rather the result, of abortion.
Asparagine has been reported to have a stimulative effect on cell division, but it is unlikely to be a stimulant to tumor formation. The data on
amino acids have shown, beyond question, that abortion of the seeds is accompanied by changes in the free amino acid composition of the tissues.

**Summary.** The main significance of these observations is that they
point to a possible approach to the incompatibility problem from an
angle frequently neglected. Several theories have in the past been pro-

posed explaining the mechanism of incompatibility, but none of them are entirely satisfactory. Valentine (1953) tried to relate incompatibility in the genus *Primula* to quantitative gene action. This is a very interesting possibility, but it does not explain the nature of the gene action. Long ago, East (1930–1931) proposed an explanation based on precipitin reactions. More recently, Brink and Cooper (1941) suggested the term "somatoplastic sterility" based on the assumption that the overgrown nucellus (apparently the same as the tumor tissue) occludes the embryo sac from nutrients entering into it at the chalazal end from the vascular bundle. This would cause starvation and subsequent abortion of both endosperm and embryo. Though this may be true for *Nicotiana*, such occlusion has never been observed in *Datura* and from what has been said above, it is clear that the tumor in *Datura* is a secondary phenomenon.

At present there is no single theory to explain seed deterioration and abortion. A possible approach seems to have been made with investigations into the biochemical changes that appear in the seed coat shortly before abortion. Most of our knowledge of seed development or failure stems from description of existing conditions in the seed. Our hope is that in the future experiments will provide us with evidence on the physiological mechanisms in the growing seed, complementing and clarifying the information we already have.

# Literature Cited

The *Datura* Bibliography of A. F. Blakeslee and Associates is entered separately on pages xxxi–xli.

ANDREWS, A. E. 1911. The active constituents of the Indian solanaceous plants, *Datura stramonium, D. fastuosa* and *D. metel.* Jour. Chem. Soc. (London) 99: 1871–1877.

ARBER, A. 1937. An interpretation of the flower: a study of some aspects of morphological thought. Biol. Rev. 12: 157–184.

ASSEYEVA, T. 1928. Bud mutations in the potato and their chimerical nature. Jour. Genetics 19: 1–26.

ASSEYEVA, T. 1931. Bud mutation in potato. Bull. Appl. Bot., Genet., and Plant Breed. 27: 135–217.

BABCOCK, E. B. 1942. Systematics, cytogenetics and evolution in *Crepis.* Bot. Rev. VIII: 139–190.

BAIN, H. F., and H. DERMEN. 1944. Sectorial polyploidy and phyllotaxy in the cranberry *Vaccinium macrocarpon* Ait. Amer. Jour. Bot. 31: 581–587.

BAKER, R. E. 1943. Induced polyploid periclinal chimeras in *Solanum tuberosum.* Amer. Jour. Bot. 30: 187–195.

BARNARD, C. 1955. Histogenesis of the inflorescence and flower of *Triticum aestivum* L. Australian Jour. Bot. 3: 1–20.

BATESON, W., and E. R. SAUNDERS. 1902. Experimental studies in the physiology of heredity. *Datura.* Reports to the Evolution Committee of the Royal Soc.

BAUHIN, C. 1623. Pinax theatri botanici. Basiliae Helvet.: 522, index.

BAUHIN, J. 1651. Historia plantarum universalis. 2: 1074. Ebroduni, index.

BAUR, E. 1909. Pfropfbastarde Periklinalchimaeren und Hyperchimaeren. Ber. Deut. Bot. Ges. 27: 603–605.

BAUR, E. 1930. Einfuehrung in die experimentelle Vererbungslehre. Zweite Auflage. Berlin, Gebr. Borntraeger. 478 pp.

BEAL, J. L., B. V. CHRISTENSEN, and A. B. COLBY. 1954. The effect of selected chemicals on the alkaloidal yield of *Datura tatula.* L. Jour. Amer. Pharm. Assoc. 43: 282–287.

BELLING, J. 1921. The behavior of homologous chromosomes in a triploid *Canna.* Proc. Nat. Acad. Sci. 7: 197–201.

BENTHAM, G., and F. VON MUELLER. 1869. Flora Australiensis. 4:576 London, L. Reeves and Co.

BERG, W. E. 1946. A microanalyzer for very small gas samples. (0.4–1 mm³) Science 104:575–576.

BERNHARDI, J. J. 1833. Ueber die Arten der Gattung *Datura.* Trommsdorf N. Jour. f. Pharm. 26: 118–158; reproduced in Linnaea. VIII Lit. Ber. 115–144.

BERSILLON, G. 1955. Recherches sur les Papavéracées contribution a l'étude du développement des Dicotylédones herbacées. Ann. des Sc. Nat. Bot. XI ser. 16: 225–443.

263

BEVERLEY, R. 1705. The history and present state of Virginia. Republished for Institute of Early American History and Culture at Williamsburg, Va., by Univ. N. C. Press, 1947.

BLAKESLEE, A. F. 1920. A dwarf mutation in *Portulaca*, showing vegetative reversions. Genetics 5: 419–433.

BLARINGHEM, L. 1911. La notion d'espèce et la disjonction des hybrides, d'après Charles Naudin (1852–1875). Progressus Rei Botanicae 4: 27–108.

BLASER, H. W., and J. EINSET. 1948. Leaf development in six periclinal chromosomal chimeras of apple varieties. Amer. Jour. Bot. 35: 473–482.

BLAYDES, G. W. 1944. Chimeras in *Lycopersicon* and *Sanseveria*. Amer. Jour. Bot. 31: 13s.

BOCCONE, P. 1674. Icones et Descriptiones rariorum plantarum Siciliae: 96, Oxonii.

BOENICKE, L. v. 1911. Zur Kenntniss der Prophasen der heterotypischen Teilung einiger Pollenmutterzellen. Ber. Deut. Bot. Ges. 29: 59–64.

BOKE, N. H. 1949. Development of stamens and carpels in *Vinca rosea* L. Amer. Jour. Bot. 36: 535–547.

BONPLAND, A., A. HUMBOLDT, and C. KUNTH. 1818. See: Humboldt, A., A. Bonpland, and C. Kunth, 1818.

BRAUN, W. 1939. The influence of long-wave ultraviolet radiation on the constituents of different drug plants. Beitr. Biol. Pflanz. 26: 331–400.

BRINK, R. A., and D. C. COOPER. 1941. Incomplete seed failure as a result of somatoplastic sterility. Genetics 26: 487–505.

BRINK, R. A., and D. C. COOPER. 1947. The endosperm in seed development. Bot. Rev. 13: 423–541.

BROWN, R. 1940. An experimental study of the permeability to gases of the seed-coat membranes of *Cucurbita pepo*. Ann. Bot. N. S. 4: 379–395.

BROWN, S. W. 1949. Endomitosis in the tapetum of tomato. Amer. Jour. Bot. 36: 703–716.

BURNHAM, C. R. 1932. An interchange in maize giving low sterility and chain configurations. Proc. Nat. Acad. Sci. 18: 434–440.

BURNHAM, C. R. 1956. Chromosomal interchanges in plants. Bot. Rev. 22: 419–552.

BUVAT, R. 1952. Structure, évolution et fonctionnement du méristème apical de quelques Dicotylédones. Ann. des Sc. Nat. Bot. 11-e ser. 13: 199–300.

CALDECOTT, R. S., E. F. FROLIK, and R. MORRIS. 1952. A comparison of the effects of x-rays and thermal neutrons on dormant seeds of barley. Proc. Nat. Acad. Sci. 38: 804–809.

CALDECOTT, R. S., and L. SMITH. 1952. A study of x-ray induced chromosomal aberrations in barley. Cytologia 17: 224–242.

CARR, F. H., and W. C. REYNOLDS. 1912. Nor-hyoscyamine and nor-atropine; alkaloids occurring in various solanaceous plants. Trans. Chem. Soc. (London) 101: 946–958.

CHATIN, J. 1874. Études sur le développement de l'ovule et de la grain dans les scrofularinées, les solanacées, les borraginées et les labiées. Ann. Sci. Natur. 5-e série 19: 1–107.

CHAZELLES, L. M. DE, and F. HOLANDRE. 1787. Dictionnaire des jardiniers et des cultivateurs par P. Miller. Traduit de l'anglais sur la 8-e ed. 3: 596. Bruxelles.

CHITTENDEN, R. J. 1927. Vegetative segregation. Bibliogr. Genetica III: 355–442.

CLARKE, C. B. 1885. Solanaceae. Hooker's flora of British India IV. London, L. Reeves and Co. 780 pp.

CLAUSEN, J. C., D. D. KECK, and W. M. HIESEY. 1940. Experimental studies on the nature of species. Carnegie Inst. Wash. Publ. 520. 452 pp.

CLAUSEN, R. E., and T. H. GOODSPEED. 1923. Inheritance in *Nicotiana tabacum*. III. The occurrence of two natural periclinal chimeras. Genetics 8: 97–105.

CLELAND, R. E. 1942. The origin of decipiens from the complexes of *Oenothera lamarckiana* and its bearing upon phylogenetic significance of similarities in segmental arrangement. Genetics 27: 55–83.

CONGER, A. D. 1954. The relative biological effectiveness of radiation from a nuclear detonation on *Tradescantia* chromosomes. Science 119: 36–42.

CONGER, A. D., and N. H. GILES, JR. 1950. The cytogenetic effect of slow neutrons. Genetics 35: 397–419.

COOPER, D. C. 1933. Nuclear divisions in the tapetal cells of certain angiosperms. Amer. Jour. Bot. 20: 358–364.

COOPER, J. M. 1949. Stimulants and narcotics. The Comparative Ethnology of South American Indians. Smithsonian Instit. Bull. No. 143, volume 5: 525–558.

COULTER, J. M. 1898. Contribution to the life-history of *Ranunculus*. Bot. Gaz. 25: 73–88.

CRAMER, P. J. S. 1954. Chimeras. Bibliogr. Genetica 16: 193–381.

CROCKER, W., and L. BARTON. 1953. Physiology of seeds. A Chronica Botanica Publication. New York: The Ronald Press Co. 267 pp.

CROMWELL, B. T. 1944a. Studies on the synthesis of hyoscyamine in *Atropa Belladonna* and *Datura stramonium* L. Biochem. Jour. 37: 717–722.

CROMWELL, B. T. 1944b. The role of putrescine in the synthesis of hyoscyamine. Biochem. Jour. 37: 722–726.

CROSS, G. L. 1938. A comparative histogenetic study of the bud scales and foliage leaves of *Viburnum opulus*. Amer. Jour. Bot. 25: 246–258.

CULLEY, J. 1936. The California Indian: their medical practice and drugs. Jour. Amer. Pharm. Assoc. 25: 332–339.

DALLEMAGNE, M. J., and C. HEYMANS. 1955. "Respiratory stimulants." In Manske and Holmes (eds.). The alkaloids. vol. 5, Chap. 40, pp. 109–139. New York, Academic Press.

DERMEN, H. 1945. The mechanism of colchicine-induced cytohistological changes in cranberry. Amer. Jour. Bot. 32: 387–394.

DERMEN, H. 1947a. Periclinal cytochimeras and histogenesis in cranberry. Amer. Jour. Bot. 34: 32–43.

DERMEN, H. 1947b. Inducing polyploidy in peach varieties. Jour. Hered. 38: 77–82.

DERMEN, H. 1951. Ontogeny of tissues in stem and leaf of cytochimeral apples. Amer. Jour. Bot. 38: 753–760.

DERMEN, H., and H. F. BAIN. 1944. A general cytohistological study of colchicine polyploidy in cranberry. Amer. Jour. Bot. 31: 451–463.

DE VRIES, H. 1900. Das Spaltungsgesetz der Bastarde. Ber. Deut. Bot. Ges. 18: 83–90.

DIAPER, D. G. M., S. KIRKWOOD, and L. MARION. 1951. The biogenesis of alkaloids. III. A study of hyoscyamine biosynthesis using isotopic putrescine. Can. J. Chem. 29: 964–969.

DOBZHANSKY, T. 1941. Genetics and the origin of species. 2d ed. New York, Columbia Univ. Press. 446 pp.

DOWD, O. J. 1933. Preliminary studies on the internal atmosphere of apples. Proc. Am. Soc. Hort. Sci. 30: 162–163.

DRAY, R. E. A., and G. E. FOSTER. 1953. The determination of tropane alkaloids in vegetable drugs by paper chromatography with special reference to the alkaloids of *Datura sanguinea*. Jour. Pharm. and Pharmacol. 5: 839–848.

DUNAL, F. 1852. Solanaceae. De Candolle Prodromus Systematis Naturalis Regni Vegetabilis. XIII, Pt. 1. Paris, Victor Masson. 690 pp.

DUNCAN, R. E., and J. G. ROSS. 1950. The nucleus in differentiation and development. III. Nuclei in maize endosperm. Jour. Hered. 41: 259–268.

DUVICK, D. N. 1952. Free amino acids in the developing endosperm of maize. Amer. Jour. Bot. 39: 656–661.

EAST, E. M. 1930–1931. Possible immunological reactions in plants. Harvey Lectures 26: 112–128.

EAST, E. M., and J. B. PARK. 1918. Studies on self-sterility. II. Pollen-tube growth. Genetics 3: 353–366.

EHRENBERG, L., A. GUSTAFSSON, and N. NYBOM. 1952. Effects of ionizing radiations in barley. Arkiv. Bot. 2 ser. 1 (17), 557–568.

EHRENBERG, L., and N. NYBOM. 1952. Chemical and biological effects of neutrons and x-rays. Hereditas 38: 481–501.

EIGSTI, O. J., and P. DUSTIN. 1955. Colchicine in agriculture, medicine, biology and chemistry. Ames, Iowa State Coll. Press. 470 pp.

EINSET, J., H. W. BLASER, and B. IMHOFE. 1946. A chromosomal chimera of the Northern Spy apple. Jour. Hered. 37: 265–266.

EVANS, W. C., and M. J. MENÉNDEZ. 1956. A note on the x-irradiation of *Datura tatula* seeds with special reference to alkaloid production. Jour. Pharm. and Pharmacol. 8: 277–279.

EVANS, W. C., and M. W. PARTRIDGE. 1949. Partition chromatography of alkaloids. Part II. Australian *Datura ferox* and Indian Henbane. Jour. Pharm. and Pharmacol. 1: 593–598.

EVANS, W. C., and M. W. PARTRIDGE. 1953a. Alkaloid biogenesis. Part I. The site of synthesis of alkaloids in *Datura*. Jour. Pharm. and Pharmacol. 5: 293–300.

EVANS, W. C., and M. W. PARTRIDGE. 1953b. Alkaloid biogenesis. Part II. Changes in the ontogenetic production of alkaloids in *Atropa* and *Datura*. Jour. Pharm. and Pharmacol. 5: 772–777.

EVANS, W. C., and M. W. PARTRIDGE. 1953c. Alkaloids of *Datura innoxia*. Nature 171: 656.

EVANS, W. C., and M. W. PARTRIDGE. 1954. Alkaloid biogenesis. Part III. Production of biosynthetic radioactive hyoscine and meteloidine. Jour. Pharm. and Pharmacol. 6: 702–706.

EVANS, W. C., and M. W. PARTRIDGE. 1957. 7-Hydroxy-3: 6 ditiglyloxytropane, a new alkaloid isolated from the roots of *Datura*. Jour. Chem. Soc., 1102–1103.

EWAN, J. 1944. Taxonomic history of perennial southwestern *Datura meteloides*. Rhodora 46: 317–323.

FELDHAUS, J. 1905. Quantitative estimation of the distribution of the alkaloids in the various parts of *D. stramonium* L. Arch. Pharm. 243: 328–348.

FERNALD, M. L. 1900. Some undescribed Mexican phanerogams, chiefly *Labiatae* and *Solanaceae*. Proc. Am. Acad. Arts and Sci. 35: 562–573. (Contr. Gray Herb. n.s. no. 19.)

FINN, W. W. 1935. Einige Bemerkungen über den mannlichen Gametophyten der Angiospermen. Ber. Deut. Bot. Ges. 53: 679–686.

FLÜCK, H., and A. NISOLI. 1954. Influence of fertilizer, suppression of blossoms and fruits, and the distance between plants on the content and ratio of scopolamine to hyoscyamine in *Datura innoxia*. Ann. Pharm. Franc. 12: 250–257.

FOCKE, W. O. 1881. Die Pflanzen-Mischlinge, ein Beitrag zur Biologie der Gewächse. Berlin, Gebr. Borntraeger. 570 pp.

FODOR, G. 1957. Recent development in the synthesis and stereochemistry of tropane alkaloids. Tetrahedron 1: 86–102.

FOSTER, A. S. 1937. Structure and behavior of the marginal meristem in the bud scales of *Rhododendron*. Amer. Jour. Bot. 24: 304–316.

FOSTER, A. S. 1941. Comparative studies on the structure of the shoot apex in seed plants. Bull. Torr. Bot. Club 68: 339–350.

FOSTER, A. S. 1949. Practical plant anatomy. 2d ed. New York, D. Van Nostrand Co., Inc. 288 pp.

FROST, H. B., and C. A. KRUG. 1942. Diploid-tetraploid periclinal chimeras as bud variants in *Citrus*. Genetics 27: 619–634.

FUCHSIUS, L. 1542. De historia stirpium commentarii insignes: 896. Basileae.

FULLER, W. C., and M. R. GIBSON. 1952. The arginase-alkaloid relationship in *Datura tatula*. Jour. Amer. Pharm. Assoc. 41: 263–266.

GAERTNER, C. F. VON. 1827. Notice sur les expériences concernant la fécondation de quelques végétaux. Ann. Sci. Natur. 10:113–144.

GERLACH, G. H. 1948. *Datura innoxia*—a potential commercial source of scopolamine. Econ. Botany 2: 436–454.

GIFFORD, E. M., JR. 1950. The structure and development of the shoot apex in certain woody *Ranales*. Amer. Jour. Bot. 37: 595–611.

GIFFORD, E. M., JR. 1954. The shoot apex in angiosperms. Bot. Rev. 20: 477–529.
GLIŠIČ, L. M. 1928. Zur Entwicklungsgeschichte der Solanaceen. Die Endosperm-bildung von *Datura metel* L. Bull. Inst. et Jard. Bot. Univ. Belgrade 1: 75–85.
GODRON, D. A. 1873. Des hybrides et des métis de *Datura* étudiés spécialement dans leurs descendance. Nancy 8: 1–75. Berger-Lerrault et Co.
GOODSPEED, T. H., and M. V. BRADLEY. 1942. Amphidiploidy. Bot. Rev. 8: 271–316.
GRAY, A. 1848. A manual of botany of the Northern United States. Boston and Cambridge, James Munro & Co. 710 pp.
GREENMAN, J. M. 1898. Diagnoses of new and critical Mexican phanerogams. Proc. Am. Acad. Arts and Sci. 33: 471–489. (Contr. Gray Herb. n.s. no. 14.)
GRÉGOIRE, V. 1938. La morphogénèse et l'autonomie morphologique de l'appareil floral. La Cellule 47: 287–452.
GUHA, M. P. 1951. The alkaloid content of *Datura metel*. Indian Pharmacist. 6: 201–206.
GUIGNARD, L. 1902. La double fécondation chez des Solanées. Jour. de Bot. 16: 145–167.
GUILLON, A. 1950. The alkaloids of *Datura stramonium* and the course of their development. Compt. Rendu. 230: 1604–1606.
GUSSONE, J. 1842. Florae Siculae Synopsis. 1: 582. Neapoli, Tramater.
GYERMEK, L., and K. NÁDOR. 1957. The pharmacology of the tropane compounds in relation to their steric structure. Jour. Pharm. and Pharmacol. 9:209–229.
HAGA, P. R. VAN. 1954. Cuscohygrine, a normal constituent alkaloid of *Atropa belladonna*. Nature 174: 833–834.
HAGA, P. R. VAN. 1956. The biogenesis of tropane alkaloids. Biochim. et Biophys. Acta 19: 562.
HÅKANSSON, A. 1928. Die Reduktionsteilung in den Samenanlagen einiger Oeno-theren. Hereditas 11: 129–181.
HANF, M. 1935. Vergleichende und entwicklungsgeschichtliche Untersuchungen ueber Morphologie und Anatomie der Griffel und Griffelaeste. Beih. Bot. Centr. Abt. A. 54: 99–141.
HANNIG, E. 1904. Zur Physiologie pflanzlicher Embryonen. I. Ueber die Cultur von Cruciferen-embryonen ausserhalb des Embryosacks. Bot. Zeit. 62: 45–80.
HANSTEIN, J. 1868. Die Scheitelzellgrouppe im Vegetationspunkt der Phaneroga-men. Festschr. Niederrhein. Ges. Natur. u. Heilk: 109–134.
HEGNAUER, R. 1951. Formation of alkaloids in *Datura stramonium*. Pharm. Acta. Helv. 26: 371–379.
HEGNAUER, R. 1953. The influence of external factors on the content of active compounds in medicinal plants. IV. The daily fluctuations of the alkaloid content in the leaves of *Atropa, Datura* and *Hyoscyamus*. Pharm. Weekblad. 88: 106–112.
HEMBERG, T., and H. FLÜCK. 1953. The daily periodicity of the content of alkaloids and other nitrogen-containing substances in *Datura stramonium*. Pharm. Acta. Helv. 28: 74–85.
HENRY, T. A. 1949. The plant alkaloids. 4th ed. London, Churchill Ltd. 804 pp.
HERMANN, P. 1698. Paradisus batavus. Lugduni batavorum: 247, 15 index. Elsevier Pub. Co., Amsterdam.
HOLFERT, J. 1890. Die Naehrschicht der Samenschalen. Flora 73: 279–313.
HOLMES, H. L. 1950. "The chemistry of the tropane alkaloids." In Manske and Holmes (eds.). The alkaloids, vol. I, 271–374. New York, Academic Press, Inc.
HUMBOLDT, A., A. BONPLAND, and C. KUNTH. 1818. Nova genera et species plan-tarum quae in peregrinatione orbis novi collegerunt. 3: 456, pl. 193–300. Paris, Libraria Greco-Latino-Germanica.
HUNT, K. W. 1937. A study of the style and stigma, with reference to the nature of the carpel. Amer. Jour. Bot. 24: 288–295.
ING, H. R. 1955. "Mydriatic alkaloids." In Manske and Holmes (eds.). The alka-loids, vol. 5, 243–263. New York, Academic Press, Inc.

JACKSON, B. P., and J. M. ROWSON. 1953. Alkaloid biogenesis in tetraploid *stramonium*. Jour. Pharm. and Pharmacol. 5: 778–793.

JACQUIN, N. J. 1776. Hortus Botanicus Vindobonensis seu Plantarum Rariorum. 3: 52, 100 plates. Vindobonae, Kaliwodo.

JACQUIN, N. J. 1798. Plantarum Rariorum Horti Caesarei Schönbrunnensis descriptiones et icones. 3: 80, plates 251–400. Vienna, C. Wappler.

JAMES, W. O. 1946. Demonstration of alkaloids in solanaceous meristems. Nature 158: 377–378.

JAMES, W. O. 1950. "Alkaloids in the plant." In Manske and Holmes (eds.). The alkaloids, vol. I. New York, Academic Press, Inc. Pp. 64–68.

JAMES, W. O. 1953. Alkaloid formation in plants. Jour. Pharm. and Pharmacol. 5: 809–822.

JAMIESON, G. S. 1943. Vegetable fats and oils. 2d ed. New York, Reinhold Pub. Corp. 508 pp.

JENTZSCH, K. 1953. Contribution to the knowledge of alkaloid formation in solanaceous plants. Sci. Pharmaceut. 21: 285–291.

JOHNSON, A. F. 1948. Improved syntheses of certain substituted pyrroles and investigations of the chlorophyll in *Datura stramonium* pale-7. Unpubl. thesis. Ohio State Univ.

JOHNSON, C. H., and E. NUÑEZ-MELENDEZ. 1942. A study of wild and cultivated *stramonium* in Puerto Rico. J. Amer. Pharm. Assoc. 31: 166–169.

JOHNSTON, G. W. 1941. Cytological studies of male gamete formation in certain angiosperms. Amer. Jour. Bot. 28: 306–319.

JØRGENSEN, C. A., and M. B. CRANE. 1927. Formation and morphology of *Solanum* chimaeras. Jour. Genet. 18: 247–273.

JOST, L. 1907. Ueber die Selbststerilität einiger Blueten. Bot. Zeitg. 65: 77–117.

KACHIDZE, N. 1932. Changes in the chromosomes and formation of chromosome chimeras under the influence of x-ray treatment in *Cephalaria syriaca*. Bull. Appl. Bot. Genet. and Plant Breed. second ser. I: 177–187.

KERNS, K. R., and J. L. COLLINS. 1947. Chimeras in the pineapple. Jour. Hered. 38: 323–330.

KILMER, F. B. 1930. The Daturas. Am. Jour. Pharm. 102: 526–534.

KIRBY-SMITH, J. S., and C. P. SWANSON. 1954. The effects of fast neutrons from a nuclear detonation on chromosome breakage in *Tradescantia*. Science 119: 42–44.

KIRCHNER, A. 1905. On the mydriatic alkaloids of *Datura*. Arch. Pharm. 243: 309–328.

KNUDSON, L. 1946. A new nutrient solution for the germination of orchid seed. Amer. Orchid Soc. Bull. 15: 214–217.

KOBLET, R. 1940. Untersuchungen über die staffichen Veränderung im wachsenden und reifenden den Weizenkorn. Ber. Schweiz. Bot. Ges. 50: 99–232.

KOELREUTER, J. G. References to his work taken from Roberts, H. F. (1929).

KOSTOFF, D. 1930. Ontogeny, genetics and cytology of *Nicotiana* hybrids. Genetica 12: 33–119.

KOSTOFF, D. 1942. The problem of haploidy. Bibliogr. Genetica 13: 1–148.

KRENKE, N. P. 1933. Wundkompensation, Transplantation und Chimaeren bei Pflanzen. (Transl. from Russian.) Berlin, Julius Springer. 934 pp.

KROEBER, A. L. 1925. Handbook of the Indians in California. Smithson. Inst. Bureau of Amer. Ethnol. Bull no. 78. Wash. 995 pp.

KUHN, E. 1937. Zur Physiologie der Pollenkeimung by *Matthiola*. Planta. 27: 304–333.

KUROWICKA-KULESZYNA, A. 1953. The effect of sunlight on the contents of alkaloids in the leaves of *Datura stramonium* var. *inermis*. Acta. Polon. Pharm. 10: 53–65.

LA COUR, L. 1931. Improvements in everyday technique in plant cytology. Jour. Roy. Microsc. Soc. 51: 119–126.

LAGERHEIM, G. 1895. Monographie der ecuadorischen Arten der Gattung *Brugmansia* Pers. A. Engler's Bot. Jahrb. fur System., Pflanzengesch. und Systematik. 20: 655–668.

Leete, E., L. Marion, and I. D. Spenser. 1954a. Biogenesis of hyoscyamine. Nature 174: 650–651.

Leete, E., L. Marion, and I. D. Spenser. 1954b. The biogenesis of alkaloids. XII. The mode of formation of the tropine base of hyoscyamine. Can. J. Chem. 32: 1116–1123.

Levan, A. 1938. The effect of colchicine on root mitosis in *Allium*. Hereditas 24: 471–486.

Lewitzky, G. A. 1931. The morphology of the chromosomes. Bull. Appl. Bot. Genet. and Pl. Breed. 27: 19–174.

Linnaeus, C. 1737. Hortus Cliffortianus. Amstelaedami. 26 unnumb. pp., i–x, 1–231, 301–501, 16 unnumb. pp. of index.

Linnaeus, C. 1753. Species plantarum. 1: 560. Holmiae, Laurentii Salvii.

Linnaeus, C. 1754. Genera plantarum. Ed. 5. XXXII: 500, 12 unnumb. pp. of index. Holmiae, Laurentii Salvii.

Linnaeus, C. 1756. Amoenitates academicae. 3: 464. Holmiae, Laurentii Salvii.

Linnaeus, C. 1759. Systema naturae. Ed. 10, reformata. 2: 825–1384. Holmiae, Laurentii Salvii.

Linnaeus, C. 1762–63. Species plantarum. Ed. 2, aucta. 2 vols.: 1684. Holmiae, Laurentii Salvii.

Linnaeus, C. von [Linnaeus filius] 1781. Supplementum plantarum systematis vegetabilium. Ed. 10, tertiae, Generum plantarum. Ed. 6, et Specierum plantarum. Ed. 2. Brunsvigae, impensis Orphanotrophaei: 467.

Linsbauer, K. 1930. Die Epidermis. Handb. d. Pflanzenanatomie. Bd. 4. Berlin, Gebr. Borntraeger. P. 284.

Lohde, H. 1874. Ueber Entwickelunsgeschichte und den Bau einiger Samenschalen. Diss. inaug. Naumburg (references taken from Marloth, R., 1883).

Lorz, A. P. 1947. Supernumerary chromonemal reproductions: polytene chromosomes, endomitosis, multiple chromosome complexes, polysomaty. Bot. Rev. 13: 597–624.

Luckwill, L. C. 1948. The hormone content of the seed in relation to endosperm development and fruit drop in the apple. J. Hort. Sci. 24: 32–44.

MacArthur, J. W. 1928. A spontaneous tomato chimera. Jour. Hered. 19: 331–334.

Maheshwari, P. 1950. An introduction to the embryology of angiosperms. New York, McGraw-Hill Book Co., Inc. 453 pp.

Marion, L., and A. F. Thomas. 1955. A further observation on the biogenesis of hyoscyamine. Can. J. Chem. 33: 1853–1854.

Marloth, R. 1883. Ueber mechanische Schutzmittel der Samen gegen schaedliche Einflusse von aussen. Englers Botan. Jahrb. IV, Bd. III: 222–265.

Mascré, M. 1919. Sur le rôle de l'assise nourricière du pollen. Compt. Rend. Acad. Sci. 168: 1120–1122.

Mascré, M. 1921. Recherches sur le développement de l'anthère chez les Solanacées. Thèses Fac. des Sc. de Paris: 1–100.

Mascré, M., and R. Thomas. 1930. Le tapis staminal assise nourricière du pollen chez les Angiospermes. Bull. Soc. Bot. Fran. 77: 654–664.

Mikaelsen, K. 1956. Studies on genetic effects of chronic gamma radiation in plants. Proc. Intern. Conf. on Peaceful Uses of Atomic Energy 12: 34–39.

Miller, P. 1768. The gardeners dictionary. Ed. 8. London. 2 vols.

Milne-Edwards, A. 1864. De la famille des Solanacées. Thèse. 1–137. Paris, Martinet.

Mortimer, P. I. 1953. A possible common biogenetic origin of the nicotine, tropane and hygrine bases. Nature 172: 74–75.

Mothes, K., and A. Romeike. 1951. Accumulation of alkaloids in organs of storage and reproduction. Biol. Zentr. 70: 97–113.

Mothes, K., A. Romeike, and H. B. Schröter. 1955. Mutation experiments with alkaloid producing plants. Die Naturwissenschaften. 42: 214.

MÜNTZING, A. 1936. The evolutionary significance of autopolyploidy. Hereditas 21: 263–378.

NAUDIN, C. 1863. References to his work taken from Blaringhem, L. (1911).

NEBEL, B. R., and M. L. RUTTLE. 1938. The cytological and genetical significance of colchicine. Jour. Hered. 29: 1–9.

NEES V. ESENBECK, C. G. 1837. Monograph of the East Indian Solaneae. Trans. Linnean Soc. of London XVII: 37–82.

NEILSON-JONES, W. 1937. Chimeras: A summary and some special aspects. Bot. Rev. 3: 545–562.

NOZERAN, R. 1955. Contribution à l'étude de quelques structures florales. Ann. des Sci. Nat. Bot. 11-e ser. 16: 1–224.

O'NEAL, C. E. 1920. Microsporogenesis in Datura stramonium. Bull. Torr. Bot. Club 47: 231–241.

ORTEGA, C. G. 1797–1800. Novarum aut rariorum plantarum horti Matritensis descriptiones decades. Centuria I: 138. (fasc. 1: 1797). Madrid, Ibarriana.

OS, F. H. L. VAN, E. DRIJFHOUT, and F. H. KLOMPSMA. 1955. The influence of pruning and the removal of flowers on the alkaloid content of Datura stramonium var. inermis. Pharm. Weekblad. 90: 209–215.

OTSUKA, K., and T. NAGATA. 1953. Effect of nitrogen levels on the alkaloid content of medicinal plants with special reference to Datura stramonium. J. Sci. Soil Manure (Japan) 24: 149–152.

OVERBEEK, J. VAN. 1942. Hormonal control of embryo and seedling. Cold Spring Harbor Symposium of Quant. Biol. 10: 126–134.

OVERBEEK, J. VAN, R. SIU, and A. J. HAAGEN-SMIT. 1944. Factors affecting the growth of Datura embryos in vitro. Amer. Jour. Bot. 31: 219–224.

PEACOCK, S. M., JR., D. B. LEYERLE, and R. F. DAWSON. 1944. Alkaloid accumulation in reciprocal grafts of Datura stramonium with tobacco and tomato. Amer. Jour. Bot. 31: 463–466.

PERSOON, C. H. 1805. Synopsis plantarum, seu Enchiridium botanicum. 1: 546. Tuebingae, Cotta.

PHILIPSON, W. R. 1949. The ontogeny of the shoot apex in dicotyledons. Biol. Rev. 24: 21–50.

PLOUGH, H. H. 1954. Symposium: Some biological effects of radiation from nuclear detonations. Introduction to the symposium. Amer. Nat. 88: 209–213.

POPHAM, R. A., and A. P. CHAN. 1950. Zonation in the vegetative stem tip of Chrysanthemum morifolium Bailey. Amer. Jour. Bot. 37: 476–484.

PRADISTH, C. S., and A. C. SANTOS. 1939a. Isolation and separation of the main constituents of Datura alba Nees. Rev. filipina med. farm. 30: 170.

PRADISTH, C. S., and A. C. SANTOS. 1939b. Alkaloids of Datura alba Nees. Univ. Philippines Nat. and Applied Sci. Bull. 7: 1–4.

PRASAD, S. 1948. Effect of pruning and exfloration on the growth and alkaloid content of Datura metel L. J. Am. Pharm. Sci. Ed. 37: 346–349.

PYMAN, F. L., and W. C. REYNOLDS. 1908. Meteloidine: a new solanaceous alkaloid. Trans. Chem. Soc. 93: 2077–2. .

RAFINESQUE, C. S. 1836. Flora telluriana. Pars secunda (Centuria 1): 33. Philadelphia, H. Probasco.

RANDOLPH, L. F. 1936. Developmental morphology of the caryopsis in maize. Jour. Agric. Res. 53: 881–916.

RANDOLPH, L. F., and L. G. COX. 1943. Factors influencing the germination of Iris seed and the relation of inhibiting substances to embryo dormancy. Amer. Soc. Hort. Sci. Proc. 43: 284–300.

RAPPAPORT, J. 1954. In vitro culture of plant embryos and factors controlling their growth. Bot. Rev. 20: 201–225.

REGEL, E. A. VON. 1859. Abgebildete Pflanzen. Datura Wrightii Hort. Gartenflora. 8: 193–194, T. 260.

RENNER, O. 1919. Zur Biologie und Morphologie der männlichen Haplonten einiger Oenotheren. Zeisch. f. Bot. 11: 305–380,

RENNER, O. 1936. Zur Entwicklung Geschichte randpanaschierter und reingrüne Blätter von *Sambucus, Veronica, Pelargonium, Spiraea, Chlorophytum.* Flora 30: 454–466.

RHEEDE TOT DRAAKENSTEIN, H. A. VON. 1679. Hortus indicus malabaricus. 2: 110, 57 pl. Amstelodami, J. Someren et J. van Dyck.

RIJVEN, A. H. G. C. 1952. In vitro studies on the embryo of *Capsella bursa-pastoris.* Acta Bot. Neerlandica I: 157–200.

ROBERTS, H. F. 1929. Plant hybridization before Mendel. Princeton, Princeton Univ. Press. 374 pp.

ROBINSON, R. 1917a. A synthesis of tropinone. J. Chem. Soc. 111: 762–768.

ROBINSON, R. 1917b. Theory of the mechanism of the phytochemical synthesis of certain alkaloids. J. Chem. Soc. 111: 876–899.

ROBINSON, R. 1936. Synthesis in biochemistry, J. Chem. Soc. 1079–1090.

ROBINSON, R. 1955. The structural relations of natural products. Oxford, Clarendon Press. 150 pp.

ROLANDO-SUÁREZ, L. 1952. Investigation of alkaloid (atropine) content and determination of hypertensive action of aqueous extracts of *Datura arborea* (cultivated variety). Anales asoc. quim. y farm. Uruguay 52: 48–55.

ROMEIKE, A., and R. ZIMMERMAN. 1958. On a hitherto unknown alkaloid in the roots of *Datura ferox* L. Die Naturwissenschaften. 45: 187–188.

ROTH, A. W. 1802. Neue Beyträge zur Botanik: 351. Frankfurt am Main, Wilman.

ROWSON, J. M. 1945. Increased alkaloidal contents of induced polyploids of *Datura, Atropa* and *Hyoscyamus.* Part I. *Datura* species. Quart. J. Pharm. Pharmacol. 18: 175–184.

RUDORF, W., and P. SCHWARZE. 1951. The polyploidy effect in *Datura tatula.* Planta. 39: 36–64.

SAFFORD, W. E. 1921a. Synopsis of the genus *Datura.* Jour. Wash. Acad. Sci. 11: 173–189.

SAFFORD, W. E. 1921b. *Datura*—an inviting genus for the study of heredity. Jour. Hered. 12: 178–190.

SAFFORD, W. E. 1922. Daturas of the old world and new. An account of their narcotic properties and their use in oracular and initiatory ceremonies. Smithsonian Report for 1920, Publ. 2644, 537–567.

SANDERS, M. E., and P. R. BURKHOLDER. 1948. Influence of amino acids on growth of *Datura* embryos in culture. Proc. Nat. Acad. Sci. 34: 516–526.

SARTORIS, G. B. 1942. Longevity of sugarcane and corn pollen. A method for long-distance shipment of sugarcane pollen by airplane. Amer. Jour. Bot. 29: 395–400.

SAWYER, M. L. 1925. Crossing *Iris pseudoacorus* and *I. versicolor.* Bot. Gaz. 79: 60–72.

SAX, K. 1950. The effect of x-rays on chromosome structure. Jour. Cellular and Comp. Physiology 35: (Supp. I) 70–81.

SCHMIDT, A. 1924. Histologische Studien an Phanerogamen Vegetationspunkten. Mez. Bot. Arch. 8: 345–404.

SCHMIDT, E. 1906. On the mydriatic alkaloids of *Datura.* Arch. Pharm. 244: 66–71.

SCHNARF, K. 1929. Embryologie der Angiospermen. Berlin, Gebr. Borntraeger. 673 pp.

SCHRATZ, C., and M. SPANING. 1942. The effect of rain on the alkaloid content of the thorn apple, *Datura stramonium.* Deut. Heilpflanze 8: 69–72.

SESSÉ, M., and J. M. MOCIÑO. 1893. Plantae novae hispaniae. ed. 2: 175. Mexico, oficina tip. de la Secretariade Fomento.

SHARMAN, B. C. 1947. The biology and developmental morphology of the shoot apex in the *Gramineae.* New Phytol. 46: 20–34.

SHIBATA, S., and I. IMASEKI. 1954. Phytochemical investigation on cultivation of medicinal plants. Part VIII. On alkaloid biogenesis in *Datura.* J. Pharm. Soc. Japan 74: 862–865.

SHIBATA, S., I. IMASEKI, and H. ITO. 1951. Phytochemical investigation on cultivation of medicinal plants. III. The effect of nutritional conditions on the alkaloid content of *Datura tatula*. Jour. Pharm. Soc. Japan 71: 806–811.

SIFTON, H. B. 1944. Developmental morphology of vascular plants. New Phytol. 43: 87–129.

SIMÕES, R. 1951. The alkaloid content of *Datura suaveolens*. Anáis faculdade farm. e odontol. Univ. São Paulo, 9: 185–188.

SIMS, J. 1812. *Datura metel*, Downy Thorn-Apple. Curtis Bot. Mag. 35. pl. 1140.

SINNOTT, E. W. 1945. The relation of growth to size in cucurbit fruits. Amer. Jour. Bot. 32: 439–446.

SIRGO, V. 1939. Various factors influencing plant growth. Pharmacia (Estonia) 19: 78–79, 113–116.

SIRKS, M. J. 1926a. Mendelian factors in *Datura*. I. Certation. Genetica VIII: 485–500.

SIRKS, M. J. 1926b. Mendelian factors in *Datura*. II. The bronze factor. Genetica VIII: 518–524.

SIRKS, M. J. 1928. Mendelian factors in *Datura*. III. Separate factors for certation and their differential value. Genetica XI: 257–266.

SMITH, W. H. 1950. Cell-multiplication and cell-enlargement in the development of the flesh of the apple fruit. Ann. Bot. N.S. 14: 23–38.

SOUÈGES, R. 1907. Développement et structure du tégument séminal chez les Solanacées. Ann. Sc. Nat. 9-e sér. Botan. VI: 1–124.

SOUÈGES, R. 1922. Recherches sur l'embryogénie des Solanacées. Bull. Soc. Bot. Fran. 69: 163–178, 236–241, 352–365, 555–585.

SOUÈGES, R. 1934. Recherches sur les Solanacées. Titres et Travaux Scient. 167 pp.

SPARROW, A. H., and W. R. SINGLETON. 1953. The use of radio-cobalt as a source of chronic irradiation on growing plants. Amer. Nat. 87: 29–48.

STADLER, L. J. 1932. On the genetic nature of induced mutations in plants. Proc. VI Intern. Cong. of Genet. I: 274–294.

STARÝ, F. 1952. The pharmacobotanical investigation of the most important medicinal herbs of the Solanaceae. Sborník Céskoslov. Akad. Zemědělské 25: 333–342.

STEBBINS, G. L., JR. 1947. Types of polyploids: Their classification and significance. Advances in Genetics I: 403–429.

STEBBINS, G. L., JR. 1950. Variation and evolution in plants. New York, Columb. Univ. Press. 643 pp.

STEENIS, C. G. G. J. VAN. 1930–1931. *Brugmansia* or *Pseudodatura*. Bull. du Jardin Botan. de Buitenzorg. Ser. III, Vol. XI: 15–18.

STEINEGGER, E. 1951. The alkaloidal content of tetraploid *Datura* species. Pharm. Acta Helv. 26: 188–194.

STEINEGGER, E. 1953a. Heteroploidy in drug plants. XX. General diploids of the *Datura* species. Pharm. Acta Helv. 28: 143–148.

STEINEGGER, E. 1953b. How can the increase in alkaloid content by polyploidy be explained? Pharm. Acta Helv. 27: 351–360.

STEINEGGER, E., and F. GESSLER. 1955. Alkaloidal biogenesis in *Datura innoxia*. Pharm. Acta Helv. 30: 115–123.

STEWARD, F. C., R. H. WETMORE, J. F. THOMPSON, and J. P. NITSCH. 1954. A quantitative chromatographic study of nitrogenous components of shoot apices. Amer. Jour. Bot. 41: 123–134.

STIENSTRA, T. M. 1954. Formation of mydriatic alkaloids in excised root cultures of *Datura stramonium* grown on a completely synthetic nutrient. Proc. Koninkl. Ned. Akad. Wetenschap. 57C: 584–593.

STRAUB, J. 1947. Zur Entwicklungsphysiologie der Selbststerilität von *Petunia*. II. Das Prinzip des Hemmungsmechanismus. Zeitschr. Naturforsch. 2-b: 433–444.

THODAY, J. M., and J. REED. 1947. Effect of oxygen on the frequency of chromosome aberrations produced by x-rays. Nature 160: 608.

THOMAS, H. H. 1932–1933. The old morphology and the new. Proc. Linn. Soc. London (Part I) 145: 17–46.

THOMPSON, J. F., and F. C. STEWARD. 1951. Investigations on nitrogen compounds and nitrogen metabolism in plants. II. Variables in two-directional paper chromatography of nitrogen compounds: A quantitative procedure. Plant Physiol. 26: 421–440.

TIMMERMAN, H. A. 1927a. Datura: The nomenclature of the species used in medicine. Pharm. Jour. 118: 571–574.

TIMMERMAN, H. A. 1927b. Stramonium and other species of Datura: a comparative study of the structure of their seeds. Pharm. Jour. 118: 742–744.

TISCHLER, G. 1927. Pflanzliche Chromosomen-zahlen. Tab. Biol. Period. 4: 1–83.

TISCHLER, G. 1931. Pflanzliche Chromosomen-zahlen. Tab. Biol. Period. 7: 109–226.

TORREY, J. 1824. A flora of the northern and middle sections of the United States. New York, J. Swords. 518 pp.

TORREY, J. 1856. Botanical report. Pacific R. R. Reports, vol. 7, pt. III: 1–28.

TORREY, J. 1857. Descriptions of plants collected along the route, by W. P. Blake, and at the mouth of the Gila. Pacific R. R. Reports, vol. 5, pt. II. Appendix, art. 1: 359–370.

TOURNEFORT, J. P. DE. 1700. Institutiones rei herbariae. 3 vols. Parisiis. 697 pp., 489 tables. (1719. Engl. transl.: The compleat herbal. 1: 625. London, Typographia Regia.)

TRAUTNER, E. M. 1947. Alkaloid formation in Duboisia myoporoides and D. leichhardtii. Australian Chem. Inst. J. and Proc. 14: 411–431.

TUKEY, H. B. 1934. Artificial culture methods for isolated embryos of deciduous fruits. Proc. Am. Soc. Hortic. Sci. 31–32: 313–322.

TUKEY, H. B. 1938. Growth patterns of plants developed from immature embryos in artificial culture. Bot. Gaz. 99: 630–665.

TURRILL, W. B. 1938. The expansion of taxonomy with special reference to the Spermatophyta. Biol. Rev. 13: 342–373.

TURRILL, W. B. 1942. Taxonomy and phylogeny. Bot. Rev. VIII: 473–532.

UFFELIE, O. F. 1951. The formation of alkaloids in the roots of Hyoscyamus and Datura. Pharm. Tijdschr. Belg. 28: 65–71.

ULLRICH, R. 1949. Extraction et analyse des gaz internes des fruits charnus. Compt. Rend. Acad. Sci. 228: 500–502.

VALENTINE, D. H. 1953. Evolutionary aspects of species differences in Primula. Symposia. Soc. Exp. Biol. VII: 146–158.

VINCENT, D., and T. DULUCQ-MATHOU. 1946. Grafting experiments on Solanaceae to locate the site of formation of alkaloids in the plant. Compt. Rend. Soc. biol. 140: 535–536.

W., W. 1894. "Datura cornucopaea." The Garden. vol. 46, part 2: 224–225.

WARDLAW, C. W. 1936. Studies in tropical fruits. II. Observations on internal gas concentrations in fruit. Ann. Bot. 50: 655–676.

WARDLAW, C. W. 1952. Phylogeny and morphogenesis. London and New York, St. Martin Press. 536 pp.

WARDLAW, C. W. 1955. The chemical concept of organization in plants. New Phytol. 54: 302–310.

WARDLAW, C. W. 1957. On the organization and reactivity of the shoot apex in vascular plants. Amer. Jour. Bot. 44: 176–185.

WARDLAW, C. W., and E. R. LEONARD. 1936. Studies in tropical fruits. I. Preliminary observations on some aspects of development, ripening and senescence with special reference to respiration. Ann. Bot. 50: 621–653.

WARMING, E. 1873. Untersuchungen ueber pollenbildende Phyllome und Kaulome. Bot. Abh. herausg. von Hanstein 2: 1–90.

WETTSTEIN, R. 1895. Solanaceae. In Engler und Prantl. Die Natürlichen Pflanzenfamilien IV. Abt.3-b: 4–38. Leipzig. Wilhelm Engelmann.

WILLAMAN, J. J., and W. R. BROWN. 1930. Carbon dioxide dissolved in plant sap and its effect on respiration measurements. Plant Physiol. 5: 535–542.

WILSON, C. L. 1942. The telome theory and the origin of the stamen. Amer. Jour. Bot. 29: 759–764.

WILSON, C. L., and T. JUST. 1939. The morphology of the flower. Bot. Rev. 5: 97–131.

WINKLER, H. 1907. Ueber Pfropfbastarde und pflanzliche Chimaeren. Ber. Deut. Bot. Ges. 25: 568–576.

WINKLER, H. 1935. Chimaeren und Burdonen. Die Loesung der Pfropfbastard-problems. Der Biologe 4: 279–290.

WITKUS, E. R. 1945. Endomitotic tapetal cell divisions in *Spinacia*. Amer. Jour. Bot. 32: 326–330.

WOODWORTH, C. M. 1919. The application of the principles of breeding to drug plants, particularly *Datura*. Bull. Univ. Wisc. Ser. no. 1005. 32 pp.

YASUDA, S. 1931. An experiment to graft the style upon the ovary in *Petunia violacea*. Proc. Imp. Acad. [Tokyo] VII(2): 72–75.

YOUNGKEN, H. W. 1924. The drugs of the North American Indian. Amer. Jour. Pharm. 96: 485–502.

YOUNGKEN, H. W. 1925. The drugs of the North American Indian. Amer. Jour. Pharm. 97: 158–185.

ZIEBUR, N. K. 1951. "Factors influencing the growth of plant embryos," Plant Growth Substances. Madison, Univ. of Wisc. Press. Pp. 253–261.

# Index

Aborted pollen
  in haploids, 72–74
  varying proportion in balanced chromosomal types, 241
Aborted seeds in incompatible crosses, 246
Agar, 198
Aged pollen inducing mutation, 123
Aged seeds inducing mutation, 123, 124
Aging of seeds and pollens, experiment with, 157, 158
*Agropyrum*, stamen initiation, 143
Alanine, 212, 213, 214, 260, 261
Albino, 111–114
Aleurone grains in embryo and endosperm in each species, 192
Alkaloid biogenesis, 54–56
Alkaloid chemistry, 49–51
Alkaloid content in *Datura* species, 52–53
Alkaloids
  biogenesis of, 54–56
  chemistry of, 49–51
  distribution of, 52–54
  found in *Datura* species, 52–53
  not characterized with certainty, 53
  pharmacology of, 51–52
Alkaloid synthesis in plants, relation of to metabolic processes, 55, 56
  and metabolic
  sites of, in species, 54
Amino acid
  effect of, 201–202
  in endosperm of *D. innoxia*, 261
  in tumors of *D. innoxia* × *D. discolor*, 261
Amino acid content in seed and seed coat
  in *D. innoxia* self, 260
  in *D. innoxia* × *D. discolor*, 260
Amino acids in *D. stramonium* seeds, 210–215

chromatograms, 211
  in embryos, 214
  in endosperm, 213
  in seed coat, 212, 213
  in young seeds, 212
  methods of determining
    paper-chromatographic method, 211
    qualitative analysis, 211, 212
Antipodal cells, 171
*Apemon crassicaule* Raf., 35
Apple, spontaneous periclinal chimera, 134
Arabic numbers for *D. stramonium* PT's, 221
Archesporial cell
  in nucellus, 168, 169
  in stamen, 173, 174
Arginine, 212, 213, 214, 260, 261
"Artificial" species, 220
Asparagine, 201, 212, 213, 214, 260, 261
Aspartic acid, 201, 212, 213, 214, 260, 261
Asymetric bivalent, 67
*Atropa*, narcotic properties of, 3
*Atropa belladonna*, 48, 49, 54, 55
Atropine, 48, 51
  as antidote to toxic insecticides, 51
  in alkaloid chemistry, 49
  in pharmacology of alkaloids, 51
Attraction of like ends in homologous chromosomes, 62, 64
Auxin, 258, 259
  damaging effect on hypocotyl and cotyledons, 202

"B" race, 12, 64, 68, 102
Balanced types, 62, 71, 89
Barriers to crossability, 15, 235–262
Belling's hypothesis of segmental interchanges in chromosomes, 64
Belling's iron-acetocarmine technique, 58

275

of seven compensating types, 104–106
of tertiary types, 103
of $3n \times 2n$, 78, 79
Oil
accumulation in growing *D. stramo-nium* seed, 206, 207
in basal cells of suspensor, 191, 192
in embryo and endosperm, 192
in hybrid embryos and proembryos of incompatible crosses, 247
Ololiuhqui, Indian name for *D. met-cloides*, 4
Optimum pH value for embryos from self, 199
Optimum temperature
for normal embryo development, 199
for rapid embryo growth, 199
Origin
and induction of mutation, 112, 121–125
of combination types, 106, 107
of compensating types, 104, 105
of periclinal chimeras, 134
of tertiaries, 102
of $2n + 1$ mutants, 87, 88
Ornithine, 55
Osmotic value of nutrient media, 201
Outermost layer of integument, 172
Overcoming prefertilization barriers, 243, 244
Ovular coat, 171–173
basal end formed by nucellar cells, 136, 172, 173
distal end formed by integument, 136, 172, 173
dual origin of, 172
Ovular tumors, 251–253, 261, 262
cause and nature of, 14
enveloping hybrid embryo, 252, 253
filling the embryo sac in hybrid seed, 253
in interspecific hybrids and in *D. stramonium* $2n \times 4n$, 251
may follow or accompany endosperm necrosis, 252
origin and growth, 251–253
Ovule
growth and shape, 136, 168, 169
initiation and early growth, 148
Oxygen concentration inside *Datura* capsule, 216
Oxygen consumption of *D. stramonium* seeds, 218

Paper-chromatographic free amino acids analysis, 211
Peach, spontaneous periclinal chimera, 134

*Pelargonium*, periclinal chimera, 132
Pentasome, 87
Periclinal chimeras
obtained experimentally, 14, 134
$6n$ and $3n$ components, 227
spontaneous formation, 134
survey of 192 plants
location of $4n$ layers, 138
morphological appearance, 140–141
types of, 138, 139
use of, in ontogenetic studies, 141–148
variability of $2n$, $4n$, $8n$ components in 100 plants, 136, 137, 139
*Petunia*, style splicing experiments, 244
Pharmacology of alkaloids, 51–52
pH, effect of, 199
of media adjusted, 198
value preferable
for hybrid embryos in advanced stage, 199
for young hybrid embryos, 199
Pineapple, periclinal chimera obtained experimentally, 134
Plastochron, 140
p.m.c.; *see* Pollen mother cell
Pollen
of haploid, 74
of tetraploids, 74, 82
of triploids, 74, 77
of $2n$ plant, 74
Pollen abortion genes, 111, 112, 119, 163
Pollen germination
failure of *in vitro*, 236–237
harmful conditions for *in vitro*, 236–237
on stigmas, varying proportion in balanced chromosomal types, 242
on stigmas of compatible and incompatible species, 237
Pollen mother cell, division of, 59, 72, 73–75, 78, 81, 175
Pollen sterility gene, 11, 12, 111, 112, 119, 120
Pollen-tube distribution in selfs of diploid *D. stramonium*, 238
Pollen-tube growth
abnormal and normal, 237–241
Buchholz's method for studying, 237, 238
in crosses between *Datura* species, 239–240
in selfs of *Datura* species, 239
in style, 11, 12
of tetraploids, effect of styles in balanced chromosomal types on, 242
Pollen tubes
correlation between the styles length and the growth rate of, 241

# Date Due

| | | | |
|---|---|---|---|
| JUL 3 00 | | | |
| DEC 12 05 | | | |
| | | | |
| | | | |
| | | | |
| | | | |
| | | | |
| | | | |
| | | | |
| | | | |
| | | | |
| | | | |
| | | | |
| | | | |
| | | | |
| | | | |

Demco 38-297